Haunted Inns of America

of America

National Directory of Haunted Hotels and Bed & Breakfast Inns

From the files of Ghost Stalkers
Terry L. Smith & Mark Jean

W0010936

CRANE HILL
PUBLISHERS

Library of Congress Cataloging-in-Publication Data

Smith, Terry (Terry L.), 1961–
  Haunted inns of America : go & know national directory of haunted
hotels and bed & breakfast inns / Terry Smith and Mark Jean.
     p. cm.
  ISBN 1-57587-201-3
 1. Haunted hotels—United States—Guidebooks. 2. Ghosts—United
States. I. Jean, Mark, 1957- II. Title.
  BF1474.5.S65 2003
  133.1'22—dc21

                          2003005399

10 9 8 7 6 5 4 3 2 1

CONTENTS

Southeast

INTRODUCTION

Since 1986, we have been investigating the mysteries that lie between life and death. Indeed, with every footstep, with every whiff of perfume from a century ago, with every misty form, we question our own mortality. We find it amusing when someone says there are no such things as ghosts. Why not? Why is it so hard to consider that we are not alone in this world? We can be assured of one thing—there are still mysteries on this earth that have yet to be explained.

As The Ghost Stalkers, we have had the opportunity to conduct an extensive amount of research on paranormal phenomena and we have come to the following conclusion—we can not tell you positively, absolutely, what a ghost is. Many speculate that ghosts are forms created from a past life that play over and over, like a broken record, often repeating the way a person died or what they were doing when they passed on. Others feel that ghosts are individuals who held too close a tie to the material objects of this world, so they are trapped with those same objects for eternity—and one of the biggest objects an individual can claim is their home. When there is a great deal of tragedy in one location, persons will often experience more supernatural activity. Some regard ghosts as benevolent presences, similar to guardian angels, that watch over the living while providing a sense of comfort, peace, and protection. We feel that ghosts do exist, and that they are peaceful spirits that bring no harm to the people with whom they come in contact.

Our web site, Ghoststalkers.com, premiered more than five years ago, and we have had the pleasure of receiving more than 100,000 internet visitors from all over the world. Thousands of individuals have written to share their own ghostly experiences. The number one question we receive from our visitors is, "Where in my area can I investigate ghosts?" Many publications on the market today cover ghost experiences, but mostly in private residences, anonymous locations, or even places that are now closed, preventing public access. Therefore, we decided to write our own ghost book as a travel directory that featured the entire country with locations to visit and stay the night— places where you're more likely to have your own "experiences."

Many of the 200 hotels and inns we have included offer a history of their location that's as fascinating as the ghostly activity itself. Steam ships, jails, hospitals, churches, bordellos, and residences have been transformed into hotels, inns, and bed & breakfasts. Although these locations have been converted to accommodate guests, they have a tendency to hold a few spirits from their early days.

Along with the history of each location, we have provided an account of the paranormal activity, even naming certain rooms in some cases where the sightings of ghosts are more prevalent. Noises will often be repeated at the same time every night, or the same ghost will make its presence known to multiple guests who happen to stay in a certain room. We have provided a ghost rating with each location that has nothing to do with the quality of the location, but merely provides the visitor a benchmark regarding the level of hauntedness.

Finally, we have included a little about the accommodations in true travel-guide fashion—including information on food, architecture, and recreation that guests can enjoy when they take a break from their ghost hunting.

Be aware that we by no means guarantee that a guest at any of the inns featured will see or sense a ghost. However, through exhaustive research, interviews, and paranormal investigations, we've narrowed down hundreds of locations to the top 200 chances for you to witness something out of the ordinary—perhaps something that you will remember all of your life and beyond.

We've organized the book by region, starting with the Northeast and moving clockwise around the United States. Within each regional section, lodgings are grouped by state, with the states in alphabetical order. For quick reference, there is also an alphabetical listing of all inns on page 240.

We hope that you, the ghost-hunting buff and lover of ghost stories, will enjoy our American travelogue into the world of ghosts and the unknown.

Terry L. Smith and Mark Jean
The Ghost Stalkers

NORTHEAST

— CONNECTICUT —

Homespun Farm Bed & Breakfast

306 Preston Road (Route 164)
Griswold, CT 06351
Near Hartford, CT
(888) 889-6673, (860) 376-5178
www.homespunfarm.com
Room rates: $95–$135
Visa, Master Card, Discover

Courtesy of Homespun Farm

History: The word "homespun" literally means hand-made, which describes this colonial farmhouse listed on the National Register of Historic Places.

Simon Brewster originally purchased the farm in 1740. Brewster was the great-great-grandson of William Brewster, who arrived in the New World in 1620 on the Mayflower. For over 200 years, the Brewster family ran the property as a dairy and orchard business.

Today, the home has been transformed into a warm and romantic bed and breakfast, complete with hand-crafted beds and hand-hewn beams.

Activity: Innkeepers Kate and Ron Bauer were working the orchard and pruning blueberries one afternoon when both had a sudden feeling that someone was watching them. They didn't talk to each other about the experience until a month later. The couple claims they saw the image of a man watching them as they worked; they felt as though the spirit was guiding them in where and how much they should prune. The spirit appeared in a plaid shirt and overalls. They now refer to him as their "guiding spirit." Weeks later, they found the spirit was that of Simon Brewster. This was confirmed after a relative of the Brewsters stayed at the inn one night. The guest showed them a picture of Simon Brewster, and it was his exact likeness the innkeepers had seen in the orchard.

The ghost of Simon's wife, Laura Brewster, also makes appearances at the farm. She is often heard walking up and down the stairs at night. Hotels that have ghosts on the premises often attract customers because of them, and today there are guests that come to Homespun Farm

primarily to hunt ghosts. Kate says that neither spirit is scary; moreover, they seem to be keeping a watchful eye over the farm they dearly loved.
Accommodations: Homespun Farm will take you back in time with all of the comforts of the present. Plunge into a sea of pillows and luxurious linens, and wake refreshed to a full country breakfast served by candlelight. Each of the two guest rooms offers a fireplace, full private bath, cable television, hair dryer, and bathrobe.

The Red Brook Inn

2750 Gold Star Highway • Mystic, CT 06372
(800) 290-5619, (860) 572-0349 • www.redbrookinn.com
Room rates: $109–$189 • All major credit cards

History: The Red Brook Inn is nestled on a hillside complemented by stone walls. Capturing colonial life at its best, the inn is composed of two beautifully restored historic buildings that are quintessentially New England. The first is the Haley Tavern (circa 1740), a center-chimney Colonial that was once a stagecoach stop and tavern. The second building is the Crary Homestead, a Colonial built in 1770 by the merchant sea captain Nathanial Crary. Each portion of the inn offers visitors rooms furnished with lovely antiques.
Activity: Guests who have stayed in the North Room of the Crary Homestead have reported seeing the ghost of an elderly woman with white hair, wrapped in a black shawl. She apparently stands near the corner watching visitors to her room.

Guests and employees of the Red Brook Inn have also experienced unexplained cold spots in certain areas of the inn and, occasionally, witnesses have heard voices coming from the 240-year-old building when no one else is present.
Accommodations: Each of the Red Brook Inn's 11 guest rooms is embellished with authentic period furnishings, wide-plank floors, and canopied beds with hand-embroidered linens. Seven of the rooms offer fireplaces, and all baths are modern. Each morning, a full breakfast is served family-style in the ancient keeping room.

Special holiday packages are available featuring colonial dinners of turkey or lamb with vegetables, cooked over the open hearth while breads and pies bake to perfection in the brick oven.

Lighthouse Inn

🕯️🕯️🕯️

6 Guthrie Place
New London, CT 06320
(888) 443-8411, (860) 443-8411
www.lighthouseinn-ct.com
Room rates: $95-$395
All major credit cards

Courtesy of The Lighthouse Inn

History: Built in 1902, the Lighthouse Inn was the grand summer home of steel magnate Charles S. Guthrie. The property was originally called "Meadow Court" for the wildflowers that surrounded the site. The home commanded a breathtaking view of Long Island Sound. Noted Boston architect William Emerson designed the home, and the formal grounds were conceived by renowned landscape architect Frederick Law Olmsted, who designed New York's Central Park. In 1927, Meadow Court began operating as an inn. It was renamed the Lighthouse Inn for the New London Harbor Light, located nearby. Soon, the inn became famous for social events and as a private retreat for film stars like Bette Davis and Joan Crawford.

Activity: A frontdesk clerk who worked the 4 P.M.-midnight shift often had the feeling of someone standing over her shoulder watching her. When she read the newspaper, the paper would move as if someone was batting at it. She would ask whoever it was to stop, and the harassment would cease.

One evening, an elderly man came down to the bar and looked quite shook up. The owner saw him and asked if anything was wrong. The guest asked if the inn was haunted. The manager was surprised, but replied that some people thought so. The elderly man told the manager that his wife was not feeling well, so she went to bed. He was tucking her into bed when he looked up to see a woman in Victorian dress standing in the corner, watching him. Since then, several guests on the third floor have reported seeing the ghosts of women in long Victorian gowns, as well as the spirit of a little girl.

On a December morning, an employee was checking to make sure a room was ready for a guest. As she was leaving the room, she heard several doors down the hallway open and slam shut. Knowing that no guests were occupying those rooms, she quickly left that floor.

There was a bad storm one night and the whole staff stayed at the inn. The employees reported hearing footsteps up and down the halls all night long. They opened the doors to their rooms repeatedly, only to find no one there. Minutes after they closed their doors again, the footsteps started back.

Accommodations: The Lighthouse Inn offers 52 exquisitely appointed guest rooms and suites that blend contemporary amenities and authentic décor. The inn overlooks a private beach on Long Island Sound as well as its own beautiful grounds.

The inn has 3 buildings. The Guthrie Mansion has 27 guest rooms filled with antiques and a lovely, winding staircase similar to the one on the Titanic. The second building, the Carriage House, has 24 rooms with French décor. The third building is the Watchman's Cottage, a large studio that can sleep up to 6 people. The cottage also has its own private patio.

For your dining pleasure, the Lighthouse Inn offers the award-winning Mansion Restaurant and the Meadow Court Lounge.

The John York House Bed & Breakfast

1 Clarks Falls Road • North Stonington, CT 06359
(860) 599-3075 • www.mystic-inns.com/johnyork.html

History: The John York House was built in 1741 for John York, a businessman and farmer. According to legend, the house was run as a tavern during the Revolutionary War.

One night, two soldiers in the Continental Army who were friends got into a fight over a woman. One soldier stabbed and killed the other in what is now the library. The floorboards were so badly stained with blood that York had to pry them up and turn them over. The murderer escaped and was said to have drowned at sea. Shortly thereafter, the house began to earn a reputation for being haunted. The Wilms family owned the home from 1963 to 1987, and Mrs. Wilms became so interested in the paranormal that she conducted seances in her home. This may be the reason that the hauntings started to increase.

Activity: In the days of Mrs. Wilms' seances, furniture would turn over, clothes and shoes would mysteriously appear piled up on the floor in the middle of the room, the sound of cannon fire would be heard, the scent of pipe smoke could be smelled, unexplained footsteps were heard, locked doors would open, and, on one occasion, the vacuum cleaner turned on by itself. The Wilms family had had enough and contacted some experts in the area of the supernatural. They found that the spirit of a soldier was present in the house, and he was consumed with sadness and guilt. They encouraged him to find his resting place. The paranormal experiences started to decrease afterwards.

Today, the innkeepers Leea and David Grote tell us they have not heard or seen anything out of the ordinary. However, their guests have reported otherwise.

Accommodations: This authentically restored 1741 Colonial farmhouse offers the warmth and elegance of early New England. It is located near Mystic, the Rhode Island beaches, and the world's largest casino. Each spacious guest room has a private bath, fireplace, air conditioner, and heirloom antiques. Guests awaken to the aroma of rich coffee and homemade breads, and can enjoy a candlelit gourmet breakfast served by a crackling fire on chilly mornings.

— DELAWARE —

Fox Lodge at Lesley Manor

123 West 7th Street • New Castle, DE 19720
(302) 328-0768
Room rates: $105–$185 • All major credit cards

History: In 1855, Dr. Allan Vorhees Lesley built this Gothic Revival mansion in Old New Castle. Designed by the builders of the Grand Opera House in Wilmington, Delaware, the Lesley Manor became home to Dr. Lesley's medical practice, where he incorporated some of most advanced medical techniques of the 19th century.

Perhaps due to its use as a place of healing, the current owners report that guests feel relaxed during their stay and rejuvenated when they leave the manor. Visitors find that it's easy to forget about the outside world in a mansion that resembles a page out of a Victorian romance or an Edgar Allan Poe mystery.

Activity: Legend has it the good doctor enjoyed his place of residence so much that he still makes house calls. The ghost of Dr. Lesley is occasionally spotted in the home, along with the spirit of Jane Lesley, the doctor's wife. She occasionally appears in the manor and seems to be inspecting the restoration work that is taking place.

Accommodations: Known locally as "the Castle," the Fox Lodge at Lesley Manor is a 33-room mansion with three creatively appointed guest rooms called the Malveen, Lesa, and Jane rooms. Upon check-in, guests are met in Piglet's Tavern with a buffet of fruits, meats, cheese, cookies, and wine or beer.

The home features stained glass, a white marble fireplace, a slate roof, and a massive cast-iron chandelier. Guests ascend the huge staircase with Gothic railings to their rooms on the second floor. The dining room offers an elaborate breakfast buffet every morning. Rose gardens encircle the house, and there are benches for relaxing. You may want to join a game of croquet on the front lawn.

— MAINE —

The Tides Inn By-The-Sea

Courtesy of The Tides Inn By-The-Sea

252 Kings Highway
Goose Rocks Beach
Kennebunkport, ME 04046
(207) 967-3757
www.tidesinnbythesea.com
Room rates: $145-$325
Personal or cashier's check only

History: The Tides Inn By-The-Sea—or the New Belvidere as she was known in her first life—was built in 1899. Emma Foss, the original owner (along with her mother), commissioned famous architect John Calvin Stevens to design the inn in the authentic shingle-style manner he was famous for in the Maine seacoast towns of Bar Harbor, Portland, and Cape Elizabeth. Under Emma's care, famous guests like Theodore Roosevelt and Sir Arthur Conan Doyle frequented the Tides Inn. The Tides Inn survived a fire that burned much of the area, and is still going strong.

Activity: Emma Foss, who built the original inn, still oversees all improvements made to her inn and lets everyone know if she disapproves of any changes made.

Emma also has a problem with uptight men. If she finds a male guest is uptight, isn't having a good time, or does not believe in ghosts, she will do her best to convince him otherwise.

Beds have been known to shake in the middle of the day, and toilets will shake as well. One male guest was convinced that an earthquake must have occurred. He even checked the weather report, and no quake occurred except for in his room.

When entering the inn, a life-size doll of Emma, located at her piano, welcomes guests.

Most of the paranormal activity has occurred on the third floor and in room 25. This is known as Emma's Room, and it features a queen-sized, four-poster bed. All the pictures are of women, since Emma has a problem with uptight males.

On one occasion, the staff experienced a problem with the fire alarms going off in the middle of the day, only to find there was no cause for the alarm. It was only Emma playing another mischievous trick.

The current innkeepers, Kristin and Marie, feel Emma must approve of their operation of the inn. This may be because they are mother and daughter. Since Emma once ran the inn with her mother, you might say they are carrying on the tradition.

Accommodations: The Tides Inn By-The-Sea offers 22 unique bedrooms, each individually decorated with designer linens and antique furnishings. Guests enjoy magnificent views of the islands and the Atlantic Ocean from the inn.

The Tides Inn presents the simple charm of a turn-of-the-19th-century Victorian inn located across from the white sands of Goose Rocks Beach. Guests can wake to the melodic sounds of sea gulls, stroll for miles over the sandy beach, search for shells, and in the evening fall asleep to the restful sounds of the surf.

Billed as an historic libation & dining "dest-inn-ation," the Belvidere Club is reminiscent of a Victorian Bar of times gone by. Located in the Inn's original dining room, it offers a magnificent view of the ocean and serves innovative regional fare in a relaxed atmosphere. There is an exceptional wine list and a fully stocked bar to complement the exceptional food. The restaurant has been welcoming the public since its Grand Opening in 1899.

1794 Watchtide . . . by the Sea

190 West Main Street • Searsport, ME 04974
(800) 698-6575, (207) 548-6575 • www.watchtide.com
Room rates: $115-$185 • All major credit cards

History: Searsport was incorporated as a town in 1845, with almost ten miles of coastline on Penobscot Bay. During Searsport's history, it served as a major shipbuilding and cargo-handling center.

In the mid 1800s, Searsport was home to ten of America's most famous sea captains, each traveling the globe and bringing home treasures from all corners of the world. Today, some of these treasures are on display in the Penobscot Marine Museum's eight historical buildings downtown.

The chemical industry played a big part in the local economy of

Searsport (during both World War II and the Korean War) with petroleum product shipping. Today lumber, fuels, paper, and chemicals continue to depart and arrive at the busy seaport.

The 1794 Watchtide . . . by the Sea is an 18th-century early American home that became well known in the early 20th century as the Collage Club Inn. Under that name, it is entered in the National Register of Historic Places. The Watchtide had the pleasure of hosting several presidential wives—Eleanor Roosevelt made frequent visits to the hotel.

Activity: The spirits at the Watchtide are said to be friendly, and they have a love for music. Radios owned by the guests and staff will randomly start playing on their own accord. When the present owners first moved in, they began to hear noises like the breaking of windows. When they investigated, nothing was found out of place.

A guest recently snapped a photograph in one of the guest rooms and was surprised to find a misty image over the bed in the developed photo.

One April, all of the inn's clocks, including digital clocks on the stove and microwave and those in each guest room, were turned ahead one hour because of the change to daylight savings time. When the owners returned after a two-week trip, they were astonished to find every single clock had been changed back.

Over the years, guests have reported numerous sightings; however, it is believed that the spirits of the Watchtide spend most of their time on the second floor of the barn. No matter how cold it gets in the winter, the second floor always gives visitors a feeling of warmth.

Accommodations: The 1794 Watchtide . . . by the Sea features five guest rooms with ocean views, making it a perfect choice for newlyweds or lovers of all ages. Each morning you will awaken to a sweet and savory breakfast lovingly prepared and served on the Inn's beautiful 60-foot long wicker-furnished sun porch, overlooking a bird sanctuary and the boats and ships as they sail along Penobscot Bay. Breakfast includes Maine's own delightful coffees, native berries, and homemade popovers with the inn's very own flavored butters. The Inn also provides an 18-hour hot refreshment bar for guests on the go.

The city of Searsport is the antique capitol of Maine, with numerous stores and outdoor flea markets to choose from. Further outdoor activities include whale-watching and sailing.

— MARYLAND —

Pleasant Springs Farm

16112 Barnesville Road
Boyd, MD 20841
Near Washington, DC
(301) 972-3452
www.pleasantspringsfarm.com
Room rates: $165-$270
Personal checks only

Courtesy of Pleasant Springs Farm

History: Built in 1768, the log cabin bed and breakfast is listed on the National Register of Historic Places. The cabin is totally secluded, yet it's only 28 miles from Washington, D.C., and it's also near Sugarloaf Mountain and the C&O Canal.

Jonathan Austin purchased the cabin in 1804, and generations of Austins lived there until 1951. In 1980, the cabin was purchased by the current owners, restored, and opened as a bed and breakfast.

As guests relax in the old cabin, sheep graze and chickens cluck just outside the door, and a trail leads to the farm pond and a blanket of wildflowers.

Activity: Malcolm Walters is the last surviving grandson of the last Austin owner. At age 96, he's a spry, sharp-witted man. He spent much of his childhood at his grandparents' cottage. One day, Walters came to the cottage for lunch, along with his wife and daughter. He and the present owner were sitting in the old log room eating, when Walters suddenly froze and grew pale. His eyes were focused for several seconds on the doorway to the stairs. He then relaxed, sat back, and told them that he saw his grandfather standing there.

Since that time, a comforting presence has been felt in and around the grounds. The presence has been especially strong when the owner is working in the garden. Apparently, Malcolm Walters mentioned that his grandmother loved to work in the garden, and she had every type of flower imaginable. Her presence is often felt there, perhaps watching as the new flowers bloom.

Accommodations: The 18th-century log cabin has been lovingly restored and makes the perfect honeymoon cottage or anniversary getaway. The house has two bedrooms upstairs and a small bedroom downstairs, as well as a stone fireplace. The property is great for weddings, family reunions, and teas, or just as a retreat for nature lovers.

Guests of the 235-year-old cabin will enjoy a gourmet breakfast prepared with exquisite care from a flexible menu of foods selected by the guests themselves. Bridal luncheons offer a dazzling array of foods to make the special day memorable. Whatever the occasion, visiting Pleasant Springs Farm will be like a step back in time.

The Davis Warner Inn

8114 Carroll Avenue • Takoma Park, MD 20912
(301) 408-3989 • www.daviswarnerinn.com
Room rates: $75-$1458 • All major credit cards

History: This historic home was built in 1855 by John B. (J.B.) Davis, a local merchant who operated a store at the corner of Carroll Avenue and University Boulevard, then called Old Bladensburg Road. After the original owners gave up the home in the 1880s, the structure was used as a veterans' hospital, a speakeasy, and in the 1930s, a gambling house. An ambush and murder occurred there during prohibition when a rival gang attempted to kill the bootlegger that lived in the house. The gang mistook a paperboy for the bootlegger and killed him instead.

In 1940, Cynthia and Harold Warner purchased the building and turned it into the Cynthia Warner School, a private school for children. The property was later purchased by the Mormon Church.

In 1991, at the brink of demolition, Mark and Kira Davis, members of the Mormon Church congregation, stopped the bulldozers and talked the church into moving the house a few dozen yards out of harm's way. Over the next four years, the building was restored to a family residence.

In 1997, the current owners, Doug Harbit and Robert Patenaude, purchased the property and renamed the house the Davis Warner Inn in honor of J.B. Davis, Mark and Kira Davis, and Cynthia Warner.

Activity: Since Doug and Robert moved into the house, they have heard the sounds of laughter coming from the front bedroom on the second floor. They feel this was J.B.'s wife Verlina's sitting room.

Guests of the inn have reported the smells of cooking from the area that is now the library, but at one time was the original kitchen.

Guests often hear the sounds of the television playing and doors slamming. It is believed that the spirit of the paperboy who was gunned down in front of the mansion is responsible for these sounds.

In the Mark and Kira Suite, guests hear the sounds of lullabies early in the morning. It has been described as harp music, and Kira Davis was known for playing the harp.

Robert, the co-owner became aware of the fact that the house was haunted early on. Starting with his first night at the inn, he would fall asleep under the sheets and wake up on top of the sheets with the comforter pulled up to his chin, covering him neatly, and tucked into the mattress. It was as if someone had tucked him into bed at night. This occurred every night for the first two weeks.

Accommodations: Located just minutes from downtown Washington, D.C., the Davis Warner Inn is a 6,400-square-foot historic mansion and is the oldest residence in the Takoma Park area. The inn has 11 bedrooms, 4$^1/_2$ baths, formal living and dining rooms, a library, two full kitchens, and a woodworking shop.

Each morning, a delicious breakfast is provided free to all guests of the inn.

— MASSACHUSETTS —

Concord's Colonial Inn

48 Monument Square • Concord, MA 01742
(800) 370-9200, (978) 369-9200
www.concordscolonialinn.com
Room rates: $145-$165 • All major credit cards

History: The Colonial Inn was originally built in 1716 as a triple house that was composed of three original buildings. Peter Bulkeley, one of Concord's original settlers, originally owned the land the buildings reside on. One of the original three structures, the East House, was built by Captain John Minot, a soldier and leading physician in Concord.

The three-part building has operated as a hotel since 1889. For over 100 years, the three houses were owned and operated as private residences, a goldsmith shop, a general store, a boarding house, and finally a hotel.

In 1900, the three structures were attached and named the Colonial Inn. Luther and Loring Grimes took over the building in 1947 and operated it for the next 17 years. Loring was the resident doctor.

Hotelier Jurgen Demisch became the proprietor in 1988, and a major renovation and redecoration began. Demisch understood that The Colonial Inn was a true landmark and often a visitor's first introduction to Concord.

Today, Concord's Colonial Inn, as it is known, offers gracious hospitality and welcome relaxation, nestled among America's revolutionary and literary history.

Activity: Ghostly occurrences surround Room 24 of the Colonial Inn. It's a large room on the second floor of the older part of the Inn, overlooking the Green. It was one of the original three homes built in 1716, called the East House. The Minot House eventually became part of the Inn, along with two 19th-century homes in the later part of the 19th century.

Several years ago, a newlywed couple stayed the night in Room 24. The next morning, the innkeeper noticed that the young bride looked a little peaked. Two weeks after their stay the innkeeper received a letter saying that the bride witnessed a ghost at the inn. She felt too foolish to admit it to anyone at the time. She was awakened in the middle of the night by a presence in the room. As she opened her eyes, she saw a grayish figure at the left side of her bed, approximately four feet away. She described it as a shadowy mass in the shape of a standing figure. It remained still for a minute and then floated to the foot of the bed in front of the fireplace. The apparition stayed there for a few seconds and then slowly disappeared. She could not fall back asleep, so she lay awake trying to rationalize a logical explanation as to what she had seen. Perhaps the moon was shining in the window? No, because the window shades were closed. In mentioning it to her husband the next morning, he replied that, "The ghost was included with the price of the room."

Accommodations: The Colonial Inn offers 56 charming guest rooms, including spacious suites and cozy apartments. Executive houses and suites are also available for both extended or short-term stays.

Some of Concord's finest dining is found at the Colonial inn, including delicious seafood and other New England fare. Dining in the traditional dining rooms is followed by musical entertainment in Village Forge Tavern.

Deerfield Inn

81 Old Main Street • Deerfield, MA 01342-0305
(800) 926-3865, (413) 774-5587 • www.deerfieldinn.com
Room rates: $149-$235 • All major credit cards and personal checks

History: The two Bradley brothers owned an inn on the village common. After they saw their inn destroyed by fire, they rebuilt the Deerfield Inn and opened it in July 1884.

Guests of the inn arrived by stagecoach, carriage, and horseback during its first 15 years of operation. Later, a trolley line ran through the village with a stop directly in front of the Deerfield Inn. The inn was later expanded by local builder George Arms, elevating it far above the average country hotel.

Activity: Room 148 is said to be the most active room in the inn. Who is haunting the room has yet to be determined. Some feel it is John Carlisle and his wife Cora, who were owners before John's death in 1932. Thereafter, Cora held seances in an attempt to contact her late husband. Others feel the ghost may be Eloise Southard, a former housekeeper who worked for many years at the inn.

In 1979, a fire started in room 148, and the guest who was staying there for the night was awakened by some unknown force. She successfully escaped the fire. Other strange events involved voices coming from the bullhorns that hang in the room. In the Carlisle suite, the staff have found it impossible to close all three doors at one time. One will inevitably swing open if the other two are shut.

Accommodations: The Deerfield Inn offers 23 guest rooms. Known as a place of tranquility, the inn enjoys a comfortable and peaceful setting. The Deerfield Inn offers breakfast, lunch, and dinner. For quick, self-serve food, the Terrace Café at the historic Deerfield provides good food for the museum visitor and casual traveler. The 330-year-old village of Deerfield is a National Historic Landmark, and it offers museums, country trails, antiques, and friendly folks.

The Lizzie Borden House

🕇🕇🕇

92 Second Street • Fall River, MA   02721
(508) 675-7333 • www.lizzie-borden.com
Call for room rates • All major credit cards

Lizzie Borden took an axe, and gave her mother forty whacks, when she saw what she had done, she gave her father forty-one.
-Anonymous

History: Only 50 miles from Boston, the Lizzie Borden House stands as a reminder of one of the most grisly murders in U.S. history, as well as one of the most famous unsolved crimes. The house was erected in 1845 and purchased by Andrew J. Borden because it was close to his bank and downtown businesses.

On a hot day in August of 1892, the small town of Fall River (and 33-year-old Lizzie Borden) made front-page headlines. The mutilated bodies of her stepmother, Abbie Durfee Borden, and her father, Andrew Jackson Borden, were found in their home. They had been murdered with 29 blows from a hatchet. Abbie's body was found in the upstairs guest bedroom, and Andrew was found dead on the couch where he'd been taking a nap. Lizzie reportedly discovered both bodies, and not a drop of blood was on her clothing.

Despite strong evidence against her, a jury of 12 men acquitted Lizzie, because they simply felt a God-fearing, charitable, well-bred woman such as she didn't have what it took to murder her father and stepmother. Though she was acquitted and released, she was ostracized by the community and regarded as guilty by many residents. Lizzie lived the remainder of her life in another home in Fall River, dying in 1927.

The home has been a city landmark ever since the infamous ax murders. In 1996, the home was transformed into a bed & breakfast and museum, named after Lizzie.

The interior and exterior of the inn has been restored to its original 1892 Victorian splendor. Guests can now not only view the crime scene, but also stay in the actual house where the murders took place, lie in the bed where Abbie met her demise, or take a nap where Andrew got "whacked."

Activity: We're not surprised to find that this house has a few souls that refuse to remain at rest. One evening, a pair of guests were startled to find their bed actually lifted off of the ground. Then they watched in amazement as one of their shoes flew across the room. The guests checked out that night.

Occasionally, body impressions have appeared on freshly made beds, and a mysterious fog has been seen hovering in the parlor.

Accommodations: The Lizzie Borden House offers 2 two-bedroom suites, each furnished with double beds and Victorian appointments. In the morning, guests are treated to a breakfast similar to the one the Bordens had on the morning of their murder, which includes Jonny-cakes, bananas, sugar cookies, and coffee. Tours of the home are available on selected days, and guests are welcome to visit the museum, which houses an extensive collection of Fall River and Borden memorabilia.

Village Green Inn

40 Main Street
Falmouth, MA 02540
(800) 237-1119, (508) 548-5621
www.villagegreeninn.com
Room rates: $95-$225
Visa, Master Card,
American Express

Courtesy of Village Green Inn

History: Originally built in 1804 by Braddock Dimmick, the property served as the Dimmick family home from 1804 to the1890s. The home was then purchased by the John Crocker family, and they converted it into a Victorian in the late 1890s. The Crockers lived there for 30 years.

In the mid 1920s, the Tripp family bought the home. Both father and son were physicians who lived in the home until the 1970s, but they maintained a practice out of the house until they sold it in the mid 1980s. The new owners transformed the home into a bed & breakfast. The current owners purchased the bed & breakfast in 1995.

Activity: When the current owners purchased the Village Green Inn in 1995, they were unaware that ghosts might inhabit their new home. Since then, whimsical things have occurred like doors locking on their own accord, melted wax appearing on light bulbs, and candy disappearing from rooms.

The first year the current owner was in the home, she was setting the table for breakfast when she looked down the hallway and saw a man walking into the parlor. She described him as having longish gray hair, stooped shoulders, and a flannel shirt. When she described him to a local resident, they told her she had described Dr. Tripp, the local physician who had lived and worked in the home for over 60 years.

One guest told the owner that she was been reading in bed the previous night when she heard the rustling of the bed skirt and felt cold air as if someone was walking past her.

The previous owner was showing the house to a family one day when their young girl became frightened, ran down the stairs and outside, and refused to come back. It turned out that the little girl had seen the images of a couple in 1800s clothing standing at the top of the stairs.

Accommodations: Village Green Inn offers 5 spacious guest rooms, each tastefully appointed. Built in Federal-style architecture and converted to Victorian, the inn sports two large porches complete with white wicker furniture and hanging geraniums. The inn is listed on the National Register of Historic Places.

Each morning guests enjoy a full breakfast of Cape Cod cranberries compote or fresh tangy ambrosia and delicious entrees of apple-cinnamon french toast or creme caramel french toast, which is complimented by an assortment of home-baked breads and cakes, along with freshly brewed coffee.

Guests can relax on the porch and enjoy the view of the historic Village Green while they sip lemonade and sample freshly baked cookies.

The Simmons Homestead Inn

288 Scudder Avenue
Hyannis Port, MA 02647
(800) 637-1649
www.simmonshomesteadinn.com
Room rates: $120-$350
All major credit cards

Courtesy of Simmons Homestead Inn

History: Built in 1800 as the homestead for the Simmons family, the inn is located on Cape Cod. Sylvanus Simmons built the house and barn, and it remained in his son Lemuel's hands until 1892. It remained a private estate until 1988, when it was fully restored and converted into a country inn. Named in honor of the Simmons family, the inn offers unique décor, rolling lawns, and a collection of 50 sports cars located in a series of garages called Toad Hall.

Activity: The Simmons Homestead Inn has a uniquely permanent resident named Susan Simmons. She is the spirit of a small 7-year-old girl who unfortunately drowned in Simmons Pond back in 1833. She apparently loves her home so much she has chosen to stay there, and resides in one of the inn's bedrooms.

When innkeeper Bill Putman was renovating the house, he began to see a small girl with brown hair in a long white dress at the end of the second floor hall, near Room 5. She would disappear around corners and then giggle.

Several years ago, one employee of the inn lived in an attic room on the third floor. She began finding her cosmetics moved around, much in the way a child might play with them. The attic room is located directly above Susan's room and was probably a place where she played.

A few years later, another employee of the inn who was staying in the same attic room would read children's books out loud at night. Occasionally, as she read, she would see the corner of her bed sink down where Susan was sitting and listening to the story.

One day, a guest who was staying in Room 5 came down to breakfast and casually asked the innkeeper if there was a ghost in her room. Bill replied that indeed there was, and asked how she knew. The guest told him that she was up half the night talking to her.

Since that time, guests (especially females) see Susan about every two years. Though some ghosts are quite bothersome, Susan is known to be an absolute gem.

Accommodations: Known as the "nicest and friendliest country inn on Cape Cod or maybe anywhere," the Simmons Homestead Inn is a pleasure to visit. The only bed & breakfast in Hyannis Port, the Simmons Homestead reflects the spirit of old Cape Cod.

The house is historically significant, but the interior and furnishings now add a sense of fun and relaxation. All 14 bedrooms have their own animal themes, like rabbits, giraffes, and elephants. Guests can sit on the porch and relax with a glass of wine after a day of exploring the Cape, the beach, Nantucket, or Martha's Vineyard. Some of Cape Cod's finest restaurants are less than a mile from the inn.

Sherburne Inn Bed and Breakfast

10 Gay Street • Nantucket, MA 02554
(888) 577-4425, (508) 228-4425 • www.sherburneinn.com
Room rates: $85-$295 • All major credit cards

History: The name Sherburne was taken from Nantucket's original name when it was just a settlement. The town's name was changed to Nantucket in 1795. The Sherburne Inn dates back to 1835, when it was first built as headquarters for the Atlantic Silk Company. The building was originally constructed on barrels, since the foundation would not be poured until the ground thawed in the spring. A steam engine, six looms, four spindles, and five hundred bobbins were purchased and installed. The Atlantic Silk Company owned one of only two power looms in the world. Both in texture and weave, the silk produced was comparable with the best on the market. Unfortunately, local merchants and internal strife caused the downfall of the factory in 1844 after losing thousands of dollars of investors' money.

What was once the original factory has now been divided into two separate dwellings. The east side of the building has been transformed into the Sherburne Inn Bed & Breakfast. Visitors are welcome to savor the charm, atmosphere, and gracious hospitality of 19th-century Nantucket.

Activity: One afternoon several years ago, the then owner of the Sherburne Inn was taking a nap with her infant son. She heard a knock at the front door, and then she witnessed the door to their room slowly open and close, as if someone had come in and left. She called out, "hello," but there was no answer. Then she saw the translucent figure of a tall woman in a dress breeze past the bedroom door at a fast pace. The owner followed her, but she found no sign of the apparition.

The figure of the woman was later seen again on the second floor of the inn. The owner was making up the beds and preparing for guests to arrive when she turned the corner and came face-to-face with the spirit. They stared at each other for a few seconds. Though it was a blurry image, the owner could clearly make out the hair around the apparition's face, and she knew it was the same woman she had seen in her room. The spirit abruptly vanished. It is still a mystery as to who she was, though some believe she may have been an employee in the silk factory who was walking around and checking on her workers.

Accommodations: The Sherburne Inn is tucked away in a quiet corner of Nantucket's historic downtown. Featuring 8 guest rooms, the Sherburne offers several one-of-a-kind architectural features that make it one of the most beautiful properties in Nantucket.

The Inn has two magnificent parlors. The first-floor parlor is an elegant room complete with a magnificent fireplace, beautiful antiques, and original artwork. The second-floor parlor, also with its own fireplace, is the perfect place to curl up with a good book or watch television.

Each morning, guests are served a delicious, home-baked Continental breakfast, complete with homemade muffins, island-made breads, and a wide selection of fresh fruits, juices, teas, and coffee.

Hawthorne Hotel on the Common

18 Washington Square West • Salem, MA 01970
(800) 729-7829, (978) 744-4080 • www.hawthornehotel.com
Room rates: $104-$309 • All major credit cards

History: In the 1920s, the townspeople of Salem joined together to raise funds to build a hotel to meet the needs of Salem's guests and visitors. Ever since it was completed in 1925, the Hawthorne Hotel has become a unique part of the city and Boston's North Shore. The beautifully restored and stately Federal-style hotel was named for author Nathaniel Hawthorne, who spent his childhood in Salem. In 1846, Hawthorne returned for three years to serve in the position of surveyor of the port at the customs house. In 1849, Hawthorne wrote *The Scarlet Letter* at his home in Salem.

Activity: The Hawthorne Hotel is surrounded by historical structures, many of them originally built by Salem's sea captains. Many believe that the spirits of these ancient mariners still return to the area they loved almost as much as the sea.

Located in the hotel's restaurant, Nathanial's at the Hawthorne Hotel is a large ship's wheel. Hotel guests and staff have witnessed the large wheel turn back and forth as though someone was steering a ghostly course. Even if the spinning wheel is physically stopped and held in place, once the restraining hand is removed, the wheel will resume its motion.

An employee of the Hawthorne Hotel has refused to work nights after he repeatedly found the silverware on the tables in Nathanial's was rearranged in the opposite order.

Accommodations: The Hawthorne Hotel features 89 guest rooms and suites and is located in the Salem Common Historic District, within walking distance of numerous historic sites.

Longfellow's Wayside Inn

Wayside Inn Road • Sudbury, MA 01776
(800) 339-1776, (978) 443-1776 • www.wayside.org
Room rates: $96-$155 • All major credit cards

History: From 1716 to 1861, Longfellow's Wayside Inn was known as Howe's Tavern, named for David Howe, a successful innkeeper who operated a "house of entertainment" in the very spot where the Wayside Inn stands today. In 1716 Howe received a license to open an inn on his property. Though the property was passed down through generations, it did not operate as an inn for 36 years, when Edward Rivers Lemon, a wool merchant from Malden, Massachusetts, purchased it in 1897. Lemon capitalized on interest generated by a popular book of poems published in 1863 by Henry Wadsworth Longfellow called *Tales of a Wayside Inn*. Longfellow had visited the Howe Inn in 1862, and he based his book on a group of fictitious characters there. Lemon renamed the old Howe Inn to Longfellow's Wayside Inn, and he and his wife Cora operated the inn until his death in 1919.

In 1923, Cora sold the inn to automobile manufacturer Henry Ford. Ford built a grist mill and moved the one-room Redstone School House to the grounds in 1925, along with the Martha-Mary Chapel in 1940.

Activity: The owner told us that the spirit "Jerusha" might be the reason strange things occur in the inn. Jerusha was sister to one of the Howe innkeepers who died in her 40s while waiting for her true love to return from England.

While renovating the inn, the owner heard the footsteps of someone walking slowly down the hall upstairs. She walked to where the footsteps were coming from, but no one was there.

Guests often report unexplained encounters. Some people see a bright light at night that does not emanate from outside. A young honeymooning couple got into an argument when the groom asked his bride what she had whispered into his ear when they were leaving the room. The bride responded by telling him she didn't whisper anything in his ear. They went back and forth several times until he realized it was not her that whispered in his ear. The owner jokingly told the young man it must have been Jerusha, asking when he was going to come back to see her.

Accommodations: Longfellow's Wayside Inn offers 10 guest rooms, and it's a popular location for weddings and special events. The inn has a bakery and gift shop, as well as museum rooms and wonderful dining. Each of the seven dining rooms, complete with fireplaces, offers New England fare from steak to lobster pie to Indian pudding, all served by staff in period costumes.

The tavern also offers unique beverages like Coow Woow, a rum-based drink that's billed as America's first cocktail, or a Stonewall that reportedly dates back to Colonial times. There's even a Meeting House Punch for large groups.

Outside, guests will enjoy visiting the old schoolhouse, chapel, gardens, and the grist mill that grinds flour for use in the Wayside Inn's baked goods.

Old Yarmouth Inn

223 Route 6A • Yarmouth Port, MA 02675
(508) 362-9962 • www.oldyarmouthinn.com
Room rates: $130 • All major credit cards

History: Claiming to be the oldest inn on Cape Cod, the Old Yarmouth Inn was established in 1696. Originally known as the Sears Tavern, it was built as a stage stop at the halfway point on the long journey between Plymouth and Provincetown.

In Colonial times, it was not uncommon for taverns to be situated close to churches. After long hours in the unheated churches, the cold parishioners would all gather at the tavern in front of the warm fire as the innkeeper provided refreshments.

Activity: At least two ghosts reportedly reside at the Old Yarmouth Inn, with most of the activity centering on one of their two rooms.

One local resident saw the ghost when he was staying Thanksgiving night. Around 4 A.M., the man awoke to find the ghost of a gentleman in his room. The ghost was just standing there with his hand resting on his chin. The spirit was described as being a little heavy and wearing late-Victorian clothing. He looked very pleasant and non-threatening. After word got around about the appearance of the ghost, a lady who lived in town brought a picture of her grandfather who once practiced dentistry in the inn. The guest who witnessed the ghost took one look at

Recently, a guest from overseas was staying at the inn when he awoke in the middle of the night and felt a chill. Then he felt someone sit on the edge of his bed. He raised up and looked, but no one was there. He then said to himself that if one more thing occurred, he would change rooms. Suddenly, something grabbed the four-poster bed and started to shake it violently. The guest decided to move.

Further activity has occurred downstairs as well. In the Old Yarmouth Inn restaurant, ash trays have been seen flying through the air, and a lamp turned on and off by itself.

Accommodations: The Old Yarmouth Inn offers 2 big, comfortable guest rooms—haunted and non-haunted—and classic fireside dining. The restaurant at the Old Yarmouth Inn has become one of the premier dining spots on Cape Cod. Guests can relax in one of three dining rooms and enjoy a wonderful array of foods or a favorite beverage at the cozy tavern.

The Old Yarmouth Inn still serves as a welcome respite for the weary traveler, a gathering spot for the locals, and a favorite dining spot for families and friends. Several excellent golf courses are located within a five-mile radius, and the beach is just a short drive from the inn.

— NEW HAMPSHIRE —

Three Chimneys Inn—ffrost Sawyer Tavern

17 Newmarket • Durham, NH 03824
(603) 868-7800
www.threechimneysinn.com
Room rates: $119-$189
All major credit cards

History: The Three Chimneys Inn is the oldest house in Durham and one of the oldest buildings in New Hampshire.

Courtesy of Three Chimneys Inn

In 1649, New England entrepreneur Valentine Hill built the original homestead, a single-story structure with a basement and an upstairs living area. The original kitchen is now used as Maples fine dining room, and the outdoor summer kitchen fireplace can now be seen in the parlor. Hill's son, Nathaniel Hill, built a two-story addition in 1699.

The house survived the Indian attack of 1694 that destroyed many nearby homes. During the Revolutionary War, the home was used as a storage place for munitions taken from the British blockades in Portsmouth and hidden for use by Revolutionary troops.

In the 1800s, George ffrost II purchased the property. The ffrosts were successful merchants, and they renovated the homestead.

The ffrost sisters lived in the home for many years and did extensive work on the gardens. James and Margaret Pepperell ffrost Sawyer took over the estate in the early 1900s, and transformed it into a Colonial Revival summer estate with the ffrost sisters' extensive formal gardens, stone wall terraces, and a reflecting pond.

Activity: The caretaker for the ffrost Sawyer Homestead maintained the building and grounds from 1952 to 1972. During that time, he had a number of inexplicable encounters. On a few occasions while walking down the hall toward the living room, he would notice the rocking chair by the fireplace swaying back and forth gently. He'd remain quiet, standing at the door, and the rocking would continue.

Footsteps have also been heard at the inn, and the form of a woman has been seen in the basement of the mansion where the original open-hearth summer kitchen fireplace is located. The spirit of the woman was seen standing by the warming stove.

The executive chef was closing up one night when he heard loud footsteps as though someone was walking across the wooden floor of the parlor. Thinking it was a guest or perhaps an intruder, he called out, but there was no response. The chef checked the rooms, but all doors were locked. Twenty minutes later the footsteps occurred again, and, though he searched, the chef could not ascertain what was causing the noise.

Accommodations: The newly restored 1649 mansion and carriage house are located on a hill overlooking the formal gardens, the Oyster River, and the Old Mill Falls.

The inn offers 23 historic rooms, fine Colonial cuisine, a cozy old tavern, outdoor dining, and banquet and meeting facilities.

Located one hour north of Boston, the inn is conveniently located in the southern Seacoast Region and is only 15 minutes from Portsmouth Strawberry Banke Museum and John Paul Jones Home. Guests can take short day trips to Canterbury Shaker Village, numerous antique stores, boutique and outlet shopping, and the picturesque fishing villages along the seacoast of Maine.

— NEW JERSEY —

Angel of the Sea

5 Trenton Avenue • Cape May, NJ 08204
(800) 848-3369, (609) 884-3369 • www.angelofthesea.com
Room rates: $95-$315 • All major credit cards

History: Around 1850, the Angel of the Sea was built as a summer cottage for William Weightman, a Philadelphia chemist known for discovering and manufacturing quinine for medical applications.

In 1881, Weightman's son, William Jr., decided that an ocean view from the broad porches of his cottage was needed, so with the help of local farmers, they decided to move the house. Finding it too large to move as a whole, they split it in half and moved it in sections. Pulling the house on rolling logs with a team of mules and horses was truly a Herculean task, and the move took the entire winter. The horses and mules brought the sections of the house to its new location, but they did not have the strength to put the two halves together. So, the house was sealed and left as it stands today, two buildings side-by-side, a house split down the middle.

Over the years the cottage has been used as a guest house, hotel, and restaurant. In 1962, a storm destroyed much of Cape May. Fortunately, the Angel of the Sea survived, yet it sustained considerable damage. After many years of renovation and rebuilding, the Angel of the Sea was transformed into a bed & breakfast and reopened in 1989.

Activity: In the 1980s, the building served as a dormitory for employees of the nearby Christian Admiral Hotel, Shelton College, and Congress Hall. One day, an employee of the Christian Admiral Hotel found she had locked herself out of her third-floor room in the second building. She decided to climb out a window at the end of the hall, move around to her window, crawl in, and unlock her door. However, when she made it out on the ledge and around to her window, she found a screen tightly connected to the outside. As she tugged on it, the screen sprung loose, striking her and causing her to fall to her death.

Today, the spirit of the teenager has been seen on the grounds of the Angel of the Sea. She is known to be a little mischievous, and occasionally she likes to turn lights and televisions on and off. Also, doors in particular areas of the inn have been found to lock and unlock on their own. This is interesting, due to the manner in which the young girl met her untimely demise.

Accommodations: Angel of the Sea features 9 guest rooms, each complete with fireplace and ocean views. An elegant oceanfront restaurant on the first floor offers the perfect dinner for two during those romantic getaways.

— NEW YORK —

The Sagamore

110 Sagamore Road • Bolton Landing, NY 12814
(800) 358-3585, (518) 644-9400 • www.thesagamore.com
Room rates: $149-$2500 • All major credit cards

History: Hotel operator Myron O. Brown enlisted the aid of four Philadelphia millionaires to finance Green Island's first Sagamore. The four men were summer residents of the area, and together they bought Green Island and formed the Green Island Improvement Company. Later, investor John Boulton Simpson of New York joined the group and became the company's president.

In 1883, the Sagamore opened to the public with luxurious and spacious accommodations, attracting an international clientele. It was damaged by fire in both 1893 and 1914, but the hotel was fully restored in 1930. Throughout its history, the Sagamore has been the social center for Green Island's wealthy residents and their stately mansions along the island's western shore, collectively called Millionaires Row.

In 1954, the Sagamore hosted the National Governor's Conference, presided over by Vice President Richard M. Nixon and hosted by Govenor Thomas E. Dewey. The hotel closed its doors in 1981. In 1983 builder and real estate developer Norman Wolgin purchased The Sagamore and restored it to its former grandeur. Today, it is listed in the National Register of Historic Places.

Activity: Legend has it that the Trillium, the Sagamore's fine dining restaurant, is visited regularly by the ghosts of a couple that were among the hotel's first guests in the 1880s. Reportedly, they descend from the second floor and actually take a seat in the restaurant's reception room before exiting.

Another of the hotel's restaurants is Mr. Brown's. That restaurant was visited by an apparition of a tall woman with flowing blond hair, dressed in a long white evening gown. She spoke to the cook, walked toward him, and then continued right through him before she disappeared. The cook decided to find a job elsewhere.

Accommodations: Located on Lake George, the Sagamore offers 174 guest rooms and 176 spacious suites. With a peaceful lakefront location, golf course, tennis club and full-service spa, this is a wonderful year-round getaway. The resort's deluxe spa is joined together with a fitness room, which offers classes, personal training, and even scuba diving lessons.

In the evenings, guests can dine on a delicious cuisine in The Sagamore's award-winning Trillium restaurant.

Ancestors Inn at the Bassett House

215 Sycamore Street
Liverpool, NY 13088
(888) 866-8591, (315) 461-1226
www.ancestorsinn.com
Room rates: $100-$235
All major credit cards

Courtesy of Ancestors Inn at the Bassett House

History: Built in the late 1850s by early settlers of the village of Liverpool, the inn is named for George and Hannah Bassett. The home was owned by several members of the Bassett family until the 1960s, when it was purchased by a dentist and turned into his office. Current owners Mary and Dan Weidman bought the inn in 1998 and have painstakingly restored the property to its former glory.

Activity: When the bed & breakfast was opened to the public in October of 1998, the Weidmans lived part-time on site and part-time at another property. What was most likely George and Hannah's original bedroom is located at the front of the house and overlooks the parking area. Each time the Weidmans left the house, they would check the rooms and make sure the lights were off. Every time they returned to the house, the lights would be on.

Early visitors of the inn would bring their cameras to take pictures downstairs. When they get ready to leave, they would be unable to find their cameras. The cameras would later be discovered in other parts of the inn. At times, photographs taken in the inn would not develop; however, if one of the Weidmans was standing with the person taking the pictures, the film would develop without any problem.

Guests who have stayed in the Valentine Room have reported that occasionally during the night, the doorknob is rattled as if someone was making sure the door was locked and the house was secure. Others have sensed a welcoming spirit in the room and in the parlor downstairs. One Thanksgiving, the Weidman's teenage son was visiting and staying in the basement bedroom. He became ill during his visit and was on medication. During the night, every two hours he was awakened by a presence of a large African-American man wearing old-fashioned clothes. He gave the young man the medicine and water he needed. The spirit told him his name was Tim, and the young man reported that his presence was comforting.

Accommodations: Located in the quiet village of Liverpool, the historic Bassett House is a beautiful, brick Italianate house which has been restored by the present innkeepers. All four of the guest rooms are specially decorated and have queen-sized beds and private baths. Books are available to borrow, and soft drinks and juices are complimentary.

Ancestors Inn at the Bassett House serves a full gourmet breakfast, and afternoon tea or lemonade is provided on the wide front porch. From the inn, guests can take a walk in Onondaga Lake Park or visit the Gleason Mansion or Salt Museum.

The Algonquin

59 West 44th Street • New York, NY 10036
(888) 304-2047, (212) 840-6800 • www.thealgonquin.net
Room rates: $269-$429 • All major credit cards

History: Located in the heart of midtown Manhattan, the Algonquin opened in 1902. The hotel was a gathering place for New York's literary set and was host to the famous "Round Table" of the 1920s, which included Dorothy Parker, Robert Benchley, Alexander Woollcott, and Zelda and F. Scott Fitzgerald. The famous Oak Room at the Algonquin has featured artists such as Michael Feinstein, Harry Connick, Jr., and Andrea Marcovicci. Today, the Algonquin continues its tradition of elegance amidst the business and cultural attractions of the city that never sleeps.

Activity: Guests of the Algonquin have reported seeing the ghosts of the Round Table. Parker, Benchley, and the Fitzgeralds may still be congregating in their favorite hotel, doing what they do best—talking and enjoying some spirits of the liquid kind. The staff of the hotel practices their own unique exorcism each New Year's Eve. At the stroke of midnight, the kitchen crew enters the hotel lobby banging pots and pans to frighten away the spirits. Considering the reputation of the ghosts in question, they may be more amused than alarmed by the spectacle.

Accommodations: The Algonquin's 12 floors offer 142 graciously appointed guest rooms and 23 club suites that contain personal libraries, CD and VCR players, and Round Table memorabilia. A decanter of sherry and a complimentary fruit bowl are also included.

In 1998, The Algonquin completed a multi-million dollar restoration, providing the newly appointed guest rooms and suites with plush carpeting, hand-selected antiques and custom wallpaper.

For guests' convenience, a restaurant, fitness facility, laundry/valet service, lounge, and meeting facility are all located onsite. Only minutes from fine dining, shopping, and world-class entertainment, The Algonquin has been named "One of America's 10 Best Historic Hotels" by *Historic Traveler Magazine*.

— PENNSYLVANIA —

Carlisle House

148 South Hanover Street • Carlisle, PA 17013
(717) 249-0350 • www.thecarlislehouse.com
Room rates: $95-$250 • Visa, Master Card, American Express

History: The Carlisle House is one of the oldest buildings in Carlisle, with the oldest portion of the house dating back to the late 1700s. Its current form was completed in 1854. The Carlisle House was standing when George Washington rode into town and it was there throughout the Civil War, during which soldiers from the North and the South occupied the house at different times. Legend has it that soldiers from both sides marched by the house and worshiped together at St. John's Episcopal Church before walking a few miles down the road to one of the bloodiest battles of the war, Gettysburg.

The Ewing family purchased the house in 1927, and it was restored to its original beauty. William Ewing was a cabinetmaker and conducted a funeral business on the side. After his death in 1936, his widow Jessie Ewing became the first licensed female funeral director in Pennsylvania. She raised her twin sons in the house and continued to live there until 1965.

For 30 years, the house remained in the family (though vacant). In 1995, a relative of the Ewings purchased the house and converted it into a banquet facility. In December of 2000, the Carlisle House became a bed and breakfast.

Activity: In the early to middle 20th century when the house was a funeral parlor, quite a few funeral services were held there. However, none of the current paranormal activity seems to be related to that aspect of the house's use. The image of someone in a long-flowing gown has been seen walking through the halls, but the owners feel this is the spirit of Jessie Ewing, not someone interred there.

Several weddings have taken place at the Carlisle House, and many pictures have been taken of brides descending the staircase to be married between the beautiful arched double doors. Several of the brides have returned to show the owners pictures taken down the hallway facing the stairway. Several of these contain an iridescent, yellowish green streak—almost as if Jessie had become the perpetual wedding guest, never missing a good ceremony.

On December 20, 1997, a fire started at the Carlisle House. By the time the owners arrived, the fire had been put out. The owner noticed that none of the doors had been damaged, so she asked the firemen how they entered the building without smashing the front doors. The firemen told the owner that when they arrived, both the double inside and outside doors were open and they just walked in. The owner knew that both doors were locked when she left the home, and she believes the ghost of Jessie opened the doors and saved the home.

Accommodations: The Carlisle House Bed and Breakfast offers 7 guest rooms that range from suites with double jacuzzi's to a 3-room apartment. Located in downtown Carlisle, only 2 blocks from main square, The Carlisle House features hand-crafted moldings, the Crystal chandeliers, a Ben Franklin Stove, and a marbelized slate fireplace.

Each morning guests will enjoy a special in-room breakfast served by the staff of the Carlisle House.

Historic Cashtown Inn

1325 Old Route 30 • Cashtown, PA 17310
(800) 367-1797, (717) 334-9722 • www.cashtowninn.com
Room rates: $100-$150 • All major credit cards or personal check

History: The Cashtown Inn was built in 1797, and it served as the first stagecoach stop west of Gettysburg. When the Gettysburg campaign of 1863 occurred, the inn served as Confederate headquarters for General A. P. Hill.

The Inn has appeared in the motion picture, "Gettysburg," and in several publications and documentaries. Renowned Civil War artist Dale Gallon has depicted the Inn in his limited edition print titled, "Serious Work Ahead," which shows General Robert E. Lee and General Hill meeting at the Inn on July 1, 1863.

Dennis and Eileen Hoover purchased the Cashtown Inn in March of 1996. The Hoovers approach innkeeping with the philosophy that prospective guests are friends in waiting. Informality and pampered individual attention are their specialties.

Activity: The Hoovers report that a few of their guests have witnessed the appearance of two ghosts at the inn.

The first is an apparition of a Confederate soldier that mysteriously appeared in a photograph they own. Oddly, the soldier is seen in a photo that was taken on the front porch of the inn in the year 1900, though he had died thirty-seven years prior to that. We encourage guests to ask to see the photograph of the eternal soldier.

The second ghost that has been seen by a select few is that of a woman who appears dressed in white. Many believe she is the wife of a former innkeeper. She has made her presence known on the third floor in the General Robert E. Lee Suite.

Accommodations: The Cashtown Inn features 7 guest rooms; a cozy tavern for lunch, dinner, or liquid spirits; and an elegant dining room for dinner and group functions. Guests will enjoy sitting or swinging on the porch, as well as strolling along the gardens.

Angelic Inn at Ragged Edge

1090 Ragged Edge Road
Fayetteville, PA 17222
(888) 900-5880, (717) 261-1195
www.angelicinn.com
Room rates: $49-$189
All major credit cards

Courtesy of Angelic Inn at Ragged Edge

History: Colonel. Moorhead C. Kennedy, president of the Cumberland Valley Railroad (CVRR) and vice-president of the Pennsylvania Railroad, built The Ragged Edge Inn (the original name). Educated at Harvard, Kennedy and his wife were revered and respected by the community. Moorhead Kennedy passed away at his beloved Ragged Edge Inn.

Ragged Edge is well known for its railroad history and its annual stag reception held on a Saturday in October each year. From 100 to 200 guests were brought in by private railroad car at the turn of the century. Some of the notable guests were Brigadier General Atterbury, French General Foch and General Purshing.

The Cumberland Valley Railroad under Kennedy's management was innovative and one of the most financially successful railroad companies. Life at the turn of the century centered around the railroad. People went to the train depot for an evening stroll, to hear some juicy gossip, or gather with friends. Townspeople would show up to hear politicians speak.

The turn-of-the-century inn now has its fourth owner, and it has been restored to its former glory. The inn was reopened to the public on August 22, 1993, and 1,200 people were in attendance.

Every year, there is a candlelight tour to benefit Women in Need, an organization serving abused women. As many as 3,000 visitors tour the inn during the benefit.

Activity: Located in Gettysburg, an area known for ghosts, the Angelic Inn at Ragged Edge has its own share of stories. Large pocket doors located in the inn often open by themselves. Photographs taken in the home by guests have revealed ghostly images on the developed pictures.

A retired couple from California always stays in the Angelic Suite. One night, the husband got up to go to the bathroom; as he returned to bed, he turned off a little angel lamp. When he woke up later, the light was back on. He turned the light back off, only to find it on again a few hours later. He finally turned the light off and unplugged the light from the wall. A few hours later, to his surprise, the light was on again. He got up and checked the light, and found it was still unplugged.

The inn has been renamed the Angelic Inn because of the owner's feeling that angels are ever-present, and guests who usually stay at the inn are there for a reason, and not by coincidence.

Accommodations: The Angelic Inn at Ragged Edge offers 12 guest rooms, each individually decorated and named after generations of notable Kennedy family members. After the inn's meticulous restoration, an old friend of the Kennedys that knew Moorhead personally told the present owner that the Colonel would probably have said that the inn is more beautiful today than when he built it.

A continental breakfast is available upon request. For an added treat, flowers and special gift baskets can be ordered prior to your visit to the Inn to help make your stay even more romantic.

The Historic Farnsworth House Inn

🕊️ 🕊️ 🕊️ 🕊️

401 Baltimore Street
Gettysburg, PA 17325
(717) 334-8838
www.farnsworthhousedining.com
Room rates: $105-$165
All major credit cards

By Michael R. McGough. Courtesy of The Historic Farnsworth House Inn

History: One only has to hear the word "Gettysburg" to imagine one of the bloodiest battles of the Civil War. The battle itself took place in only three days, July 1–3, in 1863. Though the conflict ended well over a century ago, two million visitors come to this historic town each year. It contains the largest battlefield shrine in America, and over 1,000 monuments with over 40 miles of scenic avenues.

The Farnsworth House was built in 1810, with the brick portion added in 1833. It was owned by the Sweney family during the Battle of Gettysburg. On the first day of the Battle, the Farnsworth House fell into Confederate hands after the Union troops were routed through the town. As the Northern armies poised along Culp's Hill, the house was used as a bastion for Confederate sharpshooters as part of a Confederate perimeter paralleling the base of Culp's Hill.

The area between the Farnsworth and adjacent Confederate positions and the Union troops defending against a Confederate advance on Culp's Hill became a "no man's land" where intruders of either side fell under sharpshooter fire from the opposing line. Today, the wall of the house facing the Union position is pockmarked with over 150 bullet holes.

Following the battle, the house was used as one of a number of general headquarters of the Union Army. Restoration of the Sweney House (named after its Civil War owners) began in 1972. Prior to it being named The Farnsworth House in honor of Union General Elon John Farnsworth, the bed and breakfast was known as Sleepy Hollow.

Activity: We suggest you take the Candlelight Ghost Walk into realms of the unknown as a period-dressed guide escorts you down the very streets where soldiers fought and died. Their historic tales and legends make the Ghost Walk both entertaining and educational. We encourage you to take a walk and possibly experience your own ghostly encounter, like many have before.

While staying at the Farnsworth House Inn, you'll be happy to know that its proprietors advertise several of their rooms as haunted. The Sarah Black Room, located in the old house, overlooks Baltimore Street, where Abraham Lincoln rode by to deliver the Gettysburg Address. The Jennie Wade Room, which is also located in the old house, is named for the only civilian killed in the battle. Also, the Garrett Room, Shultz Room, Catherine Sweney Room, and the McFarland Room have all played host to paranormal activity. Each of the Farnsworth's rooms is individually decorated with 19th-century antiques, fine draperies, and personal items.

Some believe a ghostly visitor still walks the corridors at night and a female ghost named Mary reportedly walks up and down the upstairs hallway. She has been seen wearing dark clothing. Sudden cold spots and the sound of a harp have also been reported.

Accommodations: The Historic Farnsworth House Inn offers 11 guest rooms and provides visitors with a huge array of activities, including fine dining, a Candlelight Ghost Walk, Mourning Theatre, a

Spirit Theatre, and a Civil War Parlor Magic Show. The authentically restored dining rooms are accented by oil paintings of the two commanding officers at Gettysburg, General Robert E. Lee and General George G. Meade. Guests can dine by candlelight among original décor and enjoy a variety of cuisine delicately prepared with extra authenticity to give visitors a touch of early period cookery. Guests will enjoy Game Pie, Pumpkin Fritters, Peanut Soup, Spoon Bread, Sweet Potato Pudding and, for dessert, Walnut-Apple Cake.

Bucksville House Bed and Breakfast

4501 Durham Road • Kintnersville, PA 18930-1610
(888) 617-6300, (610) 847-8948 • www.bucksvillehouse.com
Room rates: $125-$150 • All major credit cards

History: Built in 1795, the Bucksville House has gone through several expansions since becoming a hotel in 1830. It has also been a tavern, a speakeasy during Prohibition, and a private residence.

The décor of the Bucksville House Inn includes period-style reproduction furniture and authentic 1830-1840 pieces like four-poster beds, country kitchen table and cabinet, desk, bureau and backgammon set. Restored 19th-century pieces include antique collectables, original art, as well as nearly 100 quilts, with the earliest homespun quilt coming from the 1800s.

The inn's current breakfast room was originally a 1795 blacksmith shop with a walk-in fireplace and early-19th-century mercer tiles. The Bucksville House is a registered Bucks County historical landmark.

Activity: There are several friendly guests of the Bucksville House that don't sign the register. There have been recurring sightings of a man in a black hat who crosses between the fireplace and a bed and sometimes moves the pieces on the checkerboard. There is also a spirit of a woman in a white dress that occasionally visits the attic. Lastly, small items are often displaced by the ghost of a boy with a mischievous nature.

Accommodations: Bucksville House Bed and Breakfast offers 5 guest rooms, each containing a fireplace, canopy bed, and period antiques. The inn's décor reflects the 1790s to the 1840s period with authentic 1800s furniture, original art, and collectables.

During the cooler months, a hot breakfast is served each morning hearthside in the dining room. During warm weather, guests can enjoy their breakfast in the screened gazebo outside. Visitors can also help themselves to homemade wine from grapes grown on the premises. The four-acre site offers guests the opportunity to walk the brick and wooden patios and pathways or visit a large stocked pond with walking bridge. Gardeners or anyone with a green thumb will appreciate the water garden, perennial flower bed, grape arbor, and an herb garden patterned after one in Colonial Williamsburg.

The General Lafayette Inn & Brewery

646 Germantown Pike • Lafayette Hill, PA 19444
(800) 251-0181, (610) 941-0600 • www.generallafayetteinn.com
Room rates: $109-$189 • All major credit cards

History: The original structure was built in 1732. It is believed that during the American Revolution, General William Smallwood and General William Hull used the inn as headquarters, and General Marquis de Lafayette frequently visited his fellow officers at the inn for meetings and refreshments.

After the Revolution, the buildings at Barren Hill (now Lafayette Hill) had to be refurbished. During this time, the Dager and Hitner families intermarried and built large additions to the inn. In 1874, a horse-drawn trolley line was opened, and the old inn became a popular place for weary travelers. In 1946, owner Ludwig Zackiewicz changed the name from the Barren Hill Hotel to the Lafayette Hotel.

In the mid 1990s, the inn closed its doors after centuries of operation. In 1996, after extensive restoration, the inn opened its doors once again, maintaining its Colonial appeal.

Activity: The General Lafayette Inn, with its 270-year history, is brimming with paranormal activity.

Innkeeper Michael McGlynn was working late one night in his office on the second floor when he heard the doorknob rattle as if someone was trying to open it. He quickly looked over, and the knob was not moving. It happened a few times. Each time he would get up and walk to the door and look, but each time, no one was there.

Employees and guests of the inn have witnessed a chair in the Pool Room twirling on one leg. Witnesses have heard footsteps coming from the second floor when no one was there. Each time, guests have tried to find the source of the footsteps, but they've been unsuccessful. Several people have sighted the ghost of an older woman crossing through the smaller upstairs dining rooms.

One night, a young man in his mid 20s was exiting the tavern near the host stand around 1:00 A.M. As he walked to the door, he witnessed the apparition of an old, hunched-over man in a white nightgown walking toward the kitchen. The young man stopped in his tracks. The bartender found the young man motionless, his face white as snow, and the two are convinced he saw something supernatural.

Accommodations: The General Lafayette Inn & Brewery offers charm and professional service with modern hotel amenities. The bed and breakfast, called Lafayette's Retreat, offers 5 tastefully appointed rooms and a guest house, which is set back in the rear acreage among tall oak trees and connected to the restaurant by a brick pathway.

The restaurant provides guests with a fine upscale dining atmosphere. Local and national microbrews are available in the Inn's tavern, including beer from their own microbrewery. Local musicians perform several nights a week, playing an eclectic range of music in the lively tavern.

— RHODE ISLAND —

Edgewood Manor Bed & Breakfast

232 Norwood Avenue
Providence, RI 02905
(800) 882-3285, (401) 781-0099
www.providence-lodging.com
Room rates: $99-$245
All major credit cards

Courtesy of Edgewood Manor Bed & Breakfast

History: Edgewood was developed at the turn of the 19th century with the goal of attracting businessmen from Providence, who favored its convenient location to the city while offering the natural beauty of the bay. In 1905, a wealthy businessman by the name of Samuel Priest commissioned the three-story Greek-Revival mansion. In the decades since its creation as a private residence, Edgewood Manor has served at various times as a convent, a rooming house, hospital administrative offices, and now as an elegantly romantic bed and breakfast.

Activity: From 1950 to 1986, Edgewood Manor was used as a convent, maintained by an order of Catholic nuns. The current owner purchased the mansion in 1994, and immediately thereafter, eyewitnesses started reporting strange sightings. Since the curtains were not up at that time, the windows were open to the street. Reportedly, the images of women dressed in white were seen walking past the front windows. They appeared to be the spirits of the nuns that once lived and worked in the convent.

After the purchase, the electricity was off for a few days. Although no power was coming into the house, a buzzer kept sounding. The manager grew tired of hearing the buzzer, so he followed the wires to the third floor, where it led to a box on the wall. Although there were no power or AC cords leading to the box, the buzzer still sounded. The manager had to physically remove the box from the wall before it would stop.

Finally, guests often report that while in their rooms, items such as brushes and combs will mysteriously fly off the dressers.

Accommodations: Edgewood Manor Bed & Breakfast offers 8 guest rooms, and is nestled between beautiful Narragansett Bay and Roger Williams Park and Zoo, only two and a half miles from historic downtown Providence.

Each morning, guests will enjoy a full breakfast, served on the outdoor patio when weather permits. The inn's signature dish is Eggs Florentine, accompanied by homemade blueberry corn muffins. There are also low-fat and vegetarian meals provided upon request.

Brookside Manor

☆ ☆ ☆ ☆ ☆

380-B Post Road
Wakefield, RI 02879
(401) 788-3527
www.brooksidemanor.net
Room rates: $175-$225 • Visa,
Master Card, American Express

Courtesy of Brookside Manor

History: Brookside Manor was initially part of a large estate. Originally built in 1690 by William Mumford, Brookside was a typical Rhode Island farmhouse. In 1921, textile baron Charles Fletcher and his family took Brookside Manor, a simple saltbox farmhouse, and transformed it over the next ten years into a beautiful, 8,000-square-foot-manor for their weekend retreat. In 1965, following Fletcher's death, his heirs sold the home to the Tarzwell family, who owned it until 1996 when the Vitale family purchased the manor and started operating it as an inn.

Activity: Over the years, several people have reported that Charles Fletcher makes an appearance from time to time in the oldest part of the house. One former innkeeper stayed in the oldest bedroom in the inn after her husband passed away. She claimed that Fletcher appeared at her bedside and asked if everything was okay, and if she was all right living there alone. Prior to this encounter, the innkeeper did not believe in an afterlife.

When the Vitales purchased the home in 1996, the decorative painters claimed to have seen Fletcher's ghost on several occasions.

Late one night around midnight, guests were playing a board game in the library when they heard a bouncing or dropping sound, and then one of the guests felt a cold presence. They decided it was time for bed.

A 17th-century cemetery is located on the property. One day, the owner saw two men standing on the hill in the cemetery. Wondering what they were doing there, the owner went outside to call to them – but by the time she came outside, they had disappeared.

Accommodations: Brookside Manor features 5 uniquely decorated s. Located on nearly eight acres, the Manor offers landscaped gardens in a park-like setting, complete with brook and pond.

The dining room was added during the 1932 restoration and provides guests with a savory breakfast served in this beautiful pine-paneled room with a wood-burning fireplace. Visitors can sit and relax with a cup of coffee and admire the extensive Murano glass collection housed in the historic room.

— VERMONT —

River Mist Bed & Breakfast

☆☆☆

7 Burt Street
Bellows Falls, VT 05101
(888) 463-9023
(802) 463-9023
www.river-mist.com
Room rates: $80-$150
Visa, Master Card, Discover,
Personal Checks, Travelers Checks

Courtesy of River Mist Bed & Breakfast

History: Bellows Falls derives its importance largely from its historical relationship to the Great Falls of the Connecticut River. Native Americans used the river for travel and they came together to the Falls to catch migrating salmon and shad. Early white settlers followed suit and then developed overland transport routes that focused on the first bridge across the Connecticut River, built in 1785. To expedite the early river traffic, one of the first canals in the United States was opened in 1802 to bypass the Falls. That canal also provided water to power Bellows Falls' emerging industry.

When the railroads passed through the area around 1850, Bellows Falls became one of the most important railroad junctions in northern New England.

In the 1870s, the available water power attracted paper mills that were among the first industries in the United States to use wood pulp— as opposed to rags—for raw material. By 1900, Bellows Falls had expanded into an important manufacturing center with a business district whose architectural character reflected its drive and prosperity. Bellows Falls still retains the historic fabric of its earlier ascendancy, and recently has undertaken substantial efforts toward its preservation.

The River Mist was originally built in 1895 and served as a private residence until it was transformed into a wonderful Queen Anne Victorian Bed and Breakfast.

Activity: Ghostly footsteps have been heard on the rear servants' staircase, and they continue down the long hallway past the bedrooms on the second floor.

When the bed is made in the Garden Room, the owner will often feel something flick him on the back of the head. When he turns around, no one will be there.

Objects have disappeared throughout the inn only to reappear later in strange and inexplicable places. An expensive diamond ring was on the owner's finger one day and gone the next. She searched the inn for months, and finally gave up. She later found the ring packed in a sealed box that had been in storage since the inn was purchased.

Legend has it that, a past owner of the home, a kind old lady, died quietly in the parlor. A little more unsettling fact was that a man who owned the home prior to her hung himself in the laundry room.

Occasionally, dark shadows have moved across the walls, and guests have reported shadowy figures moving through their rooms.

The pet dogs apparently see something or someone. When they are on the front porch, they will jump to attention, their ears will perk up, and their eyes will follow someone not visible to humans. A stay at the River Mist may indeed bring visitors in touch with ghosts of the past.

Accommodations: The River Mist Bed & Breakfast has 4 beautifully appointed rooms, each with special amenities. For guests seeking a little adventure, there is great hiking, sightseeing, and antiquing.

The River Mist offers one of the finest gourmet breakfasts in Vermont, which includes homemade cinnamon rolls, stuffed french toast and baked apples, a fabulous quiche, fruit plates, and much more.

The Equinox

Historic Route 7A • Manchester Village, VT 05254
(800) 362-4747, (802) 362-4700 • www.equinoxresort.com
Room rates: $149-$1200 • All major credit cards

History: The Equinox is a Vermont landmark with six different architectural styles, 17 separate buildings, six name changes, and a history that dates back over 200 years. It was at the Equinox where Ethan Allen and the Green Mountain Boys gathered to discuss independence in the days leading up to the Revolutionary War. The 1,100-acre resort began in 1769 as the Marsh Tavern. Owner William Marsh chose to side with the British and his two-story building was the first property to be seized in the name of American independence.

The hotel almost fell into ruin by the 1970s, when Francesco Galesi took it over and conducted a major restoration. The Equinox reopened to year-round visitors in 1985. Every architectural and decorative detail was restored to its original beauty. In 1991, it was purchased by Equinox Resort Associates and Olympus Real Estate.

Today, the inn that played host to Mary Todd Lincoln, Ulysses S. Grant, William Howard Taft, Benjamin Harrison, and Theodore Roosevelt has been revitalized and modernized to continue its reputation as a landmark hotel. In 1972, the Equinox was named to the National Register of Historic Places.

Activity: Mary Todd Lincoln and her sons spent two summers at the Equinox to escape the heat of Washington, D.C. The family planned to return in the summer of 1865, but the assassination of Abraham Lincoln ended those plans. Today, employees of the Equinox claim to have seen the images of a woman and a child on the third floor. The figures of the mother and child are consistent with descriptions of Mary Todd Lincoln and one of her sons. Perhaps Mrs. Lincoln is still trying to recapture the carefree days of those summers more than a century ago.

Accommodations: The Equinox offers 136 guest rooms that includes 10 suites and nine three-bedroom townhouses in the main hotel. For more than 230 years The Equinox has offered its guests superior dining and first-class service. Guests will find delectable dishes, artfully presented in each and every restaurant.

The Marsh Tavern, the original structure that became today's resort, offers regional cuisine and fine spirits and a wonderful weekend brunch is served in the elegant Colonnade Dining Room. Open seasonally, the Dormy Grill is located at the clubhouse on Gleneagles Golf Course, with spectacular views of the Green Mountains. It serves casual lunches and spectacular weekend evening lobsterfests.

The North Hero House

🕂🕂🕂

P. O. Box 207, Champlain Islands
North Hero, VT 05474
(802) 372-4732
(888) LAKENHH (525-3644)
www.northherohouse.com
Room rates: $75-$295
Visa, Master Card, American Express

Courtesy of The North Hero House

History: North Hero, an island on Lake Champlain, is home of the Rockwell family, who produced many steam boat captains for almost one hundred years, including Eli Rockwell, the oldest captain in the world.

The North Hero House was built in 1891. Guests arrived by steamship to stay at this beautiful inn located in the Lake Champlain islands of northern Vermont. The historic country inn and bed and breakfast has a spectacular view of the Green Mountains and Mount Mansfield. The inn was beautifully restored in 1997 with period antiques and modern conveniences.

Activity: The paranormal activity at The North Hero House apparently centers around Room 301, a third-floor room that has a beautiful view of Lake Champlain, complete with a window seat. Reportedly, several people have seen the apparition of a woman who has made her presence known to guests and employees. On one occasion, a guest saw her while bathing in the claw-foot tub in the bathroom of his room. Occasionally, the spirit of the woman will travel from Room 301 to 304.

Accommodations: The inn offers 26 guest rooms and is open year-round. It is a perfect setting for weddings, family vacations, honeymoons, meetings and conferences, or just a romantic getaway.

The North Hero House has a beautiful colonial dining room with widely acclaimed cuisine. Guests can sit by the fire in the greenhouse for drinks before dinner or have dessert after dinner. Each morning visitors can enjoy breakfast on the front porch and watch the ice skaters as they go by.

The Inn at Rutland

70 North Main Street
Rutland, VT 05701
(800) 808-0575, (802) 773-0575
www.innatrutland.com
Room rates: $90-$205
All major credit cards

Courtesy of The Inn at Rutland

History: Built in 1889 by William F. Burditt for his family, this stately Victorian mansion is located within a few miles of Killington, making it the perfect place to stay for guests who want to ski in Killington, hike the Green Mountains, or enjoy the fall foliage. A large wraparound porch fronts the inn, and guests can sit and take in the breathtaking views of the Green Mountains. Once guests step inside, they are immediately transported to the 1800s. A grand oak staircase, carved plaster relief ceilings and wainscoting, huge leaded glass windows, and fine period antiques take you back in time to an era of romantic splendor.

Activity: The Burditts had a caretaker named Henry. One of Henry's weekly chores was to go to the attic and bring down some of the necessary provisions for the week. Legend has it that Henry's fiancée became sick and died, and Henry became quite despondent. After several days passed and Henry did not show up for work, the Burditts went to the attic to get their own provisions. There they found Henry hanging by the neck from the rafters.

Since then, guests have reported their own encounters with Henry. Often he will open and close doors to the guest rooms. He has thrown bath towels onto the floor, and Henry occasionally messes up the pillows that were neatly placed on the beds minutes before. His continual mischief makes it very difficult for the housekeeping staff to do their job.

Accommodations: The inn has 11 unique guest rooms. Each room has a private bath, cable television, air conditioning, designer sheets, and plush towels. Two of the rooms now have fireplaces for those wintry days, and all of their three-course breakfasts are accompanied by a fine selection of teas and the best coffee in Vermont.

Green Mountain Inn

P.O. Box 60 • Stowe, VT 05672
(800) 253-7302 • www.greenmountaininn.com
Room rates: $109-$429 • All major credit cards

History: In 1833, Peter C. Lovejoy built the inn as a home. Lovejoy traded the residence to Stillman Churchill for a 350-acre farm. Churchill added two brick wings, a front porch, and a dance hall to the original building, and he named it the Mansfield House. The property was eventually foreclosed, and W.H.H. Bingham took possession of the property.

In 1893, Mark C. Lovejoy, the great-grandson of Peter C. Lovejoy, purchased the property and renamed it the Green Mountain Inn, and four years later the Depot Building was built next door to house the Mt. Mansfield Electric Railroad.

The inn has hosted many famous people over the years, such as Lowell Thomas, who made his regular broadcasts from the inn, and President Gerald Ford, who stayed at the inn as a student. President Chester A. Arthur stayed at the inn, and even acted in a theatrical production there.

In 1989, the inn underwent a redecoration, and additional rooms were added, along with modern amenities.

Activity: Legend has it that the ghost at the Green Mountain Inn is that of Boots Berry, a tap dancer and local hero who can still be heard dancing on the third floor of the hotel during severe winter storms.

Boots was the son of the inn's horseman and chambermaid, and he was born in 1840 in Room 302. The third floor of the hotel was servants' quarters at that time. Boots is said to have grown up at the inn, and he worked there as a horseman. He became a local hero when he bravely saved the passengers of a runaway stage. He was celebrated for his heroic actions, but wine, women, and song led to his termination from the inn. He was later jailed in New Orleans. It's there that he learned to tap dance. He eventually drifted back to Stowe.

One night, a dreadful storm hit town, and a little girl became stranded on the roof of the inn. Boots climbed to the top of the inn and carefully lowered the girl to safety. Unfortunately, after she reached the ground, Boots slipped and fell to his death from the icy roof. He was above Room 302 when he fell, the very room he was born in. Now, on icy winter nights, Boots' tapping can still be heard coming from the roof of Room 302.

Accommodations: The historic Green Mountain Inn offers guests the perfect blend of modern comfort and country elegance with 100 antique-furnished rooms and fireplace suites. Green Mountain Inn's Mansfield House offers22 luxurious rooms and suites, and the new Depot Street town houses feature accommodations for multiple couples and families. The inn offers a cozy library and living room, as well as two acclaimed restaurants, a health club, game room, and a year-round outdoor heated swimming pool.

— VIRGINIA —

The Martha Washington Inn

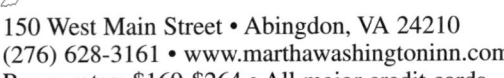

150 West Main Street • Abingdon, VA 24210
(276) 628-3161 • www.marthawashingtoninn.com
Room rates: $169-$264 • All major credit cards

History: The Martha Washington Inn was built in 1832 as a residence for General Francis Preston and his family. The United Methodist Church purchased the mansion in 1858 to establish a young girl's finishing school. In 1860, Martha Washington University opened, and remarkably, it was one of the only colleges in Virginia to operate during the Civil War. The students were affectionately known as the "Martha Girls," and their duties included the care of wounded Confederate and Union soldiers.

In 1934, an actor by the name of Bob Porterfield established the Barter Theatre housed at the old college. One year later, the college was transformed into an inn that featured elegant parlors, beautiful antique furniture, and southern hospitality.

Activity: Legend has it that during the Civil war, Union Captain John Stoves was captured near the Martha Washington Inn. A "Martha Girl" by the name of Beth reportedly tried to nursed him back to health. Though his wounds were fatal, he awoke one night and requested that Beth play something for him. She picked up her violin and played a sweet southern melody. Stoves passed away shortly thereafter, and Beth later contracted typhoid fever and died. They are buried together in Abingdon's Green Cemetery. Reportedly, on nights when there is a full moon, guests can hear Beth's haunting violin melodies on the third floor of the inn.

Accommodations: The Martha Washington Inn features 61 guest rooms, including 10 luxurious suites. Guests can select a la carte specialties from an extensive breakfast menu. At lunch, a variety of fabulous items are served and for dinner, guests can sample innovative regional fare, including steaks and chops in the region. The inn features an extensive wine list with an exclusive array of rare vintages fit for any dining occasion. Outdoor activities include croquet, tennis, work out facilities, golf, and a swimming pool, all within a two-mile radius of the hotel.

Airville Plantation Bed and Breakfast

🕴🕴🕴

6423 T. C. Walker Road • Gloucester, VA 23061 Near Williamsburg
(804) 694-0287 • www.airvilleplantation.com
Room rates: $105-$160 • Personal checks only

History: The original two-story home that's now the Airville Plantation was built in 1756 by John Dixon, sheriff of Gloucester County. His responsibilities included collecting taxes for the state, and he was personally liable for those taxes. The home was passed to his son John Dixon, Jr., who died soon after in 1788. The Dixon family lived in debt all of their lives.

In 1828, the home was sold to Thomas Smith, a local merchant and delegate to the Virginia legislature. After purchasing the home, Smith erected a large three-story addition in the Federal style. Smith brought in Philadelphia marble for the fireplaces. The new addition included a towering mahogany spiral staircase that starts at the front entrance and continues to the third floor. Located behind the main house is a row of dependencies, a smokehouse, a lumber house, a round dairy, and the overseer's cottage.

In 1841, Smith died without a will, so the executor sold the house to John Tabb Catlett. His mother was a Dixon, so once again the Dixon family was back in the house. Luck did not shine on Catlett, for he lost the property in a poker game to a man named Thomas Harwood, who moved into the house with his wife Lucy. Harwood died soon after, and Lucy was left with a sizable inheritance. She ran the working plantation until her oldest child reached maturity. The plantation stayed in the Harwood family from 1848 to 1926. During that period, Lucy carved her name into the glass in the library with her diamond ring. Whether it was the tradition of that day or perhaps Lucy was trying to make sure she had a real diamond, her signature and date of the carving are still there.

Activity: Speaking of Lucy, it appears her spirit is still very much a part of the Airville Plantation. Those who report seeing her describe Lucy with details that precisely match the tintype photographs the innkeepers still have of her. In each encounter, Lucy appears dressed in a long, white nightgown, has long flowing hair, and is barefoot. Many feel this indicates she probably died in her sleep. A benign and friendly spirit, Lucy only appears to women. No sightings have ever been reported by a male guest or employee. In fact the owner has never seen Lucy, but his wife and youngest daughter have. For some reason, she's shy around men.

Accommodations: Airville Plantation Bed & Breakfast features 3 guest rooms. Since Airville has its own orchard and vegetable gardens, each morning guests will enjoy a full breakfast which includes homemade jellies and fresh fruits and vegetables in season. The exterior of the inn is lined with ivy-covered gates and a lane bordered by tall cedar and dogwood trees. Guests can relax on the veranda, where they can sit and watch the sun set over 400 acres of gardens, meadows, and woodlands.

By the Side of the Road Bed & Breakfast

☆☆☆

491 Garbers Church Road • Harrisonburg, VA 22801
(540) 801-0430 • www.bythesideoftheroad.com
Room rates: $130-$219 • All major credit cards and personal checks

History: This large Flemish Bond-styled brick home was built around 1789, shortly after the American Revolution, by Mennonite settlers of the Shenandoah Valley. Bishop Peter Burkholder—the early Mennonite bishop of Virginia—and his descendants were longtime residents. Within walking distance of the inn lies the manor cemetery where the earliest inhabitants of this historic structure rest.

During the Civil War, the house served as a hospital following General Philip Henry Sheridan's devastating burning of the valley in 1864. Union soldiers tried three times to ignite the flame-retardant, locust-wood foundation timbers of the inn. They were unsuccessful, so they moved on. As one of the only large structures to survive the raid, the house became a natural refuge for the homeless and wounded.

Activity: The innkeepers have had their own first-hand experiences, and guests regularly report strange and unusual occurrences. A male guest was staying in a suite one evening. When he came down to breakfast the next morning, he commented jokingly about how the innkeepers must keep late hours. They asked him what he meant, and the guest replied that he heard them take their dog for a walk about 2:30 A.M. He said he clearly heard someone go down the stairs, and a few minutes later, they returned back up the stairs. The innkeepers told the guest that they had not taken the dog out at all during the night.

The innkeepers' quarters are located on the third floor in an older portion of the house built in 1789. The lady innkeeper was waiting for her daughter one evening when she heard her enter and come up the stairs. She heard the door on the landing open and close, but when she looked out and called to her daughter, there was no one there. Her daughter arrived home 45 minutes later.

The ghosts at the By the Side of the Road seem to be benevolent spirits. In fact, a previous owner felt there was an angel that lived on the roof of the inn.

One evening around 10 P.M., the innkeeper was walking around from floor to floor, turning out the lights and preparing to go to bed. He was in the 1789 portion of the house when he reached around a wall in one room to turn off the switch and felt another hand touch his. It was a little colder than his was, but he definitely felt it as a heavier hand. He left the light on that night.

A couple staying overnight in the inn reported that about 5:00 A.M. they were awakened by the sounds of footsteps in the hallway. The footsteps went back and forth, and then it was quiet again. They were the only guests in the inn that night and the innkeeper had gone to bed.

Accommodations: By the Side of the Road Bed & Breakfast offers 5 guest rooms. Amenities include whirlpools, feather beds, golf packages, and gourmet breakfasts. By the Side of the Road was the city's first official bed & breakfast. The inn offers a quiet, peaceful country retreat that's only minutes away from the thriving city of Harrisonburg.

Wayside Inn

7783 Main Street • Middleton, VA 22645
(877) 869-1797, (540) 869-1797 • www.alongthewayside.com
Room rates: $99-$159 • All major credit cards

History: The heritage of the Wayside Inn has always been service to the traveler. The first guests of the inn began arriving in 1797, stopping for room and board as they made their way across the Shenandoah Valley. Twenty years later, the inn became a stagecoach stop where weary passengers could rest and enjoy food and drink while their coach was being readied with fresh horses.

The Civil War brought soldiers from both the North and South that frequented the inn in search of friendship and refuge. Although the South's Stonewall Jackson and the North's Phil Sheridan fiercely fought throughout the valley, the inn was spared the ravages of the war, because it offered comfort to all who arrived.

During the early 20th century, the Wayside Inn catered to a new group of visitors—guests traveling through the Shenandoah Valley by way of the automobile. The inn was energetically restored and refurbished in the 1960s by a Washington financier and antique collector. He decided to decorate each room with its own unique theme.

Activity: Guests and employees of the Wayside Inn have reported seeing the images of Civil War soldiers visiting in the lobby of the inn. Each time, the apparitions have been seen right before dawn. Both soldiers and ladies will be found sitting in the parlor, or a soldier will be looking out a window. Other guests have heard footsteps and someone talking when no one was there.

Accommodations: The Wayside Inn is nestled in the Shenandoah Valley, at the foot of the Massanutten Mountains. Combining 18th-century ambience with 21st-century comfort, the inn includes 24 guest rooms and suites. Guests can choose from canopied beds; English, French, and Oriental antiques; and other appointments from a bygone era.

Visitors can dine as they would have in the colonial days with authentic regional American cuisine served in 7 antique-filled rooms. Delicacies like peanut soup, spoon bread, and country ham can be found in the Lord Fairfax Room. A variety of game, seafood, and homemade desserts can be found in the Old Servant Kitchen (Portrait Dining Room). No matter the dining room, guests will enjoy a hearty menu featuring fresh valley grown ingredients at lunch and dinner daily, as well as Wayside's special Sunday Brunch. For cocktails, the Coachyard Lounge welcomes guests to relax where horse-drawn carriages once entered the inn.

The 1763 Inn

10087 John S. Mosby Highway • Upperville, VA 20184-1742
(540) 592-3848 • www.1763inn.com
Room rates: $95-$250 • Visa, Master Card, Discover

History: Once owned by George Washington, The 1763 Inn is located in the heart of Virginia's famed Hunt county.

In 1775, Lord Fairfax deeded the land over to George Washington for survey work, but no one can say for sure if Washington actually slept here. The document transferring ownership from Fairfax to Washington is displayed in the George Washington Dining Room.

The 1763 Inn sits on 50 beautiful acres of rolling, partly wooded land at the foot of Virginia's Blue Ridge Mountains. Known originally as Greystone House, the structure and property saw a great deal of fighting during the Civil War.

Colonel John S. Mosby, known as the "Grey Ghost," staged many of his famous raids in the area. For a time, Union forces stored their horses behind The 1763 Inn until Confederate troops forced them off the property.

In 1970, the Kirchners bought the property, and they found the front door still bore the marks where Yankee soldiers had kicked it in. A major restoration to the inn took place, with the goal of creating the comforts of a modern home while retaining the property's historic charm. In April of 1986, The 1763 Inn & Restaurant was opened to the public.

Activity: Throughout its history, The 1763 Inn has remained a quiet and peaceful place. However, legend has it that apparitions continue to visit the inn. On a clear moonlit night, witnesses claim to have heard horses' hooves and have seen the ghosts of Mosby's Raiders galloping across the Blue Ridge. It seems the Grey Ghost continues to live up to his name.

In 2002, a guest visiting The 1763 Inn from Thailand claimed to have seen the ghost of a man in a long military coat. The woman who witnessed the apparition had never seen a picture of George Washington. However, after the sighting, she described in detail a soldier dressed in similar battle attire from that time period.

Accommodations: The inn offers a total of 18 unique guest rooms, 4 located in the main house, 2 in the duplex cottage, 7 in the old restored barn, 4 log cabins, and a carriage house. A tennis court and pool are available for recreation, and the Garden Pavilion provides space for large parties and weddings. There is a walking bridge across the pond that leads to the gazebo and springhouse.

A complimentary breakfast is provided each morning, and the restaurant offers German-American cuisine. Some of the activities in the area include hunting, trail rides, polo matches, fishing, rafting, vineyard tours, and historic Civil War sites.

Hewick Plantation

Courtesy of Hewick Plantation

P.O. Box 82 • Urbanna, VA 23175
(804) 758-4214 • www.hewick.com
Room rates: $109-$179
All major credit cards

History: In 1678, Christopher Robinson constructed one of the most significant manors in Virginia. Robinson had arrived from Cleasby in Yorkshire, England in 1666 and built his home by a creek coming out of the Rappahannock River, which today is Robinson's Creek. His home became a gathering place for many of the important families of Virginia who worked to shape the colony into the state it eventually became. George Washington would often come to Hewick to discuss the affairs of the colony. Christopher Robinson's son, John, was born in the house in 1683. He later became the acting governor of Virginia in 1749.

Hewick is a Virginia Historic Landmark and listed on the National Register of Historic Places. It was dedicated in May of 1995 by the Lettice Lee Chapter National Society Colonial Dames XVII Century. Today, the ivy-covered brick mansion known as Hewick is owned and resided in by 11th-generation descendants of Christopher Robinson.

Activity: For years, strange events have occurred at Hewick Plantation that have led many to claim that it may just be Virginia's most haunted house. A past resident of the home had left several furniture items in the attic. One item was a baby cradle. One night, the owner was startled to hear what sounded like a baby waking up. The sounds came from the cradle. The lady and her husband jumped up to look in the cradle, but it was empty. This occurred several times, so the cradle was placed in another bedroom. Even when the cradle was loaned out to relatives, it was promptly returned, for they too could hear the baby crying.

The sweet smell of pipe tobacco, much like that grown in colonial days, often can be detected in the area of the front hall.

An 11-year-old girl was staying in the Beverley Room at Hewick when she awoke in the middle of the night to find a white figure standing at the foot of her bed. The lighted image moved throughout the room.

Legend tells of a "Lady in Pink" that appears every seven years, and the ghost of a man dressed in a black suit has been seen as well. There have also been instances where music boxes play on their own accord, and a spinning wheel mysteriously turns. On another occasion, a relative of the owner heard a young lady singing from a north bedroom. When she opened the door to the room, the singing stopped.

Accommodations: Hewick Plantation, a 17th-century Robinson Family estate, offers 2 guest rooms and sits among 66 wooded acres. The surrounding grounds provide a glimpse of native wildlife like deer, wild turkey, red foxes, blue heron, and wild peacock. Each morning a complimentary continental "plus" breakfast is provided and banquet facilities are available for special occasions. For a journey into historical and spiritual folklore, guests may want to visit the Christopher Robinson Cemetery at Hewick, which dates back to the 17th century. The oldest marker is for the daughter of Christopher Robinson, Clara Robinson Walker, who died in 1715.

The Black Horse Inn

8393 Meetze Road
Warrenton, VA 20187
(540) 349-4020
www.blackhorseinn.com
Room rates: $125-$295
All major credit cards

Courtesy of The Black Horse Inn

History: The Black Horse Inn was originally used as a hospital during the Civil War and is rumored to have served as a courthouse for Fauquier County when the original courthouse was burned after the Civil War.

The Black Horse Inn was named after the Black Horse Cavalry, one of the local companies called to active duty by Governor Henry Wise in 1859. The Black Horse Cavalry led a successful charge against Union forces at the First Battle of Manassas, winning the special praise of Confederate President Jefferson Davis.

Today, the Inn is a comfortable home with rooms of generous proportions. A hunting stable adjoins the inn, and equine guests are welcome. The Black Horse Inn is in close proximity to wine tastings at some of Virginia's finest wineries.

Activity: The inn served as a hospital during the Civil War, and many believe the ghost of a Civil War nurse is still heard as she cheers up the soldiers. Her laughter is heard throughout the oldest portion of the house, and she is only heard by gentlemen guests. Late in the evening, male guests have heard the nurse's laughter, often in the comfort of their four-poster beds. The laughter is not threatening or frightening, and most of the gentlemen who hear the young woman's laughter are not disconcerted. The innkeeper simply tells them they must have had an ancestor in the Civil War.

Another spirit at the inn is known as "the Dancer," an apparition that has been seen at the top of the stairs, tap dancing until dawn. Some guests have heard the "tap, tap, tap" of his dancing shoes on the wooden floor.

The third ghost only frequents the inn at Christmas, and he takes great pleasure in knocking the Christmas tree over with such a vengeance that it breaks all of the bulbs and ornaments. This has happened three years in a row. The innkeeper feels this ghost must have had an unhappy Christmas experience to wreak so much havoc on the trees. Now, each year the Christmas tree is secured in the corner of the room with bailing twine and hooks to prevent further mishaps.

Accommodations: The Black Horse Inn has 9 unique rooms, each appointed with period pieces and reproductions and all with private baths. Four rooms offer fireplaces and whirlpool baths. The fields surrounding the Inn abound with whitetail deer, wild turkey, and red fox. Guests will enjoy a delicious breakfast each morning and relax after a busy day with afternoon tea and sherry, courtesy of the inn. For dinner, there is a vast array of restaurants located near the inn to suit any mood or taste.

Less than an hour's drive from Washington, D.C., The Black Horse Inn offers ample porches, landscaped grounds, boxwood gardens, and spectacular views, all of which make it a wonderful setting for weddings and wedding parties.

— WASHINGTON D.C. —

The Hay-Adams Hotel

One Lafayette Square • 16th & H Streets N.W.
Washington, DC 20006
(800) 853-6807, (202) 638-6600 • www.hayadams.com
Room rates: $199-$1600 • All major credit cards

History: In 1884, John Hay, President Abraham Lincoln's private secretary, and Henry Adams, the great-grandson of John Adams (one of the authors of the Declaration of Independence), purchased adjoining lots at the corner of H Street and 16th Street, facing the White House and Lafayette Square. The well-known architect Henry Hobson Richardson was commissioned by Adams to design a home for each of the men. The homes, both unique and Romanesque in design, eventually became the social centers of Washington, where guests like President Theodore Roosevelt came to dine with artists, writers, politicians, and other notable personalities of the times.

John Hay became Secretary of State and helped negotiate the Hay-Pauncefote Treaty, which resulted in the construction of the Panama Canal. After John Hay's death in 1905, Hay's son-in-law, Senator James Wadsworth, acquired the home. Upon Adams' death in 1918, his house became the Brazilian embassy.

In 1927, Harry Wardman, Washington's premier developer, purchased both of the properties. He razed both buildings and built an elaborate rooming house, which he called the Hay-Adams House. The 200-room hotel was opened in 1928. At the time, amenities included kitchens, servant's quarters, marble baths, and large suites. Over the next 50 years, the hotel changed hands several times until 1983, when David Murdoch purchased the hotel. He initiated a complete renovation, upgrading it to world-class standards.

Activity: Legend has it that the Hay-Adams has a permanent resident by the name of Clover Adams. Henry Adams was in the final stages of building his side-by-side mansion when his wife Clover took her own life in 1885. Rumors abound that it was actually foul play, but it was never proved.

Today, the hotel staff reports that the fourth floor of the Hay-Adams Hotel is Clover's favorite place. This happens to be the same floor where she was found dead. Activity heightens the first two weeks in December, around the anniversary of Clover's alleged suicide. During that period, the staff have witnessed the opening and closing of locked doors of unoccupied rooms, and clock radios will mysteriously turn on and off.

Witnesses have heard the sounds of a woman crying softly in one of the guest rooms or by the stairwell. The housekeeping staff has entered guest rooms to hear someone ask, "What do you want?" They will look around, only to find the room unoccupied empty. Sometimes housekeepers will be called by name, or they'll receive a big hug while cleaning the rooms.

Accommodations: The Hay-Adams Hotel offers 145 guest rooms, including 20 suites, all recently renovated and featuring views of the White House, LaFayette Square, or St. John's Church. Ornamental fireplaces, intricately carved plaster ceilings, and balconies adorn selected rooms.

From 24-hour in-room dining to the elegant LaFayette Room to the Off-the-Record Bar, you'll find several options to indulge your every mood and taste.

Located on Lafayette Park across from the White House, the Hay-Adams Hotel is world-famous for luxury and culinary excellence. Its Italian Renaissance motif creates an inviting ambiance of refinement.

— WEST VIRGINIA —

Boydville, the Inn at Martinsburg

601 South Queen Street • Martinsburg, WV 25401
(304) 263-1448 • www.boydvilleinn.com
Room rates: $125-$270 • Visa, Master Card, and personal checks

History: Known as the "Northern Gateway to the Shenandoah Valley," the land where Boydville now stands was once part of a 300-acre plantation. It was purchased by General Elisha Boyd in the 1790s from the founder of Martinsburg, Adam Stephen. General Boyd served in the War of 1812. His law office still remains on the Boydville property. The manor house, now the Inn at Martinsburg, was saved from burning during the Civil War by the direct intervention of President Lincoln.

At 16 years of age, the daughter of General Boyd, Belle Boyd, is said to have been quite a rebel. She refused to remove the Confederate flag from her bedroom window overlooking South Queen Street, and Belle even shot and killed a Union soldier from the stairway.

Stonewall Jackson was a regular guest at Boydville, and at different times, hospitals for the North and the South were located on the grounds where the inn resides; encampments for both sides were located nearby.

Activity: Several ghosts inhabit Boydville. One of the ghosts, a woman, hums and sometimes sings. Similar to a lullaby, her songs are barely audible and sound more like music than vocals. She sings in the room that used to be the nursery. When the owner spent her first night in the big house, she was alone and heard the woman singing. Since that time, over half a dozen people have heard the melodies.

Another ghost at the inn is a former slave. Many feel the slave is a protector of the inn and its owner. He has been named Henry, and several people have seen his image in the hallway. When they try to get a closer look, he disappears. While eating breakfast one morning, the owner was surprised to see someone peering in at her through a glass door. Thinking the front door must have been unlocked; she got up to see what she could do for the gentleman. As she approached the door, it swung open on its own, and the man was gone. Today, the spirit of the slave is seen at least once a month.

There is also the ghost of a Civil War soldier that has been seen walking on the front lawn carrying a light. He is occasionally seen walking in the eight acres directly in front of inn. More than 15 guests have seen the man with the light as he moves across the grounds.

One guest room in the inn is often visited by the ghost of a doctor who many believe came to the inn to help save his ill grandson. The boy passed away and the doctor became extremely grief-stricken over his death. Weeks later the doctor died in the same room. Three guests at separate times have reported other strange occurrences as well.

Accommodations: The inviting 1812 manor house and its 5 guest rooms holds a country charm from a slower, quieter, more genteel era. The grounds offer one hundred-year-old trees and a vast landscape. There are many restaurants located near the inn to suit any mood or taste. Listed on the National Register of Historic Places, Boydville is conveniently located one and a half hours west of Washington, D.C., and Baltimore, Maryland.

Pence Springs Grand Hotel

☆☆☆☆

Pence Springs, WV 24962
(888) 675-1700, (304) 445-2100
www.wvweb.com/pencespringshotel
Room rates: $85-$125
All major credit cards

Courtesy of Pence Springs Grand Hotel

History: Prehistoric Native Americans hunted buffalo at these mineral springs, and they were followed by the first European settlement around 1760.

The original Grand Hotel was built at one of the mineral spas of the Virginias. In 1918, the hotel was a premier retreat, and Pence Mineral Water won a silver medal at the 1904 St. Louis World's Fair.

The Great Depression hit the hotel very hard; visitors were unable to afford the elegant hotel, which was the most expensive place in West Virginia. Eleanor Roosevelt transformed the hotel into a lady's finishing school, and in 1947, the hotel was transformed again into the West Virginia State Prison for Women. Female inmates were housed there until 1985.

The hotel and grounds were purchased by private investors in 1986 and restored. In 2001, John and Wendy Lincoln purchased the hotel and have continued the restoration. The Grand Hotel sits on a 400-acre plantation and has once again received national attention as a place of elegance and beauty.

Activity: Reportedly, voices have been heard coming from the music room in the hotel and from the sun porch. The ghosts of past visitors have been seen dressed in formal gowns and suits of their period.

When the state acquired the building and transformed it into a women's prison for 40 years, the solitary confinement cells were located on the third floor. Between 2 and 3 A.M., sounds will be heard of the cell doors slamming shut.

The guests and management have never felt any bad feelings from the ghostly inhabitants. Still, the spirits have a tendency of playing little jokes, like turning lights off and on and rearranging the furniture in the main dining room.

From grand hotel to finishing school to women's prison and back again to an elegant historic establishment, the Pence Springs Grand Hotel offers their guests a taste of the past with the amenities of the present. **Accommodations:** The Pence Springs Grand Hotel offers a variety of 15 guest rooms to accommodate every need. Each room includes a private bath and a full breakfast.

Mystic Manor Bed & Breakfast

701 E. Myles Avenue
Pennsboro, WV 26415
(304) 659-2311
community-2.webtv.net/mysticmanorb-b
Room rates: $55 • All major credit cards

Courtesy of Mystic Manor
Bed & Breakfast

History: The Mystic Manor is one of the most unique houses in Pennsboro. It was built in 1900 as the "house of the future." It was the first house in the area to have electricity, hot and cold running water, and bathrooms. To make it fireproof, it was built with brick and stucco and a terra-cotta roof.

After the original owner experienced financial problems and lost the house, it sat empty from 1931 until 1940. Purchased by the local mayor in 1940, at that time it was still considered the prettiest and most modern house in the county. The mansion was rented out as a tourist home, and celebrities like Minnie Pearl stayed there. Known for years as the "haunted house," the home was vacant again from 1962 to 1996.

Activity: Apparently, there are two spirits that occupy the home. The spirit of Tress, a previous owner of the home who died in 1956, remains on one side of the house. There is also a plumber by the name of Rex who died in 1952. He fell down a flight of stairs in the west wing of the house. His spirit resides in the basement.

Tress is said to be a nurturing spirit. One day, she made her presence known by showing the owner she didn't like the purple candles in the dining room. He walked into the room and found the candles pulled out of the candleholders and lying on the table. Guests occasionally see the ghost of Tress near the main staircase. Her presence is said to be comforting.

Rex, on the other hand, is creepier. The ghost of the plumber stays away from the guest areas, so only the owners have to put up with his commotion. He will occasionally cause ashtrays to explode and glasses to shatter.

Accommodations: Mystic Manor is located on a national discovery rail trail, near the Ohio River. This charming old mansion offers three guest rooms, a suite, and two standard rooms. It's complete with fireplaces, gas chandeliers, a Continental breakfast each morning, and superb service. Guests may enjoy hiking, biking, boating, water skiing, tubing, fishing, hunting, golf, and much more.

SOUTHEAST

— ALABAMA —

The Victoria

1604 Quintard Avenue • Anniston, AL 36202
(256) 236-0503, (800) 260-8781 • www.thevictoria.com
Room rates: $89 • All major credit cards

History: The Victoria, built in 1888, was home to three prominent Anniston families before its conversion to a country inn and restaurant in 1985. John McKleroy built the home on the highest hill on Quintard Avenue. McKleroy, a Confederate veteran, and his family occupied the home for 25 years. William Coleman Wilson purchased the home from John's widow after it was sold at auction. When Wilson died, Frank and Robbie Kirby became the third owners in 1949 and the last full-time residents. Mr. Kirby was founder and president of Anniston Electric Company, and Mrs. Kirby was a leading community musician, entertaining visitors with her organ playing in her music room. The music room is now known as the Victoria's Piano Bar.

Activity: When Frank Kirby died, Robbie was grief-stricken and apparently grieved herself to death a year later. Since she was such a romantic and talented musician, the sounds of her organ playing are still heard in the Victoria. On other occasions, a female can be heard humming a pretty melody. The owners have been unable to find the source of this melody; they simply feel Robbie is bringing some music into the home once again. The owners do know that the sound of music is most often heard when a guest is about to propose marriage. Robbie also has a tendency to move objects in the room that was once her bedroom. The shades have been raised and lowered by themselves, doorknobs have fallen off, and objects have moved from one side to the other on the mantle and nightstand. When Robbie's niece was married at the Victoria on Thanksgiving 1999, the videotape of the wedding later showed Robbie's image on the steps as the bride and groom descend.

Accommodations: The Victoria features 60 guest rooms and a fine-dining restaurant that seats up to 100 people. The McKleroy Suite is the most Victorian room in the main house, featuring antiques from the

1880s and a mantle that looks like marble, but is actually iron. The Wilson Suite is the largest bedroom, with a half-canopied bed and claw-foot tub. The Kirby Suite has a modern bath with Victorian built-ins in the bath and entryway closet.

Oakmont

🕆 🕆 🕆

119 Pickens Street • Eutaw, AL 35462 (Near Tuscaloosa, AL)
(205) 752-7233 • www.oakmont.biz
Room rates: $100 • Cash or personal check

History: In 1908, this Greek Revival three-story home was built as a wedding present for Mary Elizabeth and Charles Alexander Webb. The Oakmont is located in Eutaw, a historic town filled with antebellum and Victorian homes. Other occupants of Oakmont over the years have included a steamboat captain and a retired colonel. In 1998, Scott and Deborah Stone bought the Oakmont and completely restored the home for the purpose of opening it as a bed and breakfast.

Activity: The first incident occurred as workers completing the restoration told the Stones of some strange experiences, including a heater that came on at will, even after the control was securely taped so that it could not be turned to the "on" position. The heater was later removed to prevent this from continuing. One day at dusk, as the Stones sat down for dinner in the formal dining room, a loud crashing noise came from upstairs, along with the sound of a slamming door. They rushed upstairs thinking one of the pictures or mirrors had fallen. They found nothing disturbed and there was no apparent sign as to what caused the noise. After that night, unexplained noises continued. The housekeeper has often heard footsteps, and now she refuses to spend the night in the house. The Stones are not sure if the ghost is that of the original owner (who killed himself in the parlor of the hotel), or if perhaps it is one of the other occupants from the house's colorful history.

Accommodations: For a taste of elegance, guests can pick from 4 beautifully appointed rooms. The Dining Room opens to the Parlor and Hall with large pocket doors. The table is set with fine china, silver, and crystal. A sumptuous southern gourmet breakfast is served in this room under the silver and crystal chandelier. The home is close to the University of Alabama for Crimson Tide fans, and there are many other attractions nearby, including Indian mounds and tours of historic homes, churches, and cemeteries. The Oakmont will take you back to a bygone era as you're pampered with southern hospitality and charm.

Rocky Mount Bed & Breakfast

2364 Rocky Mount Road
Prattville, AL 36066 near Montgomery
(800) 646-3831
www.bbonline.com/al/rockymount
Room rates: $95 • All major credit cards

Courtesy of Rocky Mount B&B

History: This family home was originally built in 1891 and renovated in 1908. A cornerstone marks the date of completion. As you walk through the front door, you'll find the 13-foot entrance hall running the full length of the house. Innkeepers Jim and Sharon Cobb now live in the same home that was originally built by Jim's great-grandfather. The original shingle roof from 1891 still covers the home and can be seen from the windows on the second floor. When Jim and Sharon Cobb began their restoration, the home had been empty for 16 years.

The story has it that great-aunt May was born and raised in the house, and that she, her two sisters, and her mother were all teachers. Aunt May once etched her name on the library door, and her name is still there. While in her 20s, she was engaged to a fellow, but something happened to prevent them from marrying. It is reported that she went off the deep end and was known for wandering in the middle of the night. One night she walked to a nearby church, sat in the dark, and played the piano. Her father would have to get up and retrieve her from these nightly walks. There are stories of May walking to Montgomery in the middle of the night in her bedclothes, but luckily a neighbor spotted her and called her father. Other times, May would get up in the middle of the night and play one of the family's pianos, perhaps dreaming of a marriage that would never be.

Activity: When the Cobbs started the bed and breakfast, Sharon would often play a compact disc of dinner music for the guests. Beautiful piano melodies would emanate through the hallway. Sharon soon found the CD player was coming on by itself and playing. The Cobbs feel it could be Aunt May, knowing her love for the piano. The Cobbs have also reported smelling a musty odor occasionally coming from a bedroom across from the original dining room. During a wedding in the home, scissors and ribbons were mysteriously moved, leading the decorator to suspect they were not alone. For years, guests have sensed that there is someone present looking over the house. Who better than Aunt May to watch over the home she dearly loved?

Accommodations: Surrounded by large oaks and tree-lined field roads, the Rocky Mount Bed & Breakfast, with its 2 spacious guest rooms, is located on 50 acres of beautiful pasture. Enjoy watching the racking horses, Thunder, Diablo, and Lightning; walk through the flower gardens, shaded patios, and porches; or stroll along the wide-open spaces. Guests will enjoy a full breakfast in the dining room or an intimate breakfast for two in the common area. Whatever your pleasure, you can relax in country style.

St. James Hotel

1200 Water Avenue • Selma, AL 36701
(888) 264-6788 • www.stjameshotelselma.com
Room rates: $65-$135 • All major credit cards

History: Built in 1837, the St. James Hotel is among the oldest functioning hotels in Alabama and one of the only antebellum riverfront hotels in the United States. This elegant hotel once played host to wealthy cotton planters, merchants, and politicians, and in its day presented the finest galas in town.

During the battle of Selma, Union troops burned two-thirds of the town, but they spared the St. James. During the war, Benjamin Sterling Turner managed the hotel. Turner later became the first African-American to serve in the U.S. Congress. Today, the St. James Hotel has been completely restored to its original splendor.

Activity: Legend has it that the ghost of a woman named Lucinda makes regular appearances at the St. James. Dressed in a pale blue and gray antebellum dress with a bustle, Lucinda has been seen walking the halls, and her dress can be heard rustling. Her hair has been described as black, her eyes are blue, and she wears lilac perfume. The image of Lucinda resembles a portrait of a lady that hangs in the hotel lobby. She has appeared for seconds at a time and on one occasion for a few minutes.

The notorious outlaw Jesse James is said to have visited the St. James, and apparently his ghost is still seen at a table in the hotel bar called the Drinking Room. He wears a white shirt and dark suspenders with a curled-brim riverboat hat. When the bar was closed one night, an employee looked through the window to see the semi-transparent image of Jesse sitting at a table to the left of the bar. Jesse was also seen by a security guard that walked in on the cowboy while making his rounds.

Finally, the spirit of a small dog has been heard in the hotel and often makes yipping sounds. He is often heard, but not seen.

Accommodations: Located near a vast array of specialty shops, the historic St. James Hotel has 42 guest rooms, with four riverfront suites offering secluded balconies. Visitors can choose views of the Garden Courtyard, St. James Place, or the beauty of the Alabama River. Guests can dine at The Troupe House Restaurant or visit the historic Drinking Room. Banquet facilities for up to 500 people are available, and surrounding the St. James Hotel are several historic museums, including the Old Depot Museum, the National Voting Rights Museum, the Smitherman Historic Building, the Confederate Foundry, and Sturdivant Hall.

— ARKANSAS —

Basin Park Hotel

12 Spring Street • Eureka Springs, AR 72632
(800) 643-4972, (877) 643-4972 • www.basinpark.com
Room rates: $79-$199 • All major credit cards

History: The Basin Park Hotel was constructed on the site of the Perry House, a four-story hotel built by Captain Joseph Perry in 1881. The captain came to Eureka Springs because of his poor health. The Perry House was one of several hotels he owned throughout the country. In 1890, the Perry House was lost in a fire, and the new Basin Park Hotel was built in 1905. The new hotel's rock exterior was provided by a limestone quarry located in the town of Beaver, and several horizontal rows of red dolomite are located around the building. The original Basin Park Hotel had 100 rooms and modern conveniences like a cage elevator, electric lights, steam heat, and telephones in each room. In 1948, an annual event known as the Barefoot Ball began—guests dance to a live band in the top-floor ballroom known as "the Roof Garden."
Activity: The Basin Park Hotel also plays host to several paranormal visitors, and numerous sightings have been witnessed by both hotel guests and staff.

In both the Grand Ballroom and room 519, guests have seen the figure of a tall, thin man with a brown beard wearing a hat and a tan suit.

Employees have felt a cold sensation as if someone was passing by them on the seventh-floor ballroom. On several occasions, a pool-ball rack has flown off of the wall and landed between two pool tables in the Rooftop Billiards Room.

On the third floor, the misty image of a young woman with blond hair and steel-blue eyes and dressed in turn-of-the-19th-century clothing has been seen floating above the floor.

The occasionally glimpsed ghost of a little girl appears to be three or four years of age, wears a yellow dress, and has long brown pigtails. She skips through the lobby and the coffeehouse.

There have also been sightings of a full-figured lady with curly red hair who eats cookies and drinks milk in the coffeehouse. Finally, there are reports of an unseen presence that supposedly "sexually charges" guests that stay in Room 408. You may want to call in advance to book this room.

Accommodations: Basin Park Hotel features 12 elegant Jacuzzi Suites, 11 spacious King Suites, and 38 premium rentals with various configurations. Visitors can eat at the Basin's Balcony Restaurant and enjoy lunch or dinner overlooking downtown Eureka Springs. On weekends great live music is featured while you relax in the fresh mountain air. Guests of the hotel only have to walk out the front door to find themselves at the very spring in Arkansas where Eureka Springs first began. Over 100 specialty shops, galleries, and eateries are available for visitors to enjoy.

1884 Bridgeford House Bed & Breakfast

263 Spring Street • Eureka Springs, AR 72632
(888) 567-2422 • www.bridgefordhouse.com
Room rates: $99-$165 • All major credit cards or cash

History: Located in the largest historic district in the United States, the Bridgeford House was built after the Civil War by Captain John Bridgeford and his wife Mary. Known as prominent Eureka Springs residents, the Bridgefords were also well known for their hospitality. Captain John was even referred to as "that large, jolly gentleman on Spring Street." The name "Uncle John" was bestowed upon him by the town's many children, as he always had sweets and loved to tell tall tales. Today, innkeepers Linda and Henry Thornton continue the tradition of hospitality, and you might even catch Henry telling some tales of Eureka Springs' past, as well as stories of the historic bed and breakfast.

Activity: When Linda and Henry moved into the inn, they found the freezer downstairs, which was full of food, pulled away from the wall three to four feet. For a week, they would slide it back to the wall, only to find it moved out again the next morning.

The second night in the home, the Thorntons were awakened to the sounds of people talking. Thinking the clock radio had come on, Henry got up to find the voices had stopped and the radio was turned off. Throughout that week, the plug from the clock radio kept coming out of the wall.

The original 1884 Bridgeford kitchen has now been converted into a guest room. The food used in that kitchen was stored in a cave under Spring Street; the entrance to the cave is now sealed with stone. Numerous sightings of the Captain and Mary Bridgeford have been reported around this room. The owners have a picture of Mary, and they confirm that the spirit they have encountered is the woman in the photograph.

Guests have reported smelling breakfast cooking at 5 A.M., and some have even commented that the owners get up awfully early to make breakfast. Actually, the ghost of Mary must be making breakfast, because the owners do not start cooking until 7:30 A.M.

Accommodations: Featured in newspapers and magazines throughout the country, the Bridgeford House is a Victorian delight, complete with 5 guest rooms. Many of the antiques and furnishings in the inn have been handed down through generations. All rooms have queen- or king-sized beds and private baths, Jacuzzis, and fireplaces. Each morning guests will enjoy a full scrumptious gourmet breakfast.

The 1881 Crescent Cottage Inn

211 Spring Street • Eureka Springs, AR 72632
(800) 223-3246 • www.1881crescentcottageinn.com
Room rates: $88-$145
Visa, Master Card, Discover

History: The Crescent Cottage Inn was built in 1881 for the first governor of Arkansas after the Civil War, General Powell Clayton. The house is the oldest and most-photographed Victorian bed and breakfast in town, with its exterior towers, sunbursts, and spindles. The property is listed on the National

Courtesy of The 1881 Crescent Cottage Inn

Register of Historic Places. The home has played host to city founders and leading citizens, and it has seen both public events and back-room wheelings and dealings over the years. There is reason to believe that some of the residual energy of these eminent personages and events may still linger.

Activity: Owners Ray and Elise Dilfield tell us the paranormal activities at the 1881 Crescent Cottage Inn have never been even remotely malevolent, though their appearance will sometimes make one pause. Throughout the years, visitors have reported seeing a dark-haired woman in a long dress leaving a room at the very moment someone walks in, while other guests have heard disembodied footsteps going up and down the stairs. There is even the occasional feeling of the floor swaying, in the absence of wind or traffic. The occurrences are not frequent, but many have sensed the feeling of being gently rocked in their bed in this Victorian painted lady of yesteryear.

Accommodations: The inn is located in a special spot at the quiet residential end of the "historic loop." Only a short walk from downtown shops and restaurants, the inn has 4 guest rooms furnished with period antiques, queen-sized beds, and private baths with Jacuzzi tubs. The two downstairs suites feature double Jacuzzis, fireplaces, refrigerators, and private entrances that open onto the lower veranda and a spectacular view of the gardens and mountains.

The Crescent Hotel

75 Prospect Avenue • Eureka Springs, AR 72632
(800) 342-9766 • www.crescent-hotel.com
Room rates: $89-$149 • All major credit cards

History: Built in 1886 by former governor Powell C. Clayton, the Crescent Hotel was constructed using white limestone brought in from the nearby White River quarry. Its architectural style has been described as both "Eclectic," "Victorian-French Gothic," "Chateausque," and "American Gothic." The Crescent operated as a first-class hotel well into the twentieth century, drawing guests from all over the world to Eureka Springs in order to sample the waters that supposedly were healing and exhilarating. The Crescent Hotel was converted in 1908 to the Crescent College for Young Women, and in 1937 it became the Baker Hospital. "Doctor" Norman Baker, who claimed to be a licensed physician, bought the hotel and operated it, claiming he had a cure for cancer. Dr. Baker, a rather eccentric fellow, always wore violet-colored shirts and drove a violet-colored car. He even painted the hotel's walls purple. Baker was planning on expanding the hotel when he was convicted of mail fraud in 1940. Closed during World War II, the Crescent Hotel was purchased in 1946 by three investors from Chicago that transformed the hotel back to its former glory. Then, in 1997, the hotel received a multi-million dollar restoration that included the addition of the New Moon Spa, which offers Vichy showers, a hydrotherapy tub, a sauna, eight massage and therapy tables, tanning beds, a sumahdi float tank, and free weights.

Activity: With such a rich and diverse history, it is no surprise that the Crescent Hotel is alive with paranormal activity. Much of it surrounds room 218. Reportedly, in the late 1880s, while construction was taking place, one of the Irish stonemasons fell to his death at the very location that is now room 218. Guests of the room have witnessed hands coming out of the bathroom mirror, the door opening and slamming shut, and the bloodcurdling cries of a falling man coming from the ceiling.

The ghost of Dr. Baker has been seen in the Crescent lobby by many of the previous owners and guests. All have described seeing a man in a violet shirt and white linen suit. Old photographs of the good doctor confirm his actual appearance. On one occasion, a guest awoke to find a mustached gentleman in a dress coat and rounded collar standing at the foot of her bed with a bottle in his hand. He was looking back and forth at her and her husband. Thinking she was experiencing a dream, she closed her eyes and opened them again. To her surprise, the entity was still there. When the guest started to wake her husband, she watched as the spirit faded away from the bottom to the top leaving his gazing eyes as her final impression.

The spirit of a nurse pushing a gurney past offices and upper hallways has often been seen and heard. The entity resides in what would have been Dr. Baker's old morgue area under the hotel. The laundry is located next to the old morgue, which still has the original autopsy table and walk-in freezer. A maintenance man refused to return to the laundry area after experiencing all of the washers and dryers coming on in the middle of the night, with no other staff on duty except him.

Finally, workmen and housekeepers have experienced meeting a spirit they call "Theodora" in room 419. She apparently introduces herself as a cancer patient of Dr. Baker's and disappears after introductions are made.

Accommodations: With 68 rooms, the elegant Crystal Dining Room, and showplace gardens with hiking and walking paths, the Crescent Hotel is a delight to visit. There are complimentary daily history tours of the hotel, and a "ghost tour" is offered throughout the week. Concierge and vacation-planning services are available for guests, and a visit to the New Moon Spa is a must. The Crescent Hotel also offers one of the finest wedding and reception locations in the Ozarks.

1890 Williams House Bed & Breakfast

㍿ ㍿

420 Quapaw Avenue
Hot Springs, AR 71901
(800) 756-4635
www.1890williamshouse.com
Room rates: $99-$165
All major credit cards

Courtesy of The 1890 Williams House B&B

History: Built in 1890 as a Victorian brownstone mansion by Dr. Aurthur Upton Williams, the inn has survived four forest fires and floods that have ravaged the city. The structure was erected by a stonemason who learned his trade working on the Aukland Castle in England.

During the 1913 fire that burned 50 blocks of Hot Springs, Dr. Williams hired helpers to protect his home. From the well on the Orange Street side, he had large quantities of water drawn and workers were placed at several locations on the roof and in the attic with buckets to drown out fire balls as they landed on the house. The roof never caught fire. A strategy to stop fires in those days was to dynamite buildings in the path of the fire. Dr. Williams, with shotgun in hand, refused to let anyone near his home for that purpose. His home and several others in the neighborhood were spared.

In 1923, Dr. Williams died, and his wife Elizabeth continued to live on the main floor with their daughter, Afton. William Wooten and his family lived on the second floor. In 1939, Elizabeth died at age of 82. The house was renovated after her passing, and Afton and Richard Wooten, William's only son, married and raised two sons in the home. A divorce and sale of the house and furnishings ended the ownership of the Williams-Wooten home in 1975. The home became a bed and breakfast in 1980, is listed on the National Register of Historic Places, and now warmly welcomes guests from around the world.

Activity: Both haunting and protective, unexplained experiences abound in the stately home. The upstairs hall light has a tendency to go off by itself. There have also been noises emanating from the attic that sound like someone walking back and forth in heavy boots. Other occurrences include the mysterious moving of large stacks of boxed books and the rearrangement of all of the seashells in a hard-to-open curio cabinet. Once, a writer spent the night at the Williams House and awoke during the night to hear someone shouting in a gruff voice to "keep those buckets moving." Recently, a home nearby burned late one afternoon. That night, the owner of the Williams House was going down the hallway about 10 P.M. when he heard the sounds of someone walking in the attic. He went upstairs to investigate, but he found nothing. Perhaps Dr. Williams was preparing to protect his home once again.

Accommodations: The house has 5 large, 12-foot-ceilinged rooms downstairs and ten-foot pocket doors with oak wainscoting in the dining room. The second floor has five rooms and a large sitting room—once Dr. Williams' billiard room.

The Empress of Little Rock

Courtesy of The
Empress of Little Rock

2120 S. Louisiana Street
Quapaw Quarter Historic District
Little Rock, AR 72206
(501) 374-7966 • www.theempress.com
Room rates: $125-$195
Visa, Master Card, American Express

History: Following the Civil War, James H. Hornibrook moved to Little Rock and became a successful saloonkeeper. He built one of the most extravagant homes in the state. The original Hornibrook mansion was completed in 1888 after six years of construction. Only Arkansas materials were used on the structure.

Legend has it that Hornibrook held illegal card games in the secret tower room so he could watch for raids on his saloon. Hornibrook died at the front gate shortly after the mansion was completed. He was only 49 years of age. His wife, Margaret McCully Hornibrook, died two years later at age 49, reportedly of a broken heart.

The Hornibrook mansion became the Empress of Little Rock. It has been described in the National Register of Historic Places as the best example of ornate Victorian architecture in Arkansas and one of the best examples of the Gothic Queen Anne style in the region. The structure includes a divided stairway, a three-story corner tower, an eight-foot stained-glass skylight, and octagonal rooms.

Activity: The ghost of a well-dressed man has been seen walking down the stairs wearing a Hamburg hat. Witnesses have confirmed that he disappears before reaching the bottom step.

One day, a painter was finishing the interior of the infamous tower room where Hornibrook once held his card games. When he stepped out and then returned, the door was locked, though the door had no lock or even a handle. He left to get a screwdriver to open the door.

Upon his return, he found the door wide open and the well-dressed man standing in the room.

A guest was spending the night in the home when she heard footsteps walking up the staircase. Her doorknob turned, and then the door opened. When she peered through the doorway, there was no one there.

Other guests have seen the spirits of a large woman who appears to be in her 30s, a heavyset man with a military-style coat, and the ghost of a maid folding laundry in the maid's closet. Some guests have reported hearing sounds early in the morning of people laughing and walking around, as well as the noise of children playing on the second floor of the hotel.

Accommodations: The Empress of Little Rock welcomes visitors to cherished family traditions and memories of what life was like for a Victorian family in the 1880s—only with some modern conveniences thrown in. Each of its 5 guest rooms is decorated with mementos and antiques that make visitors feel they are cherished guests of the "royal family." Visit the Empress of Little Rock and sample "The Forgotten Experience," the peace and magnificence of the 1880s. Guests will enjoy an elegant brunch served by candlelight and warm hospitality that is a hallmark at The Empress.

— FLORIDA —

Bryant House Bed & Breakfast

101 Sixth Street • Apalachicola, FL 32320
(888) 554-4376, (850) 653-3270 • www.romantic-retreat.com
Room rates: $87-$147 • Visa, Master Card, American Express or personal check

History: The Bryant House has seen both grandeur and poverty. Originally built in 1897 by Benjamin (Benji) Bryant, the building was rented by a housebuilder and boatwright. The porch that now has wicker rockers and cast-iron tables and chairs once had large fishing nets hanging from its rafters, hung there for repair and drying. During World War II, Rufus Owens and his wife purchased the house. They moved into one room and rented the rest of the house out to military personnel stationed in the area. Owens continued to rent out the house until 1990, when he decided to sell the place. The next occupant lived there only a year, and it sat empty until 1996. A major restoration took place that year, and the Florida room was added, complete with antique stained glass sidelights around each window. Constructed of heart pine walls, ceilings, and floors, the inn has four fireplaces with their original wooden mantels.

Activity: The Bryant House has been haunted by spirits for many years. One family that once owned the inn was even haunted by a Tasmanian Devil-type figure. Fortunately for the current owners, the figure moved with the family, so he hasn't been seen since.

Mysterious lights have been observed in the windows of the inn. Reportedly, there was one death in the home that occurred when a soldier died after falling out of the second story window in the upstairs foyer. Some feel he may still be making his presence known.

Accommodations: The Bryant House Bed & Breakfast features 3 bedrooms and 1 suite. In the back yard, visitors will find an old magnolia tree that's thought to be over 150 years old, complete with a rope swing. Guests can stroll along the beautiful garden, fountain, and koi pond. The middle of the garden offers a patio of antique brick where visitors can sit and enjoy a cool drink or afternoon tea as they watch hummingbirds darting among the flowers. Each room is tastefully decorated in period antiques and has a private bath. Guests wake up to a wonderful German-style breakfast of fresh rolls and breads, an assortment of hams and sausages, a selection of cheeses, homemade jams, fresh honey, and richly brewed European coffee.

Aunt Martha's Bed & Breakfast

315 Shell Avenue SE • Fort Walton Beach, FL 32548
(850) 243-6702 • www.auntmarthasbedandbreakfast.com
Room rates: $105-$195 • All major credit cards

History: Although Fort Walton Beach is a relatively young city, the area's history dates back thousands of years. In fact, artifacts found there date back to 10,000 B.C.

Between 1500 and 1800, there were pirates present on the island, the most notorious being William Augustus Bowles, or Billy Bowlegs, as he was known. He was a buccaneer who used the area as a pirate's playground in 1799. Many believe he buried his treasure somewhere on Okaloosa Island, and since it has never been found, treasure hunters still comb the beaches in search of Billy Bowlegs' bounty.

Today, Fort Walton Beach attracts visitors from all over the country with its beautiful waterfront, picturesque beaches, sailing, and fishing. Every June 1-4, Fort Walton celebrates the notorious Billy Bowlegs Pirate Festival with fireworks, a treasure hunt, square dancing competitions, and arts and crafts. The highlight of the event is when

Billy Bowlegs' armada sails into Fort Walton Landing and defeats the city militia in a mock battle.

Nestled by the Gulf, Aunt Martha's Bed & Breakfast opened to the public in 2001. Innkeepers Martha and Bill Garvie go out of their way to make each guest a part of their family, offering gracious southern warmth and hospitality.

Activity: Legend has it that when Billy Bowlegs buried his loot on Okaloosa Island, he left his lover (a pretty young wench), to guard his treasure while he and his pirates continued their plundering. He came back to find his lover had taken up with another beau. Billy went into a rage and cut off her head.

Today, when there is a full moon, visitors and local residents have allegedly seen Billy Bowlegs' young wench walking around the dunes on Okaloosa Island, holding her severed head in her hands and dragging her long flowing hair on the white sands of the beach. Some say she is still guarding Billy's treasure, and her long flowing hair hides her footprints in the sand.

Accommodations: Aunt Martha's Bed & Breakfast is a fine example of old Florida summerhouse charm mixed with the comforts of today. The bed and breakfast offers a large foyer, library, living room, and sunroom. French doors open onto the veranda that runs the length of the house and overlooks the water. Guests can relax and enjoy the warm Gulf breeze and sounds of the shore. A winding staircase takes visitors to the second floor, where 5 uniquely appointed guest rooms await. Decorated with a touch of Aunt Martha's southern charm, each guest room has large floor-to-ceiling windows. A separate dining room seats 12 comfortably, and each morning Martha and her staff provide an unforgettable breakfast

The Grady House

420 N.W. First Avenue
High Springs, FL 32655
(904) 454-2206 • www.gradyhouse.com
Room rates: $85-$115
All major credit cards

Courtesy of The Grady House

History: The Grady House sits upon the site of High Springs' first bakery, built in the 1890s. In 1917 the building was renovated and converted into a boarding house for railroad supervisors. The Grady House has housed many of High Springs' prominent citizens. After the railroad boom, the Grady House was turned into an apartment building and later abandoned during the 1980s. Now on the National Historic Register and restored to its early 20th century charm, The Grady House will take you to a simpler time in Floridian History when life wasn't so fast.

Activity: Innkeepers Tony and Kirk have a very social ghost by the name of Helen, who lived there when it was a boarding house. Helen lived in the Grady House all her life and she loved to have guests come over to visit and stay. Helen has been seen wearing a Victorian nightgown, and she has long, flowing hair.

Guests have repeatedly witnessed chess pieces mysteriously moving around the board. One visitor was awakened by the footsteps of someone walking back and forth in the room, while another gentleman came into his room and saw the apparition of Helen combing her long dark hair as she gazed into the mirror. Helen's presence at the Grady House has been reported to be comforting—even nurturing. Some guests have claimed that she tucked them in at night. Of the four rooms in the upstairs portion of the inn, three have been known to produce paranormal activity.

The innkeepers also purchased the building next door, which was built in 1896 and belonged to the Easterlins, a prominent family in this northern Florida town. Skeet Easterlin was an adventurous young lady who even became mayor of High Springs, but she was eventually locked up when she was caught running moonshine. She didn't reveal to the authorities that several other townspeople were involved as well, and so the townsfolk treated her like a queen when she got out of prison. Other than her time in the big house, Skeet lived in the Easterlin Home from her birth in 1910 until her death in 1997. Apparently, Skeet still occupies the dwelling. Guests who have rented the entire home have been awakened in the night to the sounds of polite conversation and the tapping of spoons being stirred in teacups, as if a grand tea party was taking place. However, every time a guest ventures down the stairs, the sounds stop before their feet touch the first floor.

Accommodations: Tony and Kirk provide warm hospitality that's rare in this fast-paced world. The Grady House features 5 bedrooms in the main building, or you can rent Skeet's cottage. A full breakfast is provided each morning.

Known as the "friendliest small town" in Florida, High Springs is a delight to visit. The tree-lined streets provide an abundance of antique shops, art galleries, a railroad museum, and numerous curio shops. You can canoe or innertube the peaceful rivers.

Eaton Lodge

☆☆☆

511 Eaton Street
Key West, FL 33040
(800) 294-2170, (305) 292-2170
www.eatonlodge.com
Room rates: $95-$295
Visa, Master Card, Discover

Courtesy of Eaton Lodge

History: In a lush and peaceful oasis just a few steps from Duval Street stand two historically significant buildings that comprise the Eaton Lodge compound. The main house, which is a fully restored Victorian mansion, was built in 1886. This three-story Greek Revival was constructed by Samuel Otis Johnson just after the great fire of 1886. One of the first ornamental gardens in the Keys once grew around the Eaton Lodge, cultivated by Genevieve Warren and her physician husband, William. Carefully refurbished to retain its original grandeur and elegance, this landmark is a favorite for today's traveler.

The second building, the Carriage House, was once a dry goods store in the early 1880s. Today, it has been converted into comfortable guest rooms with king-size beds and full kitchens.

The Eaton Lodge is on the National Register of Historic Homes and has been the recipient of a Rehabilitation Award from the Historic Florida Keys Foundation.

Activity: Countless guests have reported the same stories, and management and staff have all experienced identical ghostly phenomena. While in their rooms during the night, they'll see a shadow crossing from beneath the doorway of their room, accompanied by footsteps. However, when they open the door, no one is there.

At times, people hear the sound of someone typing on an old-fashioned typewriter late at night. It's been said that Dr. Warren gave a lot of speeches, and he may have typed them on a typewriter. It may be that the doctor is still working on his speeches.

On one occasion, a guest observed a woman in a formal dress, a man in a suit, and twin girls. The guest complained that their conversations on the other side of the wall kept her awake all night long. To add to her sleepless night, her bed shook violently. A source close to the hotel later reported that the wife of the original owner gave birth to twins in the very room where the guest was staying for the night. The guest was the only person to see the mysterious couple and their twin girls.

Accommodations: All 13 rooms of the Eaton Lodge have been decorated with antiques, wicker, and whimsical, tropical pieces. Each room has a private bath and a private terrace with outside seating. An island-style breakfast buffet is served each morning. At the end of the day visitors can meet other guests and unwind around the Jacuzzi, peruse the menu basket, or head out into Key West's famous nightlife.

Marrero's Guest Mansion

410 Fleming Street • Key West, FL 33040
(800) 459-6212 • www.marreros.com
Room rates: $95-$210 • All major credit cards

Courtesy of Marrero's
Guest Mansion

History: Francisco Marrero, a prominent cigar maker, built Marrero's Guest Mansion in 1889. His intent was to lure his young love and future bride, Enriquetta, to the town of Key West. His charm and the mansion proved successful. Francisco and Enriquetta were married and had eight children.

Francisco met an untimely death in his homeland of Cuba during a tobacco-buying trip to Havana. Though Enriquetta was named administrator of his estate, Francisco's first wife, Maria (whom he was still married to—oops!), showed up from Cuba to claim his estate. After a lengthy court battle, Maria was named administrator of Francisco's estate, inheriting everything.

Activity: She may have lost the court battle, but the old girl refuses to leave. On the day that Enriquetta and her eight children were being evicted from the house, the townspeople and sheriff gathered in front of the house. Enriquetta pleaded with Maria to leave the house for her and her children and take everything else in Francisco's estate. However, Maria was not willing to leave anything for Enriquetta.

As Enriquetta was departing her home, she turned toward the house and vowed, "With God as my witness, my spirit shall remain here forever." After making her final statement, Enriquetta and her children ventured into the streets of Key West. Tragically, Enriquetta and all eight children died from disease and malnutrition within two years of the eviction.

After Enriquetta's death, inexplicable events began to occur in the home, and today it is reported that Enriquetta still moves through her house, keeping a benevolent eye on the home she loved so dear and the guests who come to visit.

Accommodations: Marrero's Guest Mansion is a Victorian home with 12 guest rooms. Visitors can explore Key West on foot or bicycle, and the attractions of Duval Street are located only a short half-block away. Amenities of the Guest Mansion include an expanded continental breakfast, complimentary happy hour daily, and a large heated swimming pool and hot tub. There's even a clothing-optional pool area, in-room refrigerators, air conditioning, and cable television.

Casablanca Inn Bed & Breakfast

24 Avenida Menendez • St. Augustine, FL 32084
(800) 826-2626, (904) 829-0928 • www.casablancainn.com
Room rates: $99-$299 • All major credit cards and personal checks

History: In the early part of the 20th century, the city of St. Augustine became a hot spot for smuggling, due in part to prohibition. Much of the illegal rum brought into the United States from Cuba entered along the St. Augustine waterfront.

The Matanzas Hotel, now known as the Casablanca Inn, became the setting for much of the bootlegging. The owner at the time was an enterprising widow who never let a good opportunity pass. She fell into cahoots with the rum smugglers, and she took one as a lover. The rum-runners set up shop in her boarding house; they would stay at the hotel for a few days and sell liquor to the guests and locals, then move along the waterfront to their next illegal set up. It became such a lucrative business that the government sought to shut it down.

The widow was questioned but remained silent. She worked out a plan such that when the government boys were around, she would climb to the roof of the building with lantern in hand. If it wasn't safe for the rum-runners to come into town, she would wave her lantern back and forth. The rum-runners would then know to pass by until the contraband liquor could be brought ashore safely—and the lady of the inn could reap her rich rewards.

Activity: Today, the infamous "Lady with the Lantern" still visits the inn she loved so well. Reportedly, a mysterious light shining in their window has awakened guests of an adjacent property. Thinking it was coming from the lighthouse on Anastasia Island, they peered out the window to find that the light was actually coming from the Casablanca Inn.

Shrimp boats and other watercraft have sailed into the inlet after dusk on moonless nights, only to see an eerie lantern swinging in the darkness above the inn. Some witnesses spot only the light; however, some claim to have actually seen a dark figure on the distant rooftop. Perhaps the "Lady with the Lantern" is still signaling to her lover and his cohorts from the top of the Casablanca Inn.

Accommodations: The Casablanca Inn's 10 guest rooms and 10 suites are individually decorated with antiques and collectables, each carefully chosen and placed for guests' comfort. The inn boasts that no two rooms are alike. Guests can enjoy a gourmet sit-down breakfast in the dining room or on their front verandas. Within walking distance of the inn, guests will find fine restaurants, shops, galleries, museums, and frequent special events.

The Painted Lady Bed & Breakfast

47 San Marco Avenue
St. Augustine, FL 33040
(888) 753-3290
www.staugustinepaintedlady.com
Room rates: $79-$135
All major credit cards

Courtesy of The Painted Lady Bed & Breakfast

History: Charles Sequi, a local book merchant, built this grand Victorian home in 1910. It remained in the Sequi family for almost 80 years, and it's said their presence is still felt there. Charles was a great bird lover, and he raised carrier pigeons at his home. In the 1900s, a newspaper publisher from New York purchased many of his pigeons to transport messages back and forth from Cuba. Charles took his pigeon money and purchased the parcel of land he later built his home on, which is today the Painted Lady Bed & Breakfast. Charles opened a bookstore on St. George Street to cater to Flaglers Hotel guests during the winter, and he supplied local schoolbooks the rest of the year. Charles rode his bicycle to his bookstore and rode home at midday for lunch and to care for his pigeons.

The Sequis' only child was Martha Lee, and she never married. It is said that she once had a beau, a gentleman who rented a room in the house. However, her mother did not approve, so the man left and went to California. Martha never saw him again. Until the day she died, Martha spoke fondly of her only beau, whom she referred to as "the Colonel."

Activity: After purchasing the inn, the current owners entered a drab gray room and immediately felt a sad presence inhabiting the space. When they visited what they now call the Colonel's Room, it almost felt as if they were wearing tight wool uniforms. They decided to paint the room a pastel pink with cottage garden décor, and afterward, the sad energy was no longer there. They joked that the Colonel must not like pink, so he left.

On more than one occasion, witnesses have observed that, at midday, the front door of the inn will fly open and then the sound of footsteps will be heard dashing up the stairs. The staff wonders if it is just the wind—or perhaps it is Charles coming back home as usual for lunch and to care for his pigeons. Regardless of the explanation for these strange occurrences, the innkeepers feel watched over and welcomed into this happy home.

Accommodations: The Painted Lady features 3 suites. Guests will enjoy a breakfast of assorted cereals, banana nut bread, pastries, and muffins. Though it has recently been renovated, the property still retains its original warmth and charm as a peaceful oasis in the heart of "Antique Alley." The Painted Lady Bed and Breakfast is just a short stroll from the city gates and the excitement of the downtown historic district.

St. Francis Inn Bed & Breakfast

279 St. George Street • St. Augustine, FL 32084
(800) 824-6062, (904) 824-6068 • www.stfrancisinn.com
Room rates: $89-$279 • All major credit cards and personal checks

History: Around the corner from St. Augustine's historic "Oldest House," visitors will find what is unquestionably St. Augustine's "Oldest Inn," the St. Francis Inn. Dating back to 1791, the inn embodies the rich history and culture of the nation's oldest city.

The inn was built during the city's second Spanish Colonial period. Since the threat of invasion was a cause for concern, the King of Spain ordered that all houses were to be constructed so that they might "serve as a defense of fortress against those who might attempt to occupy the town."

The original owner, Gaspar Garcia, was a Sergeant in the Third Battalion of the Infantry Regiment of Cuba. He was granted the lot of land in 1791 by the King of Spain and shortly after, Garcia built his home. In 1838 it became the property of Colonel Thomas Henry Dummett, who grew up on Barbados and retired from Britain's Royal Marines. Dummett bought several hundred acres along the Tacoma River south of St. Augustine, and he built a sugar mill plantation there. Dummett passed away, and his daughter Anna converted the home into a lodging establishment in 1845.

Over the years, the elite of St. Augustine, literary figures, and educators have owned the home. In 1948, the property was christened "The St. Francis Inn," and today visitors will find the spirits of a colorful past and an air of elegance in its quiet setting.

Activity: Legend tells of a ghost named Lillie who makes regular visits to the inn. There is even a room named in her honor. Apparently, Lillie was an African-American slave girl who fell in love with the nephew of the owner of property in the 1840s. When the master of the house found out about the tryst, he sent the young boy away and punished Lillie. Brokenhearted, Lillie committed suicide. Her spirit has appeared to guests and employees on a regular basis. She is described as very playful, and witnesses are never frightened. Occasionally televisions will come on in the middle of the night when no one is around, and items such as hairbrushes move around or turn up missing. Lights also have a habit of turning off and on. A number of ghost hunters have visited the inn and have reported sensing Lilly's mischievous presence.

Accommodations: St. Francis Inn Bed & Breakfast features 11 rooms, 4 suites, a cottage, a garden hideway, and a beach house. Guests can enjoy the St. Francis Inn's colorful past through the tranquil ambiance of the enclosed courtyard. Each morning a buffet breakfast includes two hot homemade entrees, freshly baked pastries and breads, fresh fruit, special blend inn coffees and assorted teas, and a full serving of inn hospitality.

During the evening social hour, guests will enjoy complimentary beverages and tasty treats such as shrimp dip and crackers, veggies and dill dip, sausage balls and egg salad, or crab dip and spinach dip with Hawaiian bread. Visitors can take a stroll by the fountain pond fed from an artesian well and surrounded by lush banana trees, bougainvillaea, and tropical flowers.

— GEORGIA —

The Inn at Folkston

509 West Main Street
Folkston, GA 31537
(888) 509-6246, (912) 496-6256
www.innatfolkston.com
Room rates: $110-$160
All major credit cards

History: The Inn at Folkston is a fine example of the bungalow style of homes that were built in the early 20th century.

By Anole Imaging. Courtesy of
The Inn at Folkston

On May 26, 1922, Ed Shiver purchased property in Folkston to build his new home. The home traded hands several times over the next several years. J.V. Gowen, a well-known community activist and businessman, purchased the Main Street house as a second, in-city home for when his nine children were attending school in Folkston. The Gowens lived in the home for 28 years.

Elizabeth DeVane and her husband Howard bought the house in 1959 and converted the old servant's quarters into a schoolhouse. Many local residents recall attending Mrs. DeVane's kindergarten class between 1959 and 1967.

Mrs. Flink owned a bakery in an old hotel on Main Street called "Ye Olde Bakery," and for nine years she and her family lived in the home. The next owner, Virginia Stacks, purchased the home in 1985 and set out to remodel the house. Rooms were added, including a poolroom. Many of the kitchen cabinets were brought from Stacks' former home in Jacksonville. The banister and rails leading to the second floor were also replaced with 100-year-old railings she brought with her.

In 1997, Roger and Genna Wangsness were searching for a place to retire and open a bed and breakfast. They came to the small town of Folkston, known as the "Gateway to the Okefenokee Swamp." Since the town had no bed and breakfast, Roger and Genna purchased the home on Main Street and began a year-long restoration of the 12-room heart-pine bungalow. In February of 1998, after nine previous owners, the home reopened as the Inn at Folkston.

Activity: Former owners have reported the presence of a woman in a plaid dress who appears in the stairwell to the second story. Legend has it that the ghost is that of Rachel Templeton, a teacher who was a former resident of the town. One guest claimed to have seen the ghost of Rachel in the upstairs window, watching the innkeeper as he was gardening.

Accommodations: The Inn at Folkston offers guests 4 uniquely appointed rooms. Visitors are amazed at the size of the inn's interior, going on and on down a long and winding hallway to the inn's final bedrooms at the back of the structure.

The wide veranda of the inn is a typical bungalow porch, with deep overhanging eaves and high walls. It has rockers, wicker furniture, and a six-person hot tub for guests to relax in and enjoy.

Guests will savor a fit and healthy breakfast that begins with good coffee and a hearty serving of fruit, and is followed by one of Gina's specialties, such as apple or banana/poppy seed waffles, apple pancakes, baked lemon yogurt, herbed oven-roasted potatoes, Vidalia onion omelets, or other such delectables. The inn promises you will not go away hungry.

The surrounding two acres provide guests the perfect place to bird-watch, since Folkston is a designated bird sanctuary. Alternatively, visitors may want to visit the nearby Okefenokee National Wildlife Refuge, home of the famous Okefenokee Swamp.

Bonnie Castle Bed & Breakfast

2 Post Street • Grantville, GA 30220 Near Atlanta, GA
(770) 583-2080 • www.bonnie-castle.com
Room rates: $75-$110 • All major credit cards

History: Celebrating over 100 years of history, the Bonnie Castle was built in 1896 by the J. W. and Itura Colley family. The Colleys' son, Stewart, his wife Mary, and their family lived in the mansion throughout World War II. Several members of this wealthy and prominent family lived in the home until 1981. Active in both politics and the arts, the Colleys started textile mills in Grantville and were both prosperous farmers and bankers.

Throughout its history, many famous guests have stayed at the Bonnie Castle, in particular former President Jimmy Carter, Madame Chiang Kai-Shek, and Franklin D. Roosevelt, who stopped at the Bonnie Castle on his way to Warm Springs, Georgia. In an era when few women held positions of political power, Mary Colley helped create FDR's political platform.

Activity: Patti and Darwin Palmer, current owners and resident innkeepers, purchased Bonnie Castle in 1992 and converted it into a bed and breakfast in 1994. Almost immediately, the Palmers started hearing sounds of something breaking in the middle of the night. They would investigate the next morning, only to find that nothing had broken anywhere in the house.

A three-year-old daughter of a friend of the Palmers was eating blueberries on the steps of the Bonnie Castle when she started waving her hands and asked a man to come in the gate. She got up and ran to the gate asking the person to come in and play. Her mother, knowing her little girl was usually a quiet child, followed her to see what was causing the commotion. Not seeing anyone around, the mother asked the child what this man looked like. The little girl replied that he wore a yellow shirt, suspenders, and a hat.

A photograph of J. W. Colley, who died in 1898, was later found in the attic of the Bonnie Castle. In the photograph, the Palmers were surprised to find that Mr. Colley was wearing a light-colored shirt, suspenders, and a garden hat.

Accommodations: Located just south of Atlanta, the 5,000-square-foot Victorian Bonnie Castle is the ideal getaway for guests of all ages, offering four bedchambers, two private baths and two guest rooms containing a sitting area. One room in the castle is named the Prophet's Chamber, in honor of the many clergymen who visited the Colleys' home. Each morning, guests will enjoy freshly brewed European coffee as an aromatic wake-up call, set up on a sideboard outside the guest rooms. A full southern breakfast follows, which is served in the formal dining room or on the veranda. The menu varies daily and can include such items as sliced fresh fruit with orange juice, freshly baked quiche, and homemade bread (just to name a few). The beautiful countryside around Bonnie Castle is a perfect locale for the cyclist. Each fall, the Bonnie Castle sponsors the first stop on the annual Lewis Grizzard Catfish Memorial Bicycle Ride.

Woodbridge Inn

44 Chambers Street • Jasper, GA 30143
(706) 253-6293 • www.woodbridgeinn.net
Room rates: $60-$80 • All major credit cards

History: The spot where the famous Woodbridge Inn stands was once a favorite place of worship for Cherokee Indians. The Native Americans loved Sharptop Mountain, and they held their prayers there as the sun rose over the mountaintop.

Today, the mountain can be viewed from the east dining room of the inn. On the west side of the building, a view of the Old Federal Road is visible; it was this path that General Andrew Jackson and his army once traveled on their way to Florida to fight the Seminoles. At various times, both Union and Confederate forces camped in the area during the Civil War.

Making a fortune in the California gold rush of 1849, Ed Lenning fought on the side of the South, and following the Civil War, he built the structure that is now the Woodbridge Inn.

In 1884, the railroad came to Jasper, bringing guests from Florida for the summer months. The nearby wooden bridge was built in the early part of the 1900s and it is where the inn derives its name.

Ed's son, Jim Lenning, operated the hotel during the depression years of the 1930s. Throughout its history, several Georgian governors have come to the inn to dine at the long table in the Lenning house. Today, guests can eat their meals at the very place where Georgia's statesmen once dined.

Activity: When the white man came to this land, they cruelly evicted the Indians that inhabited the region. Legend has it that occasionally on dark nights, visitors can actually hear the Indians' cries. Though the present owners have not observed anything out of the ordinary, eyewitnesses claim to have seen the images of elder statesmen that once stayed in the inn. Some have even claimed to hear the shouts of Tom Watson, a guest in the hotel who was evicted by the original owner, Ed Lenning.

Accommodations: The Woodbridge Inn offers 18 guest rooms and 3 extended-stay rental houses. The guest rooms overlook the scenic Blue Ridge Mountains, as well as the inn's beautiful grounds, which include two ornamental fish ponds and detailed landscaping. The Woodbridge Inn serves dinner Monday through Saturday, and luncheons are available Wednesdays and Sundays.

Jekyll Island Club Hotel

371 Riverview Drive • Jekyll Island, GA 31527
(912) 635-2600 • www.jekyllclub.com
Room rates: $69-$109 • All major credit cards

History: On January 8, 1886, the incorporation of the Jekyll Island Club began. The island was owned by John Eugene duBignon, whose family owned the island since 1800. A group of wealthy elite that included J.P. Morgan and William Rockefeller purchased the property to form a winter hunting retreat. Architect Charles A. Alexander was commissioned to design and build the 60-room Clubhouse.

The Clubhouse was completed in 1887; an attached annex was built in 1901 to house more members of the Club. The first golf course was created in 1898, and two more were added by 1909. Recreational amenities included a marina to hold yachts, a swimming pool, tennis and boccie courts, and croquet.

Club membership started to decline during the Great Depression, and in 1942, the government asked the members not to use the island until after World War II. The club never reopened, and the island was sold to the state of Georgia in 1947.

In 1978, the 240-acre club district was designated as a National Historic Landmark.

During a meticulous $20 million restoration in 1986, the club was returned to its original elegance. Today, leaded-art glass, ornate woodwork, and Rumford fireplaces adorn the hotel. Whether it is its lofty towers, encircling verandas, or the original pine floors, the Jekyll Island Club Hotel has kept its Victorian charm. Guests can walk the hallways or stay in rooms that once offered hospitality to the country's richest and most powerful citizens.

Activity: Guests of the Jekyll Island Club Hotel have reported that during the morning hours they will occasionally find their coffee and paper mysteriously disturbed—as if the coffee had been sipped and paper read. Reportedly, each morning at the exclusive hunt club, Samuel Spencer, president of the Southern Railroad Company, insisted the Wall Street Journal be delivered to his room. For many years, it became his ritual to drink his cup of coffee and scan the morning paper. That is, until 1906, when he was killed in a train accident.

Years after that terrible accident, club members who occupied Spencer's suite would step away for a few minutes and then return to find their newspaper disturbed or moved and their coffee cup empty. Many believe Spencer is continuing his morning routine in his favorite room.

Accommodations: Located on a barrier island off the Georgia coast, Jekyll Island Club Hotel offers 157 guest rooms and suites. Guests can enjoy fine dining, championship golf, tennis, croquet, or Jekyll Island's Historic District.

Whitaker-Huntingdon Inn

601 Whitaker Street
Savannah, GA 31401
(912) 232-8911 • www.whinn.com
Room rates: $150
All major credit cards

Courtesy of Whitaker-Huntingdon Inn

History: The Whitaker-Huntingdon Inn was constructed in 1883 for Jane Gordon, Ellen Williams, and their brother Robert Lachlison. He was in one of eight parties representing city officials when Savannah surrendered to General William T. Sherman in December of 1864. Murry McGregor Stewart, president of three local cotton and insurance companies and Mayor of Savannah from 1920 to 1924, purchased the home in 1896. The third owner was Dr. Lloyd Taylor, who lived with his family in the home for 42 years. Dr. Taylor added a second floor to be used as an office. In 1958, Dr. Larence Dunn and his family became the fourth owners, adding a screen porch. The Saxmans purchased the home in 1976 and have been meticulously painting and restoring the structure ever since. In 1995, the home was opened to the public as a bed and breakfast.

Activity: Sightings began during the 1923 construction of the rear two-story addition by Dr. Taylor. This has led the innkeepers to call the ghost "the Spirit of 1923." The bricks used to construct the addition came from an old jail. Ever since the completion of the addition, the rear portion of the inn and apartment have experienced paranormal activity. Previous owners felt the spirit must have been encased within the old jail site, and when the bricks were moved, the spirit came along. A young female spirit has been seen in the late evening and early morning, wearing a flowing white gown as she glides through the rear portion of the home about three feet above the floor. Household pets react strangely in portions of the home. They let out strange noises and bristle when doors shut unexpectedly. Two separate tenants in the lower apartment have reported a spirit living in the rear bedroom. Construction workers were renovating the upstairs bathroom when they decided to go to lunch and never return. Apparently, they had found their tools rolling around the floor without anyone's assistance.

Accommodations: The 1883 Italianate inn overlooks 32 acres of beautiful Forsyth Park, including the park's historic fountain. The inn offers original heart pine floors, 12-foot ceilings, period lighting, oriental rugs and antiques, clocks, and reproduction furnishings. Three two-bedroom suites are available with queen-size poster beds. Two suites have sleeper couches, private baths, and kitchenettes as well. The third suite has two private baths and a kitchen. A continental-plus breakfast is set out for guests, so they may dine at their leisure.

— KENTUCKY —

The Homestead Bed & Breakfast

☆☆☆

3944 Bloomfield Road (Hwy 62 E)
Bardstown, KY 40004
(502)349-1777
www.bbonline.com/ky/homestead
Room rates: $95-$125
Visa, Master Card

Courtesy of The Homestead Bed & Breakfast

History: During the Civil War, only three homes existed between Bardstown and Bloomfield. One was the Homestead, a restored log home and a Historic Kentucky Landmark. In the late 1700s, the massive log portion of the home was built of huge, hand-hewn yellow poplar (tulip poplar) logs. A house-slave wing was later added, as well as a

Victorian wing that features faux marbling and woodgraining. Today, the Homestead is furnished with period antiques throughout, and a buffalo head from Kentucky graces the living room mantle.

The old slave kitchen has been restored and is now a working kitchen. The once dirt floor is now covered by old bricks from the L & N Railroad Station in Louisville. The preservation of the kitchen is in memory of 40 slaves that once worked the plantation. Their names can be found on a plaque made from the handmade roof shingles they crafted.

Outside, guests can visit the old family cemetery, which has also been restored. It dates back to the early 1800s. The stepping stones that allowed riders to step up into their buggy or onto a horse are still there.

Activity: All ghosts that inhabit the Homestead are said to be happy spirits. They all appear to be the ghosts of a slave family that once lived there. The spirits of slave children will occasionally chase the family dog. A clicking noise is heard when they are present. On Halloween one year, the manager was carrying her dog as she walked through the dining room. The dog was panicked and she could hear the clicking sound coming from behind her back. She turned and spoke out loud for them to quit because they were scaring her dog half to death. The clicking stopped. In one of the guest rooms, an old swing hangs from the ceiling. The manager will often enter the room to find it swinging back and forth by itself.

Accommodations: The Homestead is the perfect place to slow down the pace. Three guest rooms are available, along with a game room and an old built-in bar and fireplace. Guests can relax on one of the porches and listen to the frogs from the nearby pond, enjoy a tree swing, or watch the sun as it sets over the rolling pastures.

In the morning, enjoy a hearty country breakfast with farm fresh eggs that you can help gather if you wish. With the addition of homemade fruit preserves, jams, and jellies, this morning meal is a sure delight. Light supper accompanied by a nice bottle of wine from their neighbor's winery is available upon arrival.

Jailer's Inn Bed & Breakfast

👻👻👻👻

111 West Stephen Foster Avenue • Bardstown, KY 40004
(502) 348-5551, (800) 948-5551 • www.jailersinn.com
Room rates: $70-$125 • All major credit cards and personal checks

History: Located in the heart of Bluegrass Country, many an outlaw once feared the Old Nelson Jail in Bardstown. It housed prisoners from 1797 until 1987. The native limestone building in front of the property is known as the "old jail." The second floor has 30-inch-thick walls surrounding two jail cells and an upper dungeon in which prisoners were held. The stone building, located directly in back of the property, is referred to as the "new jail" and was built in 1874. The newer structure is completely surrounded by a stone wall. Following the building of the new jail, the older building was converted into a jailer's residence. Both the jail and jailer's residences were occupied up until 1987.

Activity: Innkeeper Paul McCoy reports that numerous sightings have occurred over the years in and around the old structure. In 1909, an article appeared in the local paper about a gentleman named Martin Hill who reportedly beat and shot his wife. He was tried and condemned to be hanged. Before the hanging day arrived, he contracted a deadly illness and spent his final days writhing in excruciating pain and agony. Hill died in his jail cell, which has now been converted into the Colonial Room. Sometimes, late at night, strange moaning, groaning, and blood-curdling screams can be heard coming from the former cell and the corridor outside.

A female employee was in the 1819 Room one day cleaning the mirror when she saw the reflection of a man standing directly behind her. She quickly turned, but no one was there. She turned back around and looked again and the man's reflection was still there, standing directly behind her. The employee ran downstairs and promptly quit.

On another occasion, a couple woke up in the middle of the night and saw a frail-looking woman standing over their bed. Some believe that the female spirit may be that of Mrs. Maxie McKay, a female jailer who worked in the jail for almost thirty years. Her husband, who was also a jailer, worked at the jail for 15 years prior to Maxie's tenure.

In the parlor, the Jailer's Inn has an old square grand piano. Visitors have reported that late at night sounds of someone tapping on the keys can be heard. If this weren't enough, visitors have also reported hearing people talking in the building when no one was around.

On another occasion, a female visitor was staying in The Colonial Room. She was awakened at 1:00 A.M. and witnessed a man standing on the other side of the room. He stood there for a long time and then faded away.

Accommodations: The inn has 6 guest rooms, each beautifully decorated with antiques and heirlooms. All are located in the renovated front jail. A full breakfast is served in the courtyard.

Whether it's searching for ghosts, shopping in Bardstown, or relaxing in a private Jacuzzi, the historic Jailer's Inn Bed & Breakfast is the perfect place to "do time."

George Clarke House

136 Woodland Avenue
Lexington, KY 40502
(866) 436-1890, (859) 254-2500
www.georgeclarkehouse.com
Room rates: $105-$199
All major credit cards

History: In 1865, George
Clarke, along with his two
brothers and two sisters,

Courtesy of George Clarke House
Bed & Breakfast

emigrated from County Galway, Ireland. They settled in Lexington, and
Clarke married a local girl by the name of Julia Erd. They had three
children together.

Clarke and his brother Augustine started a building company that
became a huge success. In 1890, George Clarke built the Woodland
Avenue house for his wife Julia and their family. Clarke's youngest
daughter Jessie was born in the home.

Activity: The ghost of George Clarke's wife, Julia, is believed to
inhabit the home. She is said to be a good-natured and jovial spirit, but
she's a bit of a prankster.

When innkeeper Kathryn Bux turned the original Clarke family
library into a guest room, she started to experience an enormous array
of unexplained problems. She continually had plumbing trouble, and
then various items would turn up missing. New furnishings would
break, like the door to a new armoire that simply popped off, and new
heating equipment that broke apart.

Apparently, Julia was originally an artist, and she did her painting in
that room also. Two witnesses, six months apart from each other, saw
the apparition of Julia as she stood in the same spot, outside of the old
library door.

One morning, guests had come down to breakfast when a crash was
heard in their room. A vase of sunflowers had fallen off of the mantle
onto the floor, and the flowers were tossed about five feet from the
mantle. The vase was unbroken and lying on a rug.

Often mysterious activity has occurred at precisely 5:15 A.M. A
guest was once awakened at that time when an old bell ringer on the
room's telephone gave out a single chime.

Accommodations: As guests enter the front door of the George
Clarke House, they are immediately transported back in time to the
home of an upper-class family from 1890. Visitors are graciously
welcomed by their hostess, who is dressed in period costume. The

George Clarke House features 4 guest rooms, each furnished with authentic antiques. The rooms are cast in the amber glow of gaslights that paint the fine antique furnishings with a warm radiance. The enticing gourmet menu includes orange zest crepes with Grand Marnier, strawberries and fresh whipped cream, creme brulee French toast, homemade muffins and breads, fresh fruit, and yogurt cups. Jeeves the butler will be in service most weekends.

The George Clarke house is centrally located downtown in a quiet residential historic district, within walking distance of theatres, art galleries, restaurants, shops, and cultural and sporting events.

Gratz Park Inn

Courtesy of Gratz Park Inn

120 West Second • Lexington, KY 40507
(800) 752-4166 • www.gratzparkinn.com
Room rates: $149-$239
All major credit cards

History: Gratz Park Inn is Lexington's only historic hotel. Located in the heart of the downtown historic district known as Gratz Park, the inn was originally the first medical clinic west of the Allegheny Mountains. Today, Gratz Park Inn has been restored to exemplify the southern grace and charm for which the city of Lexington has long been known.

Activity: The original Lexington city morgue was located in the basement when the inn was a medical clinic. This may explain some of the paranormal activities occurring at the bed and breakfast.

A few years ago, a gentleman who was staying in the inn reported to the desk clerk that a man had been in his room. The guest claimed to have awakened in the middle of the night to see a man sitting in the chair in his room. Startled, the guest turned on the light, and the sitting man disappeared. The guest got up and checked the door to find it locked, just as he had left it. Later that night, he awoke again to find the man sitting in the chair. This time, the guest rolled over and went back to sleep.

Another guest was checking out of her room when she was asked how she enjoyed her stay. The lady replied that the room was fine; however she had not been able to sleep due to the sounds of people socializing and laughing right outside her door. The guest got out of bed and opened the door, but the hall was empty. Later that evening, she awoke again to the same commotion. She once again got up and opened her room door, only to find no one in sight. Her room was located at the end of an empty hallway.

The majority of reported paranormal activity has originated in the laundry room and on the second floor. One day, an employee found the wall sconces on the second floor turned upside down. Many of the employees claimed to have seen a man in the laundry room. Once, when an employee addressed the man, he walked right through her.

On Easter Sunday, an employee reported that she was doing the laundry when she observed the reflection of a lady in the glass door of one of the dryers. The lady was dressed in a white gown with a large hat and was standing directly behind her. When the employee turned around, the lady in white disappeared.

Accommodations: The Gratz Park Inn offers 38 guest rooms and 6 suites, all appointed with fine 19th-century antique reproductions. Each guest room features mahogany furnishings, regional artwork, queen- or king-sized beds, and modern data port phones. The Gratz Park Inn features a continental breakfast and an elegant restaurant.

The Brown Hotel

335 West Broadway • Louisville, KY 40202
(502) 583-1234 • www.thebrownhotel.com
Room rates: $94-$375 • All major credit cards

History: The Brown Hotel has been located on Fourth and Broadway, in Theatre Square in downtown Louisville, since October of 1923. Louisville entrepreneur J. Graham Brown built the hotel, and on opening day, the first person to sign the guest register was former Prime Minister of Great Britain, David Lloyd George. A parade of dignitaries and celebrities followed. The Brown instantly became a local landmark and the city's center of activity, bringing a new energy to downtown Louisville. The hotel restaurant even received its own notoriety as the birthplace of the "Hot Brown" sandwich.

When the hotel was built, Louisville was the 34th largest city in the country with a population of 235,000. Fourth Street was already an established promenade, and The Brown became the cornerstone of "The Magic Corner," playing a central role in the activities and events of downtown Louisville over the decades.

Many well-known patrons of The Brown the Duke of Windsor, Harry Truman, Elizabeth Taylor, Robert Young, Joan Crawford, Eddie Cantor, Gene Autry, Eva Marie Saint, Don Ameche, Eddie Arcaro, Muhammad Ali, Dixie Carter, and Bo Derek, to name just a few.

Activity: The ghost of the Brown's founder, J. Graham Brown, is said to still inhabit the hotel. Several staff members have entered an empty elevator in the early hours of the morning to find the button of their desired floor has already been pushed. One longtime employee has seen on many occasions the image of Brown, outfitted in 1920s-era clothing and gazing out a window. He bears a remarkable resemblance to his statue that is located in front of the hotel.

Accommodations: The Brown offers 293 spacious rooms. The hotel features intricate plaster molding, detailed woodwork, stained glass, original chandeliers, antiques, and oil paintings.

Two floors of the hotel have been designated as The Camberley Club. The club features a private lounge with a complimentary, upscale continental breakfast, afternoon snacks, hors d'oeuvres, and evening cocktails and cordials. Rooms feature specially designed bedding with triple sheeting, 250-thread count sheets, a duvet cover and down comforter, and six down pillows. In addition to amenities like terry cloth robes and fresh flowers, a concierge is available mornings and evenings to answer questions or make dinner reservations.

Cincinnati's Weller Haus Bed & Breakfast

☆☆☆

319 Poplar Street • New Port, KY 41073
(800) 431-4287, (859) 431-6829
www.wellerhaus.com
Room rates: $89-$175
All major credit cards

History: The Weller Haus was built in the 1880s and consists of two Victorian Gothic homes in Taylor Daughter's Historic District, directly across the Ohio River from downtown Cincinnati. Original millwork and 18th-century period pieces set the tone in this Preservation Awarded

Courtesy of Cincinnati's Weller Haus Bed & Breakfast

Bed & Breakfast listed on the National Register of Historic Places.
Activity: Weller Haus' ghostly activity is centered in the kitchen. Guests in their rooms have heard unexplained movement emanating from there. Some report the sounds of someone rummaging through the cupboards. However, when they open the kitchen door, no one is there. Reportedly, the former owner spent most of his time in the kitchen, until he was found dead on the floor of that room in1989.

Visitors have also witnessed the ghost of the former owner in a guest room directly above the kitchen. The guests saw the spirit standing at the end of their bed. In this same room, the bathroom exhaust fan will mysteriously turn on and off several times during the middle of the night, usually between 3 and 4 A.M.

The ghost of a small child has also been seen in this guest room, standing beside the bed. Reportedly, a guest awoke to find the ghost of a child with her hand touching the guest's face. When the guest moved, the ghost disappeared.

Accommodations: Guests can enjoy a small-town atmosphere with all the conveniences of downtown Cincinnati. Weller Haus offers 5 spacious, uniquely decorated guest rooms, all with private baths and in-room phones. A double Jacuzzi suite is available for romantic getaways. They even provide the bubble bath! Outside, guests can stroll through a beautiful, secluded English garden. A full breakfast awaits you after a restful night's sleep.

— LOUISIANA —

1891 Castle Inn of New Orleans

1539 4th Street
New Orleans, LA 70130
(888) 826-0540, (504) 826-0540
www.castleinnofneworleans.com
Room rates: $89-$250
All major credit cards

History: The Castle Inn of New Orleans is a Victorian mansion located in the Garden District, steps way from the route of the world-famous streetcar and the Mardi Gras parades. If you are looking for something other than a run

Courtesy of 1891 Castle Inn of New Orleans

of the mill, "been there, done that," touristy vacation in a cookie-cutter hotel room, the 1891 Castle Inn of New Orleans is for you. It was built in 1891, as its name reflects. The current owners, originally from New York City, purchased the home in 1998.

To stay at the Castle Inn feels like you are visiting an old friend's grand and gracious home. The inn features over-sized rooms with balconies, hardwood floors, 13-foot high ceilings, and 10-foot tall windows. Each room has been personally decorated by the owner, Miss Karen, to celebrate a different and wonderful aspect of New Orleans culture and history.

Activity: The Castle Inn has a great deal of paranormal activity. Dozens of eyewitness reports have surfaced since 1998, both from employees and guests. Previous owners have reported nothing out of the ordinary. However, the current innkeepers tell a different story.

A staff member has repeatedly seen a male apparition standing by the window in Room 11. Occurrences have also involved objects moving by themselves and electric lights and appliances turning on and off on their own. The sounds of footsteps have also been heard, and brief glimpses of a "translucent man" have been seen standing in the corners of rooms and on the front porch late at night.

Guests have witnessed a television levitating above the floor, doorknobs turning on their own, and the sounds of coughing and whistling in the hallways when no one is there.

Often objects will move by themselves, to be found hidden in the most unlikely places. One day, a couple was checking out and could not find their receipts of the past four days of shopping and travel, which the husband had collected in his wallet. After a lengthy search, his wife found them all inside the microwave. They were both perplexed about how the receipts got there.

Accommodations: The 1891 Castle Inn is a 9,500-square-foot Gilded Age mansion with 9 suites and rooms. Located in the heart of the Garden District, it's only a few steps from St. Charles Avenue and a seven-minute ride by streetcar to the French Quarter. The annual Mardi Gras parades are viewable from the windows of the Castle Inn.

Dauphine House

Courtesy of The
Dauphine House

1830 Dauphine Street
New Orleans, LA 70116
(504) 940-0943 • www.dauphinehouse.com
Room rates: $65-$90
Visa, Master Card, American Express and
personal checks

History: What is today known as New Orleans' French Quarter was established in 1718 as a military outpost and commercial port. The Quarter spent the first half-century of its existence as a French settlement. Unlike English colonies of the time—who often hoped to distance themselves from their mother country—the original citizens of New Orleans proudly embraced and celebrated their French heritage.

The Spanish acquired New Orleans in 1763, and there was a melding of the two cultures, combined with African influences from the slave population. Thus, Creole society and cuisine were born. The "French" architecture for which the Quarter is famous is, in large part, actually Spanish; most buildings were constructed after the city burned in 1788 and again in 1794.

The United States made the Louisiana Purchase in 1803, and New Orleans became American. This caused a physical and spiritual separation. The newly created Canal Street became the boundary that would last over a century and would further insulate the French Quarter from the bustling city around it.

Each year, millions of visitors and residents enjoy the French Quarter's world of narrow streets, eclectic shops, and historic houses. One such home is the Dauphine House, which was built as a residence in 1860.

Activity: The innkeeper of the Dauphine House, Karen Jefferies, told us that she has seen the ghosts of a couple dressed in Victorian clothing. One day while renovations were being completed and the electricity was shut off in the house, Jefferies ran up the stairs to pick something up before leaving for work. As she looked up to the top of the stairs, she saw the ghosts of the young man and woman, both looking at her and smiling. She paused, feeling unafraid, and proceeded to thank them for their beautiful home and assured the couple she would restore it to its original beauty.

Since the inn was opened to the public, the couple has made their benign presence known on several occasions to staff and guests. One guest was very distraught over a relationship that had ended. At the close of her stay, the guest reported seeing the couple three times during the weekend. She felt they were there to comfort her.

There have also been other reports of the ghost of a gentleman who has been seen walking on the balcony of the inn. Witnesses say that he appears to be waiting for someone to come home.

Accommodations: The Dauphine House has 3 exquisite guest rooms, all with hardwood floors, 12-foot ceilings, and private baths. World-renowned restaurants are located within a short walk of the inn, and the historic French Quarter is only one block away.

While in New Orleans, visitors can enjoy river cruises on the mighty Mississippi, ride a trolley through the Garden District, or take a leisurely stroll through the lush grounds of Audubon Park and the New Orleans Zoo.

The Maison de Ville

Courtesy of The Maison de Ville

727 Rue Toulouse
New Orleans, LA 70130
(504) 561-5858
www.maisondeville.com
Room rates: $215-$980
All major credit cards

History: The name Maison de Ville means "town house" in French. This inn is just that: a two-story dwelling built in 1783 by Jean Baptiste Lilie Sarpy, in what was then the center of New Orleans.

An early resident of the home was Antoine Amede Peychaud, an apothecary who invented the first cocktail, a concoction of bitters and brands. Peychauds' bitters are still used today in a well-known New Orleans drink called the Sazerac.

Today, the main building contains the reception room, a parlor, concierge, and guest rooms. Across the courtyard, visitors will find four former slave quarters. These cottages are believed to be some of the oldest buildings in New Orleans.

With the combined efforts of Madeline Erlich, a native of Pennsylvania, and her friend, Mary McDougall, the hotel known as the Maison de Ville was created. Erlich and McDougall set about assembling just the right furniture and decorations, acquiring a door that came from the St. Louis Hotel. The door, with its etched glass between two panels of beautifully carved wood, had nearly been destroyed by a hurricane in 1915. It now graces the Maison de Ville's main entrance.

Activity: The Maison de Ville has experienced several paranormal sightings over the past several years. Jewel France, the executive housekeeper and a 23-year employee of the Maison de Ville, was the first person to encounter "the soldier." Around 20 years ago, she opened the door to cottage #4 to allow a guest in. To their amazement, they saw a man dressed in a Confederate soldier's uniform in the room. She felt a chill and began to shake as the vision disappeared.

The hotel plays classical music in the rooms as guests arrive. Apparently the soldier doesn't like classical music on the radio, for as soon as Jewel leaves, the ghost will change the station to loud country music. She'll go back in and reset the radio, but when she leaves, it changes back once more.

The image of a lady dressed in white appears in the alleyway between the hotel and the restaurant next door. The chef and employees of the restaurant have frequently seen her walking by.

Finally, in the two-bedroom, two-story cottages, guests have reported to the hotel management that while they were sitting in the living area downstairs, they heard the sounds of people in chains, walking across the floor upstairs.

Accommodations: The Maison de Ville offers 23 guest rooms. Guests can choose from two main buildings on Toulouse, former slave quarters, or seven cottages. The guest quarters and suites are exquisitely furnished with antiques, four-poster beds, and marble basins. Brick walls and fireplaces help set an atmosphere of casual elegance. Guests will enjoy relaxing in the courtyard, with its cast-iron fountain, tropical foliage, and a swimming pool nestled among the private cottage courtyards.

Le Pavillon Hotel

833 Poydras Street • New Orleans, LA 70112
(504) 581-3111 • www.lepavillon.com
Room rates: $129-$475 • All major credit cards

History: The grounds of the Le Pavillon Hotel were originally the site of one of the area's first great plantation homes. Located in the heart of New Orleans, the hotel opened in 1907 and received immediate acclaim as one of the country's most notable new hotels. A seemingly endless parade of famous personalities passed through its doors, and many elaborate parties and cotillions took place under its roof. It survived wars, prohibition, and the Great Depression to maintain its reputation as one of the grandest hotels in the world.

In 1970, a major restoration took place, and a bevy of modern features were added while retaining the hotel's original architecture and interior design. A rooftop pool and patio were created, allowing guests to take a relaxing swim while overlooking the Crescent City and the Mississippi River.

On June 24, 1991, the U.S. Department of the Interior placed Le Pavillon on the National Register of Historic Places. Guests can now enjoy luxury and magnificent service that are a reminder of a sophisticated time.

Activity: Legend has it that the ghost of a teenage girl inhabits Le Pavillon. Believed to have lived in the 1840s, she was preparing to leave on a ship when a carriage struck her. She died from the injuries. Her presence is still very much felt at the hotel, along with that of a young aristocratic couple from the 1920s and the ghost of a man in a dark suit who occasionally plays pranks on the hotel staff.

Accommodations: Today, Le Pavillon Hotel—"The Belle of New Orleans"—has been lovingly restored and features 219 guest rooms and 7 suites, as well as a breathtaking lobby with beautiful marble floors, statuary, and priceless Czechoslovakian crystal chandeliers. Both American and European antique furnishings and artwork adorn the hotel and complement the grand architecture. The Antique Plantation suite is a special treat; it's authentically furnished and is dedicated to the preservation of Louisiana's rich heritage. The Castle Suite features a magnificent hand-carved marble bathtub that was a gift from Napoleon to a wealthy Louisiana plantation owner. The only other tub belonging to Napoleon is located in the Louvre. On the front porch, guests will find the largest gas lantern in the United States. It still burns daily.

Olde Victorian Inn

914 N. Rampart Street • New Orleans, LA 70116
(800) 725-2446, (504) 522-2446 • www.oldevictorianinn.com
Room rates: $135-$185 • All major credit cards

History: In 1722, the de la Tour map recorded the site which was dubbed Lot No. 542 and granted to Monsieur Faverot and Monsurier de Benac. In 1852, Lucien Mansion built the house now known as the Olde Victorian Inn. Lucien Mansion was an enormously wealthy sugarcane plantation owner. In 1883, he deeded the property to Elizabeth Agnes Frances, who lived in the home for years and was reportedly his mistress. Rumor has it that the property later operated as a brothel.

The home traded hands several times over the years until 1940, when Leo Marchand ("Uncle Leo"), and his wife, Marie Blappert, bought the home. Leo lived the rest of his life in the house, and he died in what is now the dining room in 1977.

P. J. Holbrook purchased the home in 1989. After years of disrepair, the local government gave her five months to complete renovations and open it to the public. Repairs were completed in record time, and the inn was open for business. The interior was decorated with hand-picked antiques from all over the South, and furniture chosen by P.J. Her labor of love was sometimes booked solid a year in advance. In 1999, she retired, and sold the inn to Keith and Andre West-Harrison.

Activity: Legend has it that Leo Marchand still claims the house, and he has been seen, heard, and felt by the owners and numerous guests. Leo died from complications due to emphysema, and his heavy breathing has been heard in several rooms in the inn.

A guest was staying in the Chantilly Room one night when he awoke to find the figure of an old man sitting motionless in one of the Victorian chairs. The guest admitted he had visited Bourbon Street, but was not by any means drunk. He saw the man clearly, and when he rubbed his eyes and looked back, the man was gone. The guest described the mysterious visitor in his room, and when the owner showed him a picture of Uncle Leo, the guest exclaimed, "That's him!"

Uncle Leo's picture is hanging in the hallway near the door to the living room for visitors who want to see what he looks like. That way, they'll be able to recognize him if he should pay them a visit.

Often lights will turn off and on, water faucets will run on their own, and items will mysteriously disappear only to reappear hours later.

A maid was cleaning the Chateau Room one morning when the door slammed shut. Though she tried, the maid couldn't open the door. A contractor was called and he had to take the door off of its hinges to free the maid. No explanation was found for the sticking door.

Accommodations: Upon arrival and after you're settled into one of 6 beautifully decorated rooms, each with private baths, you will be invited to freshly made tea or special home-made lemonade and goodies while you relax in the tropical courtyard. The Olde Victorian Inn provides the elegance and romanticism of the 1840s. High ceilings, floor-to-ceiling windows, long staircases, and ruffles and lace allow visitors to step back in time. Three times a week "Chef's Tasting" is prepared by Keith and Andre with a menu of delicious New Orleans cuisine.

St. Vincent's Guest House

★ ★ ★ ★

1507 Magazine Street • New Orleans, LA 70130
(504) 566-1515, (504) 523-3411
www.stvincentsguesthouse.com
Room rate: $59-$89 • All major credit cards

History: Only minutes from the French Quarter and Convention Center, St. Vincent's Guest House offers charm, history, and comfort at reasonable prices. Built in the 1860s as an orphanage, the facility was run by the nuns of the Daughters of Charity. Its chief founder was Margaret Haughery, the famous philanthropist who began life in the U.S. as an illiterate Irish immigrant. She was orphaned herself and later lost her own baby to yellow fever; she vowed to spend the rest of her life alleviating the sufferings of children. St. Vincent's is a testimony to her exceptional life and dedication.

Activity: Since the Guest House opened its doors to the public in the mid 1990s as a boutique hotel, there have been numerous reports by guests of children running through the halls at night. A British guest approached the manager and complained about the children and threatened to check out if he didn't do something about their constant noises. The manager explained to the guest that there were no children staying in the hotel, which made the guest more angry, as if he was making the whole thing up. So the manager placed signs saying, "No Running – Quiet Please" in the hallway that night. The next morning, the guest reported that the halls were much quieter that evening and that the children kept their voices down. Seeing that the signs did the trick, the manager regularly places the signs in the halls where he receives complaints, and the disturbances have decreased.

During the restoration of the hotel, the foreman moved into the attic above the first wing. He decided to move out two weeks later because he was enduring sleepless nights caused by incessant giggling behind the walls. Also, he was worried because the furniture kept moving. A scientifically minded fellow, he drew a chalk outline around the exact spot where the chair and armoire were each night before he went to bed. The next morning, the chair and armoire were moved several inches outside the chalked outlines. He was able to duplicate this several days in a row.

During renovations on the second wing, workers refused to enter the attic after they witnessed the spirit of a nun watching them from the far end of the room. Also in the attic is a somewhat-hidden room approximately 15 ft. x 15 ft., which has a long iron bar along its length with chains attached. During the war, prisoners were shackled to the bar. Occasionally, guests and workers have heard moans and sighs coming from this room. Although the attic rooms are large and would make great guest rooms, the owner has been unable to find a crew that would be willing to work there. Which is just as well since the manager feels the unusual activity in the rooms would bring more trouble than it is worth.

Accommodations: St. Vincent's is a beautiful inn offering 80 guest rooms; it has been recognized by the Historic Commission. The décor features white wicker furnishings, charming floral fabrics, and handmade patchwork quilts.

Myrtles Plantation

🎃🎃🎃🎃

7747 U.S. Highway 61
St. Francisville, LA 70775
(225) 635-6277
www.myrtlesplantation.com
Room rates: $115-$230
All major credit cards

By Grant L. Robertson. Courtesy of
Myrtles Plantation

History: Built in 1796 by General David Bradford, the Myrtles Plantation is on the Smithsonian Institute's list of the most haunted places in the world. Legend has it that Sara Matilda, the daughter of General Bradford, married Judge Clark Woodruffe and they moved into the Myrtles.

The judge began an intimate relationship with one of his slaves, a girl named Chloe. The judge soon tired of Chloe, however, and moved on to another mistress. Chloe started eavesdropping on the family's conversations. The judge caught her listening in, and he ordered that one of her ears be cut off to teach her a lesson. After that, Chloe always wore a green turban around her head to hide her missing ear.

Reportedly, Chloe devised a scheme to make the family sick so she could nurse them back to health and earn the Judge's gratitude. She put a small amount of herbs similar to arsenic into a birthday cake meant for the Judge's oldest daughter. Sara Matilda and her two children each had a slice of the cake, but the judge did not. By nightfall, the mother and daughters were sick, and Chloe attended to their needs, not realizing she had given them too much poison. In a matter of a few hours, Sara and her children were dead.

The other slaves, afraid the judge would punish them as well, dragged Chloe out of the house and hanged her from a tree. Her body was later cut down, weighted with rocks, and thrown into the river.

Activity: The ghost of Chloe has been seen at the Myrtles on several occasions, and her image has even appeared in photographs as a shadowy figure wearing a turban, standing near the building.

Witnesses have also seen the spirits of the Woodruffe children who died from the poisonous cake. They have been seen playing on the veranda, in the hallways, and in the old children's dining room, which today is the game room. The children have even been spotted on top of a hanging chandelier.

Around the time of the Civil War, a man was shot and killed in the hallway on the first floor. Recently, a maid was mopping the floor of the hallway when she came to a strange spot near the front door.

Though she pushed the mop with all her might, whatever was there prevented her from mopping. The impregnable area of the floor was the size of a human body. The mop did not work on that spot for a month. When thunderstorms approach, a fourth apparition appears. The spirit of a young girl with long curly hair wearing an ankle-length dress has been seen drifting outside of the game room window, with her hands cupped. She is trying to look in the room.

Another spirit is that of a French woman who walks from room to room in search of someone she never seems to find. An employee once quit because he observed a woman dressed in white walk up to the house and through the front door (literally).

Some guests have heard the sounds of a baby crying in different parts of the house. A grand piano on the first floor plays by itself and practices the same chord over and over. It continues on through the night until someone enters the room. The music stops only to start again when they leave the room.

In the "French" bedroom, witnesses have seen the ghost of a woman wearing a long black skirt floating about a foot above the floor, dancing to music only she can hear.

Accommodations: The antebellum Myrtles Plantation features 11 bed and breakfast rooms and is filled with fine antiques and architectural treasures of the South. Step onto the 120-foot veranda and relax in the oversized rockers, or stroll the majestic ten acres of beautiful live oaks. A 5,000-square-foot brick courtyard is the perfect place for guests to unwind before attending a delicious candlelight dinner at the Carriage House Restaurant.

Oak Alley Plantation, Restaurant, & Inn

3645 Highway 18 (Great River Road) • Vacherie, LA 70090
(800)- 44ALLEY • www.oakalleyplantation.com
Room rates: $115-$135 • All major credit cards

History: Built in 1839 by Jacques T. Roman, a wealthy French Creole sugar planter from New Orleans, the Oak Alley Plantation has been called the "Grande Dame" of Great River Road. The plantation resides over one of the prettiest settings in the South, complete with rows of oak trees.

Activity: Oak Alley Plantation offers a few mysteries along with its picturesque scenery. On several occasions during tours of the home, the sound of a horse-drawn carriage and horses are heard coming from outside. When witnesses have peered out the door, nothing is in sight. The lights sometimes flicker on and off during tours. This happens only during tours.

One tour guide saw the spirit of a person seated on one of the beds in the mansion, and on another occasion, she saw the ghost of a man standing in the kitchen.

An office worker reported empty rocking chairs rocking in unison and items moving from table to desktop.

During a recent tour, a candlestick flew across the room on its own accord. There were 35 witnesses to this oddity. On one occasion, the tour guide walked upstairs to make sure there were no stragglers. He looked into one of the rooms and he clearly heard someone say, "Pssst," behind him. The guide turned around, but found no one there.

Recently, a guest snapped a photograph of an antique mirror. In the mirror was the reflection of a mannequin across the room, wearing an old dress. When the photographs where developed, something else was in the reflection. It was the image of a young girl with long hair. She appears to be gazing through the French doors down the alley.

Accommodations: Oak Alley offers 5 turn-of-the-century creole cottages on the grounds of the plantation close to the antebellum mansion. The quarter-mile canopy of giant live oak trees, believed to be nearly 300 years old, forms an impressive avenue leading to this Greek Revival–style antebellum inn. Daily plantation tours are offered, and bed and breakfast accommodations are available in turn-of-the-century Creole cottages. There is also a wonderful restaurant and gift shop. The Oak Alley is the ideal setting for weddings, parties, and other private functions.

— MISSISSIPPI —

1902–08 Stained Glass Manor Oak Hall

2430 Drummond Street • Vicksburg, MS 39180
(800) 771-8893 • www.vickbnb.com
Room rates: $70-$185 • All major credit cards

History: Bob & Shirley Smollen, the owners, are not exactly sure when construction began on the bed & breakfast inn. However, they do know that it was well underway by 1902 and finished in 1908. The architect, George Washington Maher, was known as the "Father of

Indigenous American Architecture." Maher is remembered for training a young draftsman by the name of Frank Lloyd Wright. In January of 1910, Louise Tiffany, of the famed Tiffany's in New York, traveled to the Stained Glass Manor and personally supervised the installation of a crystal chandelier in the main dining room. The thirty-six stained glass windows in the manor were created by Louis J. Millet, the first Dean of Architecture in Chicago and the head of the Chicago Art Institute.

Activity: When Bob and Shirley Smollen first purchased the historic manor in 1990, they began to remodel and renovate the property. Soon, they began to notice tape measures disappearing. Bob says he had at least six to seven vanish, then they'd all turn up together. The same thing started occurring with hammers, and then other pieces of hardware. The owners believe they have just one ghost: the original proprietor of the home, Fanny Vick Willis Johnson, who lived in the house from 1908 until her death in 1931. Seven people have reportedly seen a female apparition, and when each was shown a photograph of Fanny, each confirmed that it was indeed Fanny that made the surprise appearance.

One guest told the Smollens that while staying at the inn, she was grieving from a personal loss. That night, when she was alone in her room, she felt someone sit down beside her and hold her, and all of her grief disappeared. Over Fanny's grave, her tombstone actually reads, "She lived for others," and perhaps in her own way, she still does. Fanny has been seen in the yard and in the house, and many have reported that they felt her presence. The Smollens say Fanny makes herself known rather infrequently—about every six months or so.

Accommodations: The 1902–08 Stained Glass Manor features 5 guest rooms. Possibly the finest example of Mission-style architecture in Mississippi, the manor contains one of the most lavish residential displays of leaded and stained glass we've seen anywhere. Featuring 38 stained glass windows, fine oak panels, and a spectacular staircase, the interior glows from light borne through panes of gold, rose, salmon, blue, and green. The artwork of each panel is unbelievably delicate, and it is no wonder that the property is listed in the National Register of Historic Places. Each morning in the dining room, guests can enjoy a New Orleans-style breakfast to prepare them for their journey through Vicksburg.

The Duff Green Mansion

1114 First East Street • Vicksburg, MS 39180
(800) 992-0037 • www.duffgreenmansion.com
Room rates: $75-$160 • All major credit cards

History: Built in 1856 in historic Vicksburg, the Duff Green was almost destroyed during the Civil War when a Union-fired cannon ball tore through the roof and third floor before settling in the second floor library. After five similar attacks, owners Duff and Mary Green converted the home into a hospital for soldiers from both the North and the South.

The Greens often took refuge in a pair of caves they had built into the side of the hill where the mansion sits. The house was used as a hospital after the war, then became an orphanage, and then a nursing home. In 1931, it was sold to the Salvation Army as their local headquarters. A complete restoration was accomplished, replacing original fixtures, chandeliers, and original iron grillwork balconies.

Activity: Legend has it that five ghosts reside at the Duff Green Mansion. They include the former owner Mrs. Green, her daughter, and three soldiers from the war.

The spirit of Mrs. Green is said to visit the breakfast cook daily. She makes her presence known through a cold draft that travels around the kitchen. The soldiers have been seen on the first floor, one in the corner of a guest room and the other in the old kitchen, which was a surgical operating room during the war.

Footsteps have been heard in the home; many believe these are the sounds of Mrs. Green's daughter who died as a young child.

Another ghost is that of a soldier who died while waiting for surgery. During the grisly conflict, death was common in the battle hospital.

Accommodations: The Duff Green Mansion offers 7 luxurious bedrooms and suites, each with individual character, open fireplaces, and porches where guests can relax in the evening air. A full plantation breakfast is served each morning, including biscuits that many describe as the best in Vicksburg. Guests can enjoy the complimentary bar during happy hour or sunbathe during the day on the secluded patio.

This magnificent mansion is situated in the historic district of Vicksburg and is considered to be one of the finest examples of Palladian architecture in the state. Beneath its high ceilings and richly decorated walls, the polished floors still carry bloodstains from that tragic time.

— NORTH CAROLINA —

Blake House Inn

150 Royal Pines Drive
Asheville, NC 28704
(888) 353-5227, (828) 681-5227
www.blakehouse.com
Room rates: $155-$225
All major credit cards

Courtesy of Blake House Inn

History: The Blake House Inn was built in 1847 by Joseph B. Pyatt.
The house originally served as a summer home for Dr. Frederick Blake,
a wealthy rice plantation owner from Charleston, South Carolina.
During the final days of the Civil War, the house also served as a
Confederate field hospital. Confederate soldiers were treated and cared
for in bedrooms upstairs, and some of the nurses took pity on injured
Union soldiers and cared for them in the tunnel system under the inn.

The Blake House Inn, with its 22-inch native stone walls laid in lime
and clay mortar and its original 14-foot ornamental plaster ceilings, is
one of the best examples of Italianate architecture with Gothic influence
in Asheville.

Activity: On the first floor of the inn, guests will find an intricate
tunnel system with trap doors located in each room. Reportedly, the
Blake family had three generations of slaves, and many believe that
although Dr. Blake was a Confederate physician, the home and its
secret tunnels may have been used by the Underground Railroad.

Legend has it that a woman by the name of Helen was a Confederate
nurse at the end of the Civil War when the home was used as a field
hospital. Helen's husband was critically injured, and he was cared for in
what was Mrs. Blake's master bedroom (now the Lilac Room). As the
story goes, Helen tried to get to her husband, but by the time she
arrived, he had died. She became so distraught that she walked off the
balcony of the Lilac Room and committed suicide. She had red hair,
and wore a floor-length green dress at the time.

Two weeks after owners Nancy and Terry Rice purchased the inn in
June of 1998, a guest asked if she knew about the story of Helen. The
guest felt compelled to approach Nancy because there were some major
similarities between her and Helen. Mysteriously, Nancy also has red
hair like Helen did, and she also chose to wear a green dress that night.

Witnesses at the inn have reported seeing rocking chairs rocking

in several places in the hotel, a tremendous amount of activity has taken place in Room 545, two stories directly above the Palm Court atrium floor where the young woman is said to have died.

On several occasions, a cold brush of air will rush past visitors to Room 545. The manager of Elaine's, the Grove Park Inn nightclub, has seen an image described as dense smoke—a form of pinkish pastel that just flows. Another guest swore that a lady sat down beside him while he was making a phone call in his room.

In another incident, two employees were locking up for the winter. As they stood outside, they looked up and saw that all of the sixth floor room lights were on; as they watched, the lights went off, followed by the main inn lights.

The Pink Lady has also made her presence known at the inn's accounting office, where two employees saw her after a party. They heard someone come in the back door of the office and saw a woman dressed in party clothes walk quickly past. Thinking it was a guest, they got up to assist her, but she was gone.

Accommodations: Completely renovated and expanded, the Grove Park Inn Resort and Spa offers 510 rooms (including 12 suites and 28 oversized Club Floor rooms) and 50,000 square feet of meeting space (including 2 ballrooms and 42 conference rooms). Amenities include golf, tennis, two pools, an indoor sports complex, an 18-station fitness center, shops, fine dining, and children's programs, as well as one of the finest spas in North America.

Owl's Nest Inn at Engadine

2630 Smokey Park Highway • Candler (West Asheville), NC 28715
(800) 665-8868, (828) 665-8325 • www.engadineinn.com
Room rates: $80-$195 • All major credit cards

History: Built in 1885, Captain John Keais Hoyt (Company K, 3rd Alabama Infantry, Confederate States of America), moved his family into the house, which the Captain named "Engadine" after a valley in Switzerland. The house had all of the modern conveniences of the day, like running water and a coal furnace.

In 1944, Glen Howell purchased the house and raised his family there. He restored the home and moved the kitchen into what is now the den. In 1988, the house was sold and again restored and modernized. In 1994, the home was sold again and the new owners converted it into a bed and breakfast. In August of 1998, the current owners, Marg Dente and Gail Kinney, purchased the inn and changed the name, adding

Owl's Nest Inn to the original Engadine Inn. The inn is listed in the National Register of Historic Places.

Activity: Even locals tell of the inn's haunted history, and they have the pictures to prove it. Apparently, photographs of the ghost that visits the inn have been taken, and the owner feels certain that it's Mary Hoyt, the daughter of Captain John K. Hoyt, who haunts the inn. Mary's image has been captured on film as she stands outside with a white shroud around her head. She has also been seen standing in the window behind the lattice staircase.

Guests in the Captain's Bedroom have heard the sounds of a young man and woman laughing and chasing each other up and down the stairs at night.

The sound of a child playing marbles has been heard upstairs, late at night, in an empty room. The smell of tobacco smoke has appeared inexplicably (this is a nonsmoking hotel). Some think it's the Captain smoking his pipe.

The owner was cleaning the rooms one day alone on the second floor of the house when she heard the sound of someone opening the door downstairs, which is impossible since she has the only key. The visitor shouted up "yoo-hoo," she "yoo-hooed" back and went downstairs, only to find no one anywhere in the house.

The Mary Hoyt room has experienced some strange activity, like the alarm clock turning on by itself and the gas fireplace igniting and turning off by itself. That is until manager, Gail Kinney went into the room and said, "That is not funny, nor is it safe. Please stop." It has not happened since.

Accommodations: Located on 12 acres in the beautiful mountains just outside of Asheville, the Owl's Nest Inn is convenient to Great Smoky Mountains National Park and the Blue Ridge Parkway. The inn features 4 guest rooms and 1 suite. Wraparound porches surround the inn, and picnic areas and benches are available in the meadow for guests to enjoy the mountain views. Each morning, a full breakfast is served by the fireplace in the formal dining room. The inn has central air conditioning, private baths, and fireplaces.

Black Mountain Inn

֏ ֏ ֏

718 Old Highway 70
Black Mountain, NC 28711
(800) 735-6128
(828) 669-6528
www.blackmountaininn.com
Room rates: $98-$158
Visa, Master Card, American
Express

Courtesy of Black Mountain Inn

History: The house was originally built about 170 years ago as a stagecoach stop. Martha Mallory owned the home around 1900 and converted it into a tuberculosis sanatorium, which she ran until her untimely death on the railroad tracks on her way home from town.

After her death, the house fell into ruin and became a squatter's camp. Cattle were even stabled in the dining room. In 1940, Mary Aleshire and Daisey Erb purchased the property and refurbished it as a summer home. Aleshire was the manager of the Norton Art Gallery in Palm Beach, Florida. After two years of restoration, the historic property was opened to the public as the Oak Knoll Art Studio. The home also served as a summer retreat for Aleshire and her famous guests, such as Ernest Hemingway, John Steinbeck, Norman Rockwell, and Helen Keller. Huge garden parties were held at the home during summer months.

In 1989, the house was purchased by June Bergeron, and it started its next life as the Black Mountain Inn.

Activity: Witnesses occasionally see the image of a woman at different locations around the inn, dressed in turn-of-the-century clothing. Many believe it is Martha Mallory, the original owner.

Guests have reported their encounters with the ghost, and they have never been scared during the sightings. At other times, the sounds of conversations are heard from empty rooms in the inn, and the tapping of a typewriter has been heard as well.

Finally, guests and staff have witnessed the appearance of three young African-American children. Their spirits have been seen on the third floor, in the attic. Since slaves originally built this antebellum home and stagecoach stop, the children may be connected with that time period. Today, when the Black Mountain Inn has its big annual parties, there always seems to be an increase of paranormal activity.

Accommodations: Worlds away from the hustle and bustle of daily routine, the Black Mountain Inn is a peaceful retreat for the body and soul. Seven comfortable guest rooms and 1 suite (The Artist's Loft) are decorated with casual, old-fashioned furnishings, and each room has its own private bath. Delicious breakfast buffets are served in the great room each morning featuring June's fabulous homemade granola, fresh fruits and homemade breads and biscuits. Three acres of wooded property surround the inn, making it an ideal location for guests who travel with pets.

The Carolina Inn

211 Pittsboro Street • Chapel Hill, NC 27516
(800) 962-8519, (919) 933-2001 • www.carolinainn.com
Room rates: $139-$274 • All major credit cards

History: Ever since its grand opening in 1924, the Carolina Inn has played an important role in the life of the University of North Carolina and the Chapel Hill community. The inn was built by UNC graduate John Sprunt Hill, who donated the inn to the University in 1935. He referred to the inn as "a cheerful inn for visitors, a town hall for the state, and a home for returning sons and daughters of alma mater." The University of North Carolina still owns the inn, and it is managed by Doubletree Hotels.

The Carolina Inn blends elements of antebellum southern plantation houses with Georgian and neoclassical features, a style regularly found in the Northeast. The original front of the Carolina Inn was modeled after the Potomac River face of Mt. Vernon.

An extensive renovation and expansion was completed in 1996, adding modern amenities while preserving the inn's traditional warmth and grandeur. For over 75 years, the Carolina Inn has offered guests the finest in food, lodging, and hospitality.

Activity: Dr. William P. Jacocks, a physician with the International Health Division of the Rockefeller Foundation, retired to Chapel Hill and lived at the inn until his death in 1965. He had a reputation as a kind and gentle man with a fun-loving sense of humor. Supposedly, the spirit of Dr. Jacocks likes to tease guests who stay in his room on the third floor of the Carolina Inn. He apparently enjoys locking guests out of their room. One couple returned to their room to find that their electronic keys would not open the door. Hotel maintenance workers were unsuccessful in opening the door also. They had to climb a ladder and crawl through a window to finally get the door open. On another occasion, the good doctor struck again and the door had to be taken off of its hinges because it could not be unlocked.

Accommodations: The Carolina Inn offers 184 guest rooms and suites and the Carolina Crossroads Restaurant offers fine dining. Within the inn, visitors will find an extensive collection of antiques that includes objects used at the inn around 1924.

The Summit Inn

210 East Rogers Street • Franklin, NC 28734
(828) 524-2006, (828) 349-1246 • www.summitinn.net
Room rates: $59-$99 • Visa, Master Card, American Express

History: The Summit Inn was originally built in 1898 as a family residence for Samuel L. Rogers and his family. Rogers, a wealthy government official, and his wife Mamie had six children, and their family was at the center of the social scene in western North Carolina. Their home, known as Rogers Hall, held many glamorous parties and gatherings. Today, Rogers Hall has been transformed into the Summit Inn.

Activity: Since its creation, the 104-year-old Summit Inn has hosted thousands of visitors. The most infamous resident was Esther Louise Rogers, the young daughter of Samuel Rogers. Esther was intelligent, beautiful, and destined for a bright future. Her father hoped she would find a wealthy suitor and thrust the family even further into the limelight.

However, at 16 years of age, Esther fell in love with the 18-year-old stable boy. Esther soon became pregnant with his child. When Esther told her lover that she was expecting, he informed her he was to be married to another girl who was also expecting his child. When Esther told her mother about this, the stable boy was immediately fired.

Samuel Rogers came home from Washington and, fearing scandal, he and his wife Mamie concocted a plan by which Esther would go into hiding so the baby could be born in secret. The town's physician and Samuel's uncle, Wiley Rogers, delivered the child, and Esther was forced to give the baby up.

Esther was heartbroken and soon fell into a deep depression. She would pace the floors of Rogers Hall crying for the return of her baby girl. The distraught Esther eventually took her own life.

Today, visitors at the Summit Inn will hear the faint muffled sobs of a woman and the cries of her newborn baby late at night.

Accommodations: The Summit Inn offers 14 guest rooms, each with its own unique charm. Guests can kick back and relax on antique brass beds piled high with pillows and comforters, or they can enjoy bedrooms with carved highboy beds and armoires. From the front porch, visitors will enjoy one of the best vistas in Franklin, with panoramic views of Wayah Bald, Standing Indian, and Nantahala Range. Aside from the overnight accommodations, the Summit Inn features an elegant restaurant, offering fine dining.

Mountain Magnolia Inn and Retreat

Courtesy of Mountain Magnolia Inn and Retreat

P.O. Box 6
Hot Springs, NC 28743
(828) 622-3543
www.mountainmagnoliainn.com
Room rates: $95-$250
All major credit cards

History: The original owners of the inn were Colonel James Henry Rumbough and his wife Carrie. She was the daughter of federal judge Joseph Powell. The judge was the only member of the South Carolina legislature to vote against succession from the Union. The Colonel's parents were Jacob Rumbough and Ann Danridge, herself a descendent of Martha Washington.

When Colonel Rumbough decided to join the Confederate army, he wanted his family to live in a safe place, since he didn't know if he would survive the Civil War. After the war ended they moved to Warm Springs and what is now the Mountain Magnolia Inn. Carrie, who came from a Union family, hosted many guests from both sides of the war. The Colonel died in 1924 and the house remained in the family until 1988.

In 1997, Pete and Karen Nagle bought the house, and plans began for reconstruction. The Mountain Magnolia Inn opened to the public in May of 1999.

Activity: Between 20 to 30 guests and staff members have witnessed strange activity at the Mountain Magnolia Inn. Many believe the pranks originate from the ghost of Aunt Dickie, one of the Colonel's daughters. She was a known prankster in life, and she apparently has carried it on in the afterlife. Aunt Dickie's bedroom is now called the Walnut Room, and it's located on the second floor. Most of the paranormal activity has occurred in that room.

One evening, a couple was staying in the Walnut Room. He liked it warm, and she liked it cold. She opened the French doors and turned the ceiling fan on. He came out of the bathroom and told her they didn't need it that cold, so he turned off the fan and closed the French doors. He woke up the next morning, and the fan was blowing and the doors were opened. He became quite upset with his wife until he learned she was not to blame. She hadn't touched the fan or the doors.

One day, the housekeeper was cleaning the bathroom in the Walnut Room. She looked up to see a lid from a canister located on top of a shelf suddenly jump off the canister and land in the toilet. Another time, the innkeeper was in the hallway outside of the room putting an Oriental rug down. The same top to the canister fell off of the shelf in the bathroom and rolled out of the bathroom, out the room door, and came to rest at her feet.

Accommodations: Located just above Spring Creek, the Mountain Magnolia Inn and Retreat has three acres of beautifully landscaped grounds and flower gardens.

The 130-year-old, three-story inn offers 14 guest rooms, with two-bedroom suites, as well as beautiful parlors, a dining room, mountain-view porches, a message/meditation room, and a commercial kitchen.

Behind the inn, guests can follow the path to the Garden House, a three-bedroom cottage that's perfect for families and retreat groups.

Inn on Main Street Bed & Breakfast

88 S. Main Street
Weaverville, NC 28787
(828) 645-4935, (877) 873-6074
www.innonmain.com
Room rates: $95-$145
Visa, Master Card, Discover

Courtesy of Inn on Main Street B&B

History: The Inn on Main Street was built in 1900 by Dr. Zebulon Vance Robinson. The doctor used the first floor as his office, and the second floor was used to board patients and as his private residence. Surgery was occasionally performed in the downstairs office, and there's still a blood stain in one of the bathrooms that could not be sanded out.

Legend has it one of the doctor's patients may have been the author O. Henry, a.k.a. William Sydney Porter, who wrote and recuperated only a half-mile away. Porter stayed in Weaverville for several months before returning to New York City, where he relapsed, drank heavily, and soon died in 1910.

Activity: Though the ghosts' visits are infrequent, the inn has had its share of paranormal phenomena. On New Year's Eve 1998, the innkeepers were sharing a glass of champagne with their guests in the parlor when they suddenly heard a crash come from the dining room. They rushed in to see what had fallen, but found nothing disturbed. After returning to their guests, the crash was heard again. They went back to the dining room and still found nothing out of place. Later that night, the sound of the back door opening and closing was heard. There was even the creak of the floor as if someone was walking through the door. The innkeepers knew that the guests were either in the parlor or out at parties, so they went to see who was leaving or arriving. To their surprise, no one was there, inside the house or out.

Voices have occasionally been heard, as if someone is calling for the innkeeper. The voices are faint but are definitely female. When the innkeepers try to find the source of the voice, no one is ever around. Guests have heard the same voices.

Two guests were staying in the Lee Room that was once Doc Robinson's waiting room for patients. The guests reportedly heard a soft, whispering voice coming from the corner of the room.

Accommodations: The Inn on Main Street is a romantic, air-conditioned bed and breakfast, which features 7 guest rooms and is located only ten minutes from Asheville and 15 minutes from the Biltmore Estate. Nearby, whitewater rafting, skiing, golf, trail rides, and private mineral baths at Hot Springs are available for guests' enjoyment and relaxation. Each morning guests can enjoy a full hot breakfast, plus fresh fruit, cereals, juices and coffees are served. A picnic lunch and dinner are available with prior notice.

The Buffalo Tavern Bed & Breakfast

958 West Buffalo Road • West Jefferson, NC 28694
(877) 615-9678, (336) 877-2873 • www.buffalotavern.com
Room rates: $115-$140 • Visa, Master Card, American Express

History: The Buffalo Tavern was built in 1872 as a residence for George Washington Ray. It was built on 500 acres of land purchased from the state of North Carolina for five cents an acre. The house was built with timber cut from trees on the property, and the bricks were handmade on site. It was the first house in Ashe County to have glass windows, and people would come from miles around just to look through those windows.

In the late 1800s, the Buffalo Road became a major roadway from Tennessee to Jefferson, and in the late 1800s to early 1900s, the Ray family began operating a tavern and brothel out of their home. Cottages and a pond were later added behind the house for use by early tourists traveling in the mountains. A large grape vineyard and cornfields provided wine and corn liquor for the tavern customers, and the tavern even managed to continue liquor sales through Prohibition. Some believe there may have been a "special" agreement between the Rays and the local sheriff.

Activity: Happy spirits are said to inhabit the Buffalo. The ghosts live on the stairs, and come down and party at night. One previous owner's pocketknife would regularly turn up missing, but would always be returned on the stairs with the blade pointing down. The owner felt the ghosts needed it for some reason. Water faucets have turned on by themselves, and the manager once heard her name called in a soft male voice when no one was around.

The land on which the inn sits was once Native American hunting ground, and buffalo were hunted all over the mountain in front of the inn. Locals believe that Bluff Mountain was an Indian burial ground and is still haunted by Indian spirits of the past.

When the current owner purchased the home, it had been vacant for $2^1/_2$ years. She feels the happy spirits are probably so grateful to see someone occupying the home, they wouldn't dare scare her away.

Accommodations: The Buffalo Tavern offers 3 large guest rooms. The Madam's Room and Flapper's Room are located on the second floor, and all rooms feature private baths with showers, as well as queen-sized beds dressed with Egyptian cotton sheets and down comforters, fireplaces, CD players, and 1920s claw-foot soaking tubs. Each morning guests can enjoy a candlelight breakfast, and fine dining is located near the inn.

— SOUTH CAROLINA —

1843 Battery Carriage House Inn Bed & Breakfast

⛄⛄⛄

20 South Battery • Charleston, SC 29401
(800) 775-5575, (843) 727-3100 • www.batterycarriagehouse.com
Room rates: $99-$279 • All major credit cards

History: The inn was built during Charleston's golden years by Samuel Stevens, a wealthy businessman. John F. Blacklock purchased the home in 1859 and lived there until 1870. During the Civil War, the entire area was bombarded, but the house was spared.

The home, known as "No. 20," became the childhood summer home of the current owner's grandmother, Sara Calhoun Simonds. Sara grew up in the home in the 1890s with her father Andrew Simonds, a founder and president of the First National Bank of Charleston and the Imperial Fertilizer Company. The Simonds family lived there for the next 45 years. When Sara Simonds was a child, she fell through the ballroom skylight, but she was saved when she landed in the chandelier.

Activity: Employees of the 1843 Battery Carriage House Inn have witnessed the presence of a spirit they refer to as the gentleman ghost. He has been given the title because he has a fondness for the ladies and will sometimes enter a room where a lady is present. If she shows objection to his presence, he disappears.

In Room 10, the spirit of a young man has been seen both in the room and strolling outside. The story goes that in the 1800s, the young man was a graduate of Yale. While staying at the home, he became depressed over his future. Seeing no relief from his despair, he jumped from the roof, taking his own life. The ghost of the young man appears to be in his early twenties and stands about five feet tall.

Finally, the ghost of a Confederate soldier has been witnessed in the lobby of the inn and in a few of the guest rooms. He is reported to be headless and wears a coarse wool uniform. The soldier has been known to moan as if in pain, ring the front desk bell, open doors, march by the foot of the beds, or simply stand in front of surprised guests. Many believe he may be the victim of an ammunition explosion during the war.

Accommodations: The 1843 features 11 intimate guest rooms overlooking the mansion's beautiful private gardens. A continental breakfast is served each morning. Guests can choose to have breakfast in their room or in the garden under the Lady Bankshire rose arbor.

DuPre House Bed and Breakfast Inn

921 Prince Street • Georgetown, SC 29440
(877) 519-9499, (843) 546-0298 • www.duprehouse.com
Room rates: $90-$125 • Visa, Master Card, American Express

History: Originally built in 1740, the house was sold in 1753 to Susannah Gignilliat. She lived in the home until 1776. Records show she filed a claim that year for reimbursement during the American Revolution for supplies she gave to American troops. The house passed through many hands since, though records destroyed during the Civil War obscure details from the early 19th century.

Though the inn has undergone extensive renovation, the DuPre House is a reminder of the architectural heritage of early Georgetown. In particular, the second-floor wall overhang on the northwestern facade remains as an example of an old building design not typically found in the southeastern states.

Activity: The current owners, Richard and Judy Barnett, do not believe they have any ghosts at their inn. However a different story comes from former owners, employees, and guests.

Legend has it that a widow and her child lived in the home after the Civil War. A fire swept through the house, and the mother was able to get her child out safely, but perished herself. This may be why the majority of the paranormal activity appears to center around the second and third floors and involves a child and her mother.

While a former owner was renovating the inn, a local resident walking by outside spotted a child crawling out of a bedroom window on the third floor. A few months later, the owner heard a child's voice calling for her mother. Both times the owner searched, but no child was found. Guests have even seen the misty form of a child in their rooms. On one occasion, in a third-floor guest room, the previous owner found the footprints of a child on a freshly vacuumed carpet. The footprints led from the door to a bare wall. Another guest heard a child playing and humming a song on the third floor. The child has even been heard running up and down the stairs, and items in the guest rooms will sometimes be found rearranged on their own.

Other encounters center on the appearance of a woman. Occasionally, guests and employees will smell smoke when no fire is present. One day, a guest smelled the smoke, then witnessed the appearance of a lady in an apron and long dress.

Accommodations: The DuPre House features 5 guest rooms, each uniquely decorated and furnished with private baths and reproduction four-poster beds. Some rooms have private verandas that overlook the gardens, a soaking tub, and fireplace. For guests' comfort, plush robes and nightly turndown service are provided. Each morning guests are served a full breakfast that includes juices, fruits, and a main entree.

While enjoying a southern afternoon, guests are invited to take a leisurely swim in the pool, relax in the hot tub, or snooze in the hammocks under the shade of century-old live oak trees.

Walnut Lane Inn

110 Ridge Road
Lyman, SC 29365
(888) 892-6020
www.walnutlaneinn.com
Room rates: $90-$115
All major credit cards

Courtesy of Walnut Lane Inn

History: The Walnut Lane Inn is nestled under a canopy of majestic walnut trees on the grounds of this circa-1902 cotton plantation.

Activity: One day, innkeeper Hoyt Dottry witnessed the appearance of a ghost of a gentleman in the kitchen of the inn. After seeing the figure out of the corner of his eye, he turned around and the figure was gone.

The innkeeper feels there are two other ghosts present, both female. One likes to move pictures on the wall. They'll be straightened only to be found tilted minutes later. Lampshades often tilt on their own as well.

One day, the innkeeper witnessed a figure in a black skirt walking up the stairs. He followed the woman, only to find the stairs vacant.

Finally, one afternoon the innkeeper heard the voice of a young woman at the back door saying, "Hey, pretty puppies." The owners' dogs immediately started barking, but when he went to see who was at the door, no one was there. He stepped outside to see if someone was walking away, but no one could be seen on either side of the building. Dottry knows that he heard the woman's voice, and the dogs reacted to it as well.

Accommodations: The Inn offers six guest rooms and is conveniently located between Greenville and Spartanburg. Guests can stroll under century-old oaks surrounded by lush landscaping. Beverages are available on both the east and west porches, and in the front parlor. The Walnut Lane Inn also offers dinner with a complimentary dessert. Nearby is a vast array of antique shops and many fine universities and cultural centers. If you're in the mood for a drive, the Blue Ridge Mountains are located only 55 miles from the inn.

The Inn At Merridun

🚶 🚶 🚶 🚶

Courtesy of The Inn at Merridun

100 Merridun Place
Union, SC 29379
(888) 892-6020
www.merridun.com
Room rates: $89-$115
All major credit cards

History: The original home was built during 1855–1857 by William Keenan. The property included 4,000 acres known as the Keenan Plantation. The house later changed hands to Benjamin H. Rice, a local attorney and mayor of Union. Two farms were joined together to form an 8,000-acre plantation. Cotton was their main industry, and in the early 1880s, the home went through some major renovations. Around that time, Thomas Cary (T.C.) Duncan, son of Bishop W. W. Duncan and Medora Rice Duncan, moved to Union to live and work with his grandfather, B. H. Rice.

In 1885, T.C. Duncan brought his new bride, Fannie Merriman, to live in Union. T. C. Duncan inherited the house from his maternal grandparents and renamed it "Merridun"—which was a combination of the three family names (Merriman, Rice, Duncan) that lived in the ancestral home. In 1990, Peggy and Jim Waller purchased the inn from the Duncan heirs, and after much restoration, they opened it as a bed and breakfast in 1992.

Activity: Legend has it that ten ghosts inhabit the Inn at Merridun and the grounds outside. Over the course of eight years, many guests have witnessed something out of the ordinary. A clairvoyant once identified ten "energy forces" in the home, and among those ten were T. C. Duncan and his wife, Fannie, who often materialize to make sure the home is in proper working order. Their presence is usually felt by the smell of a cigar and the fragrance of an old-fashioned perfume. Another paranormal houseguest is reportedly the spirit of Mary Ann Wallace, the spinster sister of one of the former owners. She has been seen from the neck down, in a blue-green 1880s-style dress with a bustle. The ghosts of two children, a boy and a girl, are also present, along with the spirit of an African-American housekeeper. She has been seen outside the inn doing chores. Finally, guests have also seen the ghosts of a well-dressed woman and her dog. Peggy admits the dog can get pretty temperamental sometimes, driving her cats to the brink!

While restoring the home, Peggy and Jim often found pennies laying on the floor or on a wooden table that had been cleaned earlier. Perhaps it is a sign of good luck from the other world. According to one eyewitness, it means "Pennies on the floor, money through the door."

Accommodations: The beautiful Inn at Merridun has a wonderful curved staircase, large foyers on both floors, a music room, a parlor, library, seven bedrooms, and a third-story cupola. The large dining room can seat thirty people comfortably. The carriage barn, located behind the brick wing, still houses the Duncan's horse carriage. You will find frescoed ceilings throughout the mansion, along with mosaic tile and turn-of-the-19th-century stenciling and faux graining in the main foyer. Also, several beautiful chandeliers decorate the stately mansion. Guests can enjoy special teas at Miss Fannie's 2003 Tea Room which also has an assortment of sandwiches and sweet temptations and, on designated days, there is a special Sunday brunch.

— TENNESSEE —

White Elephant Bed & Breakfast Inn

☆☆☆☆

200 Church Street • Savannah, TN 38372
(731) 925-6410 • www.whiteelephantbb.com
Room rates: $100-$120 • Cash or personal check

History: Built in 1901, the White Elephant Bed & Breakfast Inn served as a home for Daniel Welch, a local merchant, banker, and Confederate soldier, and his wife, Cornelia Irwin Welch. The young Cornelia had been arrested and imprisoned while in her teens for being a Confederate spy.

Cornelia's family home was originally built on this very site during the 1880s, and her parents, James and Nancy Irwin, died in the home. The family home and surrounding grounds were used as a hospital for wounded Union soldiers and some captured Confederates after the bloody Civil War battle of Shiloh, fought on April 6th and 7th, 1862, that saw 3,500 soldiers killed and 16,000 wounded.

The old family home was torn down in 1901 to make way for the "modern" Queen Anne style Victorian house.

Activity: Some of the spirits of Shiloh may not be at rest. Whether they are the spirits of fallen soldiers or past residents is still debated; regardless, several guests have reported unsettling encounters.

On one occasion, a couple staying at the inn reported that their curtains moved as if from a sudden draft, though no window was open at the time. One guest swears a door closed on its own accord, and another guest awoke in the middle of the night to find her bedside lamp had been turned on.

Innkeeper Sharon Hansgen reports that even she has heard voices and footsteps coming from the second level of the two-story inn when no one was occupying the second floor. During each experience, the spirits have been described as peaceful. In fact, guests will often report that they've had a great night's sleep while staying at the inn.

Accommodations: Located on one-and-a-half acres, the elegant White Elephant Bed & Breakfast Inn offers three upscale guest rooms, each with queen-sized beds and antique furnishings. Guests will enjoy amenities like plush robes, turndown service, bubble bath, and afternoon refreshments. Innkeeper and historian Ken Hansgen presents battlefield tours of Shiloh and other notable Civil War sites.

While at the White Elephant Bed & Breakfast Inn, guests can dine on breakfast and snacks, including White Elephant Scottish scones, blue ribbon oatmeal, chocolate chip cookies, and southern pecan pancakes.

MIDWEST

— ILLINOIS —

The Wheeler Mansion

🎋🎋🎋🎋

2020 South Calumet Avenue • Chicago, IL 60616
(312) 945-2020 • www.wheelermansion.com
Room rates: $230-$365 • All major credit cards

History: The Wheeler Mansion was built in 1870, one year before the great Chicago fire. Calvin T. Wheeler, a prominent banker and president of the Chicago Board of Trade, built the mansion and occupied it for four years. The Wheeler Mansion is one of the last survivors of the stately mansions on the city's Near South Side.

Wheeler sold the home in 1874 to Joseph Kohn, a successful clothing wholesaler. Kohn lived in the home until 1908. In the 1910–1920s, the houses in the area were purchased by businesses and either remodeled or torn down. In 1922, Wartenburg Publishing purchased the Wheeler Mansion, and then it was purchased by Murphy Butter and Egg Company in 1944.

Today, the neighborhood has come full circle with the conversion of many commercial buildings into new residential lofts. The Wheeler Mansion Bed & Breakfast provides visitors a taste of the elegance of the past.

Activity: The paranormal activity in the Wheeler Mansion centers on Room 35. Called the Red Room, it has a 13-foot ceiling, "glow in the dark" red walls, black carpet, and black and white marble in the bathroom.

The most reasonably priced room in the hotel, Room 35 offers a few strange amenities for adventurous guests. Reportedly, if you are sleeping there between 2–2:45 A.M., the floor will begin to shake, and soon the bed will shake so violently that the door of the armoire nearby will open. There are no trains in the vicinity, and the walls are two-and-a-half feet thick, so no outside disturbance causes the quakes. Over ten guests and the innkeeper have experienced the mysterious tremors, and to date they have gone unexplained.

Accommodations: The Wheeler Mansion offers a style and elegance of yesteryear with the modern conveniences of a contemporary hotel. Eleven guest rooms are available, and a two-story bay window has been added to the front of the building, along with an elaborate front-porch canopy. The dining room has the original ceiling, and there are two doors that lead to the veranda, so that guests can enjoy their complimentary gourmet breakfast at their private table indoors or outside. Listed in *Travel & Leisure Magazine* as one of the top eight bed and breakfasts nationally for business travelers, the Wheeler Mansion will inspire you with its beauty and comfort.

Tibbetts House Bed & Breakfast

801 9th Street • Highland, IL 62249
(618) 654-4619
www.bbonline.com/il/tibbetts
Room rates: $75-$120
All major credit cards

Courtesy of Tibbetts House B&B

History: The structure was originally built in 1914 by Dr. Moses Tibbetts to be used as his office and home. The doctor must have been concerned with safety, because the walls of this Frank Lloyd Wright–style prairie home are extremely thick, and a tornado shelter is located in the basement.

Today, the home has been converted into a chocolate shop on the first floor and a bed and breakfast upstairs. Visitors can literally eat chocolate all day long and even step downstairs to grab a few morsels during the night.

Activity: Dr. Tibbetts' grandchildren always felt their grandfathers' cleaning lady, Maude, haunted the home. When the Greiners purchased the building and turned it into a bed and breakfast, they noticed that when they travelled, the inn was always clean when they returned. Now they realize it may have been Maude keeping things so tidy.

Clock radios on the second floor turn on when no one is around, and there is a sofa bed located in one of the bedrooms that some say is haunted. When the room is cleaned each day, there is a quilt on the sofa. No matter how many times it is straightened, hours later, it will be bunched up as though someone had been sitting or lying on it. This will occur even when there are no guests in the room.

Tibbetts House isn't the only building in the area that's reportedly haunted—actually, the whole street has experienced paranormal activity. Across from Tibbetts is the Highland House of Plenty Restaurant. A ghost by the name of Michael has been seen at the restaurant, and on one occasion, witnesses have seen a flashing light coming from the third-floor window.

The establishment on the corner is named the Family Inn, and it too has some ghostly tales to tell. An elderly aunt who once frequented the inn may still be there. A photograph was taken of her in 1940 as she sat at the bar and smoked a cigarette. Oddly, another photograph was taken in 1985 at the same location; an impression of a smoky cloud appeared on the picture after it was developed. The smoke formed what looked to be a face. While in Highland, visitors can conduct their own ghost tour as they stay at the Tibbetts House and eat lunch at one restaurant and have dinner at the other, for a total of three chances to spot a ghost.

Accommodations: Tibbetts House offers three guest rooms with private baths. For chocoholics, Tibbetts offers the "Chocolate Lover's Special," which includes chocolate bath products, a basket of chocolate goodies, a chocolate cake baked especially for the guest, and a chocolate fondue to dip your strawberries in as you enjoy your continental breakfast.

Hotel Baker

100 West Main Street • St. Charles, IL 60174
(630) 584-2100
Room rates: $165-$200 • All major credit cards

History: Edward J. Baker, a local philanthropist, built the Hotel Baker in 1928. In 1997, after an extensive $10 million renovation, it reopened. To compliment its Spanish architecture, the marble floors, hand-stenciled wood trim, carved terracotta detailing, and original antique furnishings were restored to their original grandeur. Hotel Baker was known in the 1930s and 1940s as the "Honeymoon Hotel," and today it remains a popular location for weddings, as well as the ideal destination for business travelers and families. The Rainbow Room ballroom features its original glass dance floor, lit from beneath in red, blue, amber, and green. Famous entertainers appeared there during the early years. The Rainbow Room featured the likes of Tommy Dorsey and Louis Armstrong. Local and national politicians also frequented the hotel. Among those who visited were Mayor Richard Daley and John F. Kennedy.

Activity: Legend has it that the notorious Chicago gangster Al Capone would sail down the Fox River and dock at the Hotel Baker for an evening of gambling with his friends. Reportedly, his presence is still felt at the hotel.

A year ago, a husband and wife were driving to the hotel for a night of relaxation. While they stood on the balcony of the Rainbow Room, the wife witnessed a tall, skinny man dressed in black slowly dance across the dance floor. The next evening, she witnessed the same apparition drifting along the path in the rose garden. Many people believe that the skinny man, who has been seen by both guests and staff, may be the ghost of someone who fell victim to Al Capone and his gang.

Accommodations: Hotel Baker features 53 guest rooms, including 10 suites. Modern amenities include marble-accented baths, desks, and telephones with voice mail and data ports.

— INDIANA —

The Old Bridge Inn Bed & Breakfast
𝄢 𝄢

131 W. Chestnut Street
Jeffersonville, IN 47130
(812) 284-3580
www.oldbridgeinn.com
Room rates: $65-$115
All major credit cards

Courtesy of The Old Bridge Inn

History: In the grand old days of rail travel, mighty locomotives passed through Jeffersonville by way of the Big-Four Railroad Bridge. Many a man lost his life during construction of the bridge that can still be seen from the middle of town. Today, the railroad tracks are no longer there; but the bridge still stands as a reminder of Indiana's industrial age.

Located only seconds from Louisville, Kentucky, The Old Bridge Inn, named after the Big-Four Railroad Bridge, is a Georgian colonial inn built in 1840 by a prominent Jeffersonville family. No further records exist pertaining to the original construction because the Jeffersonville Courthouse burned in the 1880s. The earliest records available date back to 1893.

The home was known as "Old Doc Hancock's House." There the good doctor raised four boys, with one of his sons becoming a doctor himself. Passed down through generations, the house stayed in the Hancock family until 1960.

Today, the home has been converted into the Old Bridge Inn Bed & Breakfast. There's a wood-burning fireplace in the parlor, and the place is decorated throughout with antiques.

back and forth by themselves, and one of the chefs at the inn had a recurring dream about the ghost of a red-haired lady in a green dress (and this was before Rice told him about Helen).

Silverware has occasionally moved from one location to another, and the housekeeping staff will constantly find their cleaning supplies moved. Further, witnesses have seen one of the fans go very, very fast on its own accord, and when visitors are alone at night, they will sometimes feel a brush of air pass by or something will touch their shoulder.

Accommodations: The Blake House Inn is surrounded by 150-year-old pine and sycamore trees and features five well-appointed guest rooms and one suite. Conveniently located in the Historic Royal Pines area, Blake House Inn was built to take advantage of the cool summer breezes in the mountains of North Carolina. The inn features two formal dining rooms and the LaGrador Landing Pub, which is decorated with LaGrador prints, portraits, and other wildlife scenes.

The Grove Park Inn Resort & Spa

290 Macon Avenue
Asheville, NC 28804
(800) 438-5800, (828) 252-2711
www.groveparkinn.com
Room rates: $119-$1119
All major credit cards

Courtesy of Grove Park Inn

History: The Grove Park Inn is located nearly 2,500 feet above sea level on a grassy mountain slope with panoramic views of Asheville's skyline and the Blue Ridge Mountains.

In 1912, Edwin W. Grove's dream of building a resort hotel came to fruition. Hundreds of mules, wagons, pulleys, and ropes were used to move massive granite stones quarried from nearby mountainsides—some weighing as much as 10,000 pounds. Workers from all over the South joined in on this extraordinary project that became one of the finest resorts in the world.

The hotel is on the National Register of Historic Places and is a member of Historic Hotels of America. The inn houses a large collection of arts and crafts and antiques.

Activity: Legend tells of a young woman dressed in pink who fell to her death in the Palm Court atrium around 1920. For more than a half century, a ghost known as "the Pink Lady" has been seen, felt, and experienced by hotel employees and guests. Though she has been seen

Activity: Gentle spirits maintain residence in the Old Bridge Inn. Innkeeper Linda Williams has informed us that lights often have a tendency of turning off and on by themselves. On one occasion, witnesses were amazed to see all of the lit candles in the room fade down at the same time.

Although no one has ever witnessed any form of apparition in the inn, doors have opened and closed and the television has turned on and off on their own. Perhaps the lost souls of the Big-Four Railroad Bridge are still around to watch over the inn and its guests.

Accommodations: The Old Bridge Inn Bed & Breakfast offers 3 beautiful guest rooms. Amenities include a full breakfast and complimentary beverages. The historic inn is located within walking distance of antique shops, restaurants, and the Ohio River. A short drive from the inn, guests can visit the Falls of the Ohio Fossil Beds and tour the Howard Steamboat Museum.

The Story Inn

6404 South State Road 135 • Nashville, IN 47448
Near Mount Pleasant, IN
(800) 881-1183 • www.storyinn.com
Room rates: $107-$210 • Visa, Master Card

History: President Millard Fillmore issued a land grant patent to Dr. George Story in 1851. The Story family was successful timber harvesters from southern Ohio who were attracted to this area by the vast expanse of hardwoods. The town, once called Storyville, grew into a vibrant community where settlers came to trade goods. George Story Jr., Dr. Story's son, founded a prosperous general merchandise business. After his retirement, he turned the store over to Alra Wheeler, a local merchant. After a fire in 1915, the store was rebuilt. Today, the main floor of the general store is virtually unaltered, and it houses a gourmet restaurant. The second floor of the building has been renovated into four charming, 19th-century–style guest rooms furnished with period antiques and restored artifacts. The remaining structures have been tastefully renovated into ten guest cottages.

Activity: One night, the previous owner was standing in the kitchen when she felt a cold breeze. She walked to the top of the stairs leading to the basement wine cellar. To her surprise, she saw a woman in a flowing white robe at the bottom of the stairs. As she watched, the apparition disappeared.

Several employees confirmed their own sighting of a female ghost, but that's not all. One waitress was carrying food to a guest when the plate literally exploded in her hand. Several witnesses observed this bizarre event.

Many witnesses believe the ghost—known as the "Blue Lady" because she can be summoned by turning on a blue light in one of the rooms—is one of the wives of Dr. Story. Over nine guests have written in the room journals, claiming to have experienced the appearance of the apparition. One notation from guests of the haunted room described the spirit and claimed she was calling their name. The room's history is so remarkable that it was named after the blue lady in 2001.

The present owner has not experienced anything out of the ordinary. However, he's convinced it's not an urban legend because there are too many first-hand accounts from credible witnesses. Being an attorney, the owner told us that, "as a lawyer, I have won cases on evidence that was less compelling."

Accommodations: The Story Inn offers 14 tastefully appointed rooms and cottages. Each is individually decorated and has its own history, so each room has a name instead of a number. Accommodations include hot tubs, kitchenettes, and private decks. To preserve the bucolic setting, the rooms do not have televisions, telephones, clocks, or radios. Your cell phone will not work in the Story Inn either, so take off your wristwatch, relax, and switch to "Story time."

— Iowa —

The Mason House Inn

☩☩☩

21982 Hawk Drive
Bentonsport, IA 52565
(800) 592-3133, (319) 592-3133
www.masonhouseinn.com
Room rates: $59-$85
Visa, Master Card

Courtesy of The Mason House Inn

History: The Mason House is the oldest steamboat hotel on the Des Moines River. It was built in 1846 to serve steamboat travelers journeying from St. Louis to Des Moines. The hotel was constructed by Mormon craftsmen who stayed in Bentonsport a few years during their famous trek to Utah.

Lewis Mason, a furniture maker from New York, purchased the inn in 1857. For over 99 years, Mason's sons, daughters, nieces, and nephews ran the inn. The Mason House Inn went through an extensive refurbishing in 1989 that included the remodeling of an old railroad station connected to the inn.

There are several antique and craft shops near the inn. You'll also enjoy the "wild nightlife" in Bentonsport that includes owls, bald eagles, and frogs, set along the lazy Des Moines River

Activity: The previous owners have described several sightings of the ghost of Mary Mason, Lewis Mason's daughter. She lived at the inn from 1857 until her death in 1911. Apparently, her spirit likes to walk the halls and check on the guest rooms. Old photographs of Mary Mason confirmed that it was indeed her image seen in the hallways.

Legend has it that around 1850, a young woman was shot by her estranged husband in the inn. As he stood on the stairs after the shooting, the woman's dog leaped onto the man and tore his throat out. He died on the steps, the young woman died three days later in the parlor, and the dog died a week after that of a broken heart. If the moonlight is just right, the dog can still be seen waiting outside the parlor window.

Finally, we encourage you to ask the present owners about their infamous tree in the backyard. Apparently, a man once hanged himself from that tree, and the limb will creak even when there is no wind—as if someone is still "hanging around."

Accommodations: The Mason House Inn offers 9 guest rooms. Today, more than half of the inn has the original antique furnishings from 1857. The Wild Rose Room houses a massive, nine-foot walnut headboard. The Mason Room contains a nine-foot mirror as well as the Masons' original bedroom set. There are no closets; in the 1840s, houses were taxed in part on the number of closets they contained. There are coat hooks on the walls instead. Visitors can play tunes on the 1882 Estey pump organ or on the 1905 Kimball piano located in the formal parlor. A filled cookie jar is in each room and lunch and private dinners are available with prior reservations. Large groups may eat breakfast in front of the fireplace in the 40-foot dining room. Each guest room has central heat, air conditioning, and a private bath. Guests who don't insist on privacy are welcome to bathe in the Murphy copper-lined tub that unfolds from a keeping room (or closet) wall cabinet. It's the only one in Iowa.

The Blue Belle Inn

Courtesy of The Blue Belle Inn

513 W. 4th Street
St. Ansgar, IA 50472
(641) 713-3113, (877) 736-2225
www.bluebelleinn.com
Room rates: $40-$150
All major credit Cards

History: The town of St. Ansgar is known as "The Best Little Hometown in Iowa," and it offers a multitude of unique Victorians, antique and country stores, a tea room, and a bridal theatre. The Blue Belle Inn was built here in 1896. Fireplaces, hardwood floors, tin ceilings with ornate moldings, and eight-foot maple pocket doors highlight the interior of this Queen Anne Victorian inn. Stained glass and crystal chandeliers adorn the inn with the accompaniment of bay and curved windows. A beautiful maple banister winds to the second floor and opens onto the balcony, which overlooks a flower garden, sprawling maple trees, and a fish pond. An unforgettable dining experience awaits the visitor, featuring German, English, French, Italian, and American cuisines.

Activity: The previous owners of the house believed the inn is haunted by a friendly spirit, perhaps a maiden aunt who lived in the home until her death.

On one occasion, the previous owners were cleaning the attic when cardboard tubes containing the original floor plans of the house were inadvertently taken to the city dump. The owner was extremely upset that he had thrown away these plans. To his surprise, a few months later he stepped into the attic and found the floor plans returned to their original place on the shelves. The owner felt the spirit must have cared for the floor plans as much as he did.

After the new owners purchased the inn, overnight guests came down to dinner one evening and told the employee on duty that they had been locked out of their room. The strange thing was that the safety locks on the doors could only be locked from the inside; the guests had not locked the doors themselves, and their key would not open it. The employee walked to the room with the guests and tried the key, but it would not open. They tried to climb through the transom, and from that vantage point, they could see the fireplace in the room burning with a large fire. They were still unable to get into the room. The frustrated employee exclaimed, "I wish whoever is in there would just let us in." Suddenly, the door to the room popped open.

Accommodations: Rediscover the romance and adventure of the 1890s while enjoying the comfort and convenience of the new millennium in one of the Blue Belle Inn's six distinctively decorated guest rooms.

The inn has concerts, murder mysteries, horse-drawn sleigh rides, cooking, craft workshops, and other activities throughout the year.

— KANSAS —

Beaumont Hotel

11651 S.E. Main • Beaumont, KS 67012
(620) 843-2422 • www.hotelbeaumontks.com
Room rates: $75-$149 • All major credit cards

History: The historic Beaumont Hotel was established by Edwin Russell in the beautiful scenic Flint Hills of Kansas in 1879. The structure was originally a stagecoach station and stopping place for travelers from Fredonia and Wichita. In 1885, Beaumont was established as a railroad town.

The Beaumont Hotel, then known as the Summit Hotel, was the highest point on the Frisco Railroad Line from Ellsworth, Kansas, to St. Louis. Cattle barons from Texas and Oklahoma and the elite of the Frisco Railroad were regular guests at the hotel. It was also used as a headquarters for those who shipped or brought cattle into town. While the ranchers and cattle barons stayed in the hotel, the cowboys camped outside, preferring the wide open spaces.

The hotel changed hands several times over the years until J. C. Squier bought the place in 1953 and added running water and heat. He removed the old rope ladders used for fire escapes and added decks, which provide a beautiful view of the Flint Hills. For the convenience of cattle buyers, a grass airstrip was built to allow planes to taxi up the street and park south of the hotel.

Today, the Beaumont Hotel has evolved into a destination for private pilots and city dwellers wishing to explore the charm and beauty of the Flint Hills and Kansas plains.

Activity: Witnesses have reportedly seen and heard the spirit of a cowboy who walks the halls of the top floor of this 19th-century building at night. Though inquiries have been made and research conducted, to this day no one knows who the mysterious cowboy is or why he makes his periodic sojourn up and down the halls.

Accommodations: The hotel features 6 guest suites and 5 guest rooms on two floors, all in a park-like setting. Amenities include a private porch, television with VCR, and complimentary breakfast for overnight guests.

The 50s Café/Diner and a private dining room provide delicious meals with a view of the breathtaking prairie landscape.

The Eldridge Hotel

By Ernst Ulmer. Courtesy of Eldridge Hotel

7th and Massachusetts
Lawrence, KS 66044
(800) 527-0909, (785) 749-5011
www.eldridgehotel.com
Room rates: $69-$160
All major credit cards

History: The Eldridge Hotel occupies the exact spot that its forerunners did during Kansas' territorial days and during the Civil War. At various times in its history, the property has been known as the Free State Hotel, Eldridge House, and the Hotel Eldridge. The names have changed, but the quality and fine service have remained.

On May 21, 1856, while known as the Free State Hotel, pro-slavery forces rode into Lawrence and burned the hotel because it served as a safe haven for settlers coming to Kansas in the name of abolitionism. After the fire, Shalor Eldridge rebuilt the hotel and declared that each time the hotel was destroyed, another story would be added. Quantrill's Raiders rode into town on August 21, 1863 and made the Eldridge Hotel the focus of their attack on Lawrence. They destroyed what many felt was the finest building in Kansas at that time. The hotel was rebuilt and stood until 1924, when it was replaced by an even newer, grander Eldridge Hotel, which stands today.

Activity: Marge, the head of housekeeping, is the ghost expert at the Eldridge Hotel. She reported to us that they often have visitors that come to the hotel primarily because of the ghosts.

The majority of the paranormal activity takes place in Room 506. In the bedroom of that guest room is the original cornerstone of the hotel. Many people feel that cornerstone is a portal to the next world. Often guests and staff have witnessed the appearance of ghosts in the room.

On one occasion, a couple saw what appeared to be a tea party taking place in Room 506. The misty images of ladies in long Victorian gowns were sitting, walking around, and chatting and drinking their tea, oblivious to the humans in the room staring at them dumfounded.

The fifth floor is very active, and on that floor, lights have turned off and on, equipment has malfunctioned, and a vacuum cleaner has been moved down the hall away from the housekeeper. Recently, doors have been slamming shut on their own. A couple was walking down the hall when they turned to see a guest room door open and then slam shut.

Accommodations: The Eldridge Hotel offers guests 48 luxurious suites on five floors. The lobby is made of rich woods and furnishings with a quiet elegance from a simpler time.

The newest incarnation of the Eldridge highlights the contrast between a legendary Civil War past and the quiet elegance of a beautifully restored present. Guests can dine in Shalor's Restaurant in the hotel for breakfast, lunch, or dinner, or relax at the Jayhawker Lounge.

— MICHIGAN —

Big Bay Point Lighthouse Bed & Breakfast

#3 Lighthouse Road • Big Bay, MI 49808
(906) 345-9957 • www.bigbaylighthouse.com
Room rates: $99-$185 • Cash or personal check

History: Between Marquette and Keweenaw Portage Entry stands the Big Bay Lighthouse. In 1882, the plans for a lighthouse were presented to the lighthouse board, and on February 15, 1893, Congress authorized the creation of a lighthouse station on Big Bay Point.

The lighthouse was built as a two-story duplex dwelling. The light tower extended from the center of the house, rising 105 feet above Lake Superior. The head keeper maintained residence in the duplex dwelling with his family on one side, and the assistant keeper and his family lived on the other side. The lighthouse's steady white light was increased to a brilliant white flash every 20 seconds by rotating bulls-eye panels in the lens system. In 1941, the last keeper was reassigned, and the Big Bay Lighthouse was automated.

Activity: On August 15, 1896, H. William Prior was appointed the first head keeper at Big Bay after transferring in from Stannard's Rock Lighthouse.

Prior was a perfectionist who took his job very seriously. After several of his assistant keepers failed to meet his standards, Prior gave his son the job. Unfortunately, Prior's son accidentally cut himself while working at the lighthouse in April of 1901. Though his son's injury was very serious and it became infected, Prior waited until June to take him

30 miles to Marquette for medical treatment. By then gangrene had set in, and the young man died.

Immediately after his son's funeral, Prior returned to his post at Big Bay. However, his grief over his son's death and his own guilt proved too great for the man, and the day after his return, Prior disappeared. Three months later, Prior's body was found in the woods. He had committed suicide.

Today, the current owners have seen the ghost of William Prior in the keeper's dwelling and on the grounds. Forever the perfectionist, Prior's spirit has turned the shower water off when the shower is not being used, and lights will be turned off, undoubtedly to conserve energy.

A young lady named Sarah visited the lighthouse with friends many years ago. They were goofing off, and she fell, broke her neck, and died. Frightened, her friends left her where she fell, and her family did not find her for days. Witnesses have seen the ghost of a young woman on the second floor of the assistant keeper's quarters. She appears to be a modern-dressed girl in her late teens. Many believe she is the ghost of Sarah.

Accommodations: In 1986, the two-story brick building and its adjoining 52-foot square tower were transformed into a bed and breakfast. The inn offers 14 guest rooms, and features private baths, a common living room, a library, and a sauna, and a full breakfast is included. There are three acres of lawn and 40 acres of woods with trails for exploring.

Guests can climb to the lighthouse lantern 120 feet above the lake surface. From this vantage point, visitors can survey open fields of native grasses, wildflowers, pine forests, and the majestic Huron Mountains and Lake Superior.

Lakeside Inn

15251 Lakeshore Road • Lakeside, MI 49116
(269) 469-0600 • www.lakesideinns.com
Room rates: $75-$175 • Visa, Master Card, Discover

History: The Lakeside Inn was built on 78 acres that were owned in 1844 by Alfred Ames of Vermont. He started a resort called Pleasant Grove, a prime location for the annual meeting of the Lakeside Anti-Horse Thief Association. Legend has it that a horse thief was once hanged from a beech tree near the inn. The property was purchased by the Aylesworth family and later willed to Arthur Aylesworth. He was a world adventurer, film producer, casino operator, and big-game hunter who had toured with Buffalo Bill's Wild West Show. The property became known as the Aylesworth Hotel.

Throughout the early 1900s the hotel was expanded to three stories, with a basement and six ground-floor entrances.

The Lakeside Inn prospered in the 1920s and became a major vacation retreat for Chicagoans. But in the 1930s, the economic depression brought hard times. Aylesworth and the Lakeside Inn went bankrupt several times until the property was finally lost in foreclosure.

In 1968, John and Kay Wilson purchased the inn and renamed it the Lakeside Center for the Arts. The Wilson's print business was conducted in several rooms on the ground floor of the inn.

The current owner, Devereux Bowly, purchased the inn and started a massive renovation, updating amenities, adding new furniture, antiques, and a restaurant called the Lakeside Café.

Activity: Arthur Aylesworth owned the property into the 1950s. He reportedly shot and wounded his second wife, Virginia Harned. Though he claimed it was an accident, many believed otherwise. She eventually died. When the inn was refurbished, a towel with Aylesworth's initials was found hidden behind the wall. It was stained with blood. To this day, the spirit of Virginia is felt in the inn, especially in and around Room 30.

In his golden years, it is said that Aylesworth would watch a small television in the lobby of the inn until he fell asleep. At 10 P.M. each night, the ghost of Virginia would awake the handyman who lived in a small building outside the inn. He would go then to the inn, wake up Aylesworth, and tell him it was time for bed.

A wedding guest recently saw the outline of a gentleman at a party that was being held in the ballroom. He described the apparition as being Aylesworth, complete with a pet raccoon on his shoulder.

Accommodations: The Lakeside Inn has 31 guest rooms, each with a private bath and many with lake views. Five rooms offer Jacuzzi tubs. Sauna and exercise equipment, as well as a café are located on the premises. The inn has two large stone fireplaces—one in the lobby and one in the ballroom. A 100-foot long front porch is lined with rockers, allowing guests to relax and enjoy the lake breezes. Directly across from the inn is a private beach.

Nahma Inn Bed & Breakfast

13747 Main Street • Nahma, MI 49864
(906) 644-2486 • www.exploringthenorth.com/nahma/inn.html
Room rates: $50-$80 • All major credit cards and personal checks

History: The Historic Nahma Inn was built in 1902 and served as the
company hotel for the Bay de Noquet Lumber and Sawmill Company.
It's located in the tiny village of Nahma on the shores of Lake Michigan
in Michigan's Upper Peninsula.

Activity: A lady by the name of Miss Nell lived and worked in the inn
during the late 1930s. She had a special friend named Charles Good. He
also lived at the hotel, and he actually owned the nearby Bay de Noquet
Lumber and Sawmill Company (the patron company of the hotel). In
the late 1950s, Miss Nell died of cancer. However, several guests have
witnessed her presence as she roams throughout the hotel. Often found
in the kitchen, the ghost of Miss Nell occasionally throws items around.
Other guests have seen her shadow near her room. The spirit of Charles
Good has also been seen wearing a suit and walking though the halls,
perhaps looking for Miss Nell. Guests are welcome to stay in either
Miss Nell's or Charles Good's rooms.

Accommodations: Nahma Inn Bed & Breakfast features 14 guest
rooms, each decorated with antique furnishings. Guests are invited to
dine in the Bay de Noc Room and enjoy homemade soup, whitefish,
steak, and barbecue ribs. A continental breakfast is served each morning
and the Arrowhead Lounge is the ideal spot to relax with your favorite
beverage. The Old Post Office and General Store are located next to the
inn. Only a half mile from the inn is the nine-hole Nahma Golf Course
on the shores of Lake Michigan. A boat launch for fishing boats is
available, or guests can fish from the shore or from the bridge over the
Sturgeon River.

The Terrace Inn

1549 Glendale • Petoskey, MI 49770
(800) 530-9898, (231) 347-2410
www.theterraceinn.com
Room rates: $49-$340
Visa, Master Card, American
Express

Courtesy of The Terrace Inn

History: The Terrace Inn is located in Bay View, a fairy-tale village with over 400 Victorian cottages. Bay View is adjacent to Petoskey and Little Traverse Bay in northwest Michigan. W. J. DeVol, a prosperous banker from northern Indiana, built the Terrace Inn in 1911. After completion, summer vacationers from Detroit, Chicago, and southern Michigan began arriving by train and steamship to stay at the Terrace Inn.

In 1987, Bay View was recognized as a National Historic Landmark, and the Terrace Inn received permission to open year-round.

Most of the furnishings in the inn are original antiques, giving the property its turn-of-the-19th-century charm and elegance.

Activity: Legend has it that the ghost of a young woman named Elizabeth roams the halls of the Terrace Inn in search of her husband Edmond, who passed away at the inn in 1920. Guests describe Elizabeth as wearing a white, flowing gown, and she's been seen gliding through the halls and sometimes through the walls of the guest rooms. Some have heard her mournful cry, calling out for Edmond. Her presence has been described as a calming experience, and witnesses never seem to be fearful.

The guests and management have never experienced any negative energy surrounding the ghosts of the Terrace Inn. In fact, innkeeper Tom Erhart tells us the ghosts often protect the inn and its inhabitants from harm. Once, a caretaker known to be a sound sleeper was staying on the lower level of the inn. In the middle of night, he was awakened by someone shaking him. He didn't know what to think of it, but he decided to get up and inspect the building. To his surprise, he found a compressor smoking downstairs. He was able to unplug it and take care of the problem without any harm being done to the inn.

The innkeeper's wife was baking in the kitchen late one night. When she finished, she turned off the lights and left the room. She immediately heard dishes rattling. She returned to the kitchen to find she had left a stove burner on. She extinguished the burner and left once more. She heard the rattling of dishes once again. She came back to the kitchen and found she had left a fan on. She turned the fan off, and the rattling of the dishes stopped.

Accommodations: The Terrace Inn offers guests 43 rooms and a unique vantage of Bay View. Guests of the inn have full use of the private Bay View beach, as well as tennis courts, hiking, cross-country ski trails, and sailboat rentals. All room rates include a continental breakfast plus a "Northern Michigan Buffet" dinner is featured.

— MINNESOTA —

Thayer's Historic Bed 'n Breakfast

ᛒ ᛒ ᛒ

60 West Elm Street
Annandale, MN 55302
(800) 944-6595, (320) 274-8222
www.thayers.net
Room rates: $145-$245
All major credit cards

Courtesy of Thayer's Historic B&B

History: The building that is now Thayer's Historic Bed 'n Breakfast was built in 1895 by Gus and Caroline Thayer and the Sooline Railroad. Apparently, the railroad needed a convenient place to bring workers out to that region. Through some smooth business dealings, Gus received a land grant and the finances to build his new home. Built in the traditional railroad-box shape, Thayer's distinct Victorian balconies led to its inclusion on the National Register of Historic Places. It is said that these balconies were the first of their kind to be built this far west.

In 1993, Sharon Gammell purchased Thayer's, and since that time it has gone through extensive restoration, providing some modern conveniences like whirlpools, a hot tub, and sauna, along with fireplaces and private baths. Another feature of the facility is the "Interactive Mystery Dinner," which involves a collection of different plots. There are mysteries from 400 BC up to today, including different suspects, characters, victims, and murderers, changing every time they are played out.

Sharon has been a psychic for over thirty years. During that time she has given lectures, taught classes in psychic development, and she has clients from all over the United States. Visitors are welcome to have readings for a nominal fee. During her "Dinner with a Psychic" evening, Sharon prepares dinner and serves it in the quaint Victorian dining room, and she offers each guest a mini-reading during the course of the evening.

Activity: Thayer's experiences quite a lot of activity, and the real mysteries come after the Interactive Mystery Dinner. When Sharon bought the property, she immediately felt a presence in the home. The farther she walked into the house, the stronger it became. Sharon says that even though the ghosts appear on a regular basis, they are friendly, helpful and never intrusive. Gus Thayer even makes frequent visits.

You'll know he's there, because he'll leave you a penny. Helpers in the home have cleaned rooms, only to return and find pennies on the dresser. In a room on the third floor called "Wedding Dreams," young couples have found pennies showering the threshold.

Along with Gus, Caroline Thayer makes an appearance every once in a while to make sure the home is in proper working order. There is also a ghost of a kitten that likes to sleep at the foot of the bed in a second-floor room. You can actually see the indention in the bed where the kitten lays.

Sharon Gammell, owner, chef, and psychic, sums it up well: "It's nice to have a house that's full of caring energies."

Accommodations: Thayer's offers 11 guest rooms, each decorated in authentic period antiques. The bed and breakfast accommodations include a full four-course breakfast, theme dinners, and the psychic powers of the owner/chef.

Quill and Quilt Bed & Breakfast

615 W. Hoffman Street
Cannon Falls, MN 55009
(800) 488-3849, (507) 488-3849
www.quillandquilt.com
Room rates: $79-$169 • All major credit cards

History: In 1897, this grand three-story hotel was built by Dr. A. T. Conley, a physician who practiced in Cannon Falls for over 40 years. The home is a classic example of Colonial Revival architecture, and it is noted for its six bay windows, six-column front porch, and double dormers.

By George W. Gardner. Courtesy of Quill and Quilt B&B

The home was converted into a bed and breakfast in 1987. Tom and Jean Schulte purchased the business in 2000 and have proceeded to lovingly renovate the home. They've had the rare opportunity to meet several of the past owners, and together they've shared memories of the home and a few ghost stories as well.

Activity: On one occasion, two boys were staying in what is now the Colvill Suite. Both of the lads were lying in bed when a ball of light entered the room. The boys stared in amazement as the strange light illuminated the entire room. One of the boys then became frightened and ran to get his mother. As the mother opened the door to the room, the light immediately vanished.

The innkeeper was once in the process of converting the third floor quarters into a new guest room called Writer's Haven. The innkeeper had visited a citywide garage sale the day prior and had placed the items she purchased in a plastic bag on the rocking chair along with her jeans, which had change in the pockets. About 2 A.M., she woke to the sound of a plastic bag rustling and the sound of the change falling out of her jeans pocket. She rolled over in bed and immediately she saw someone small take off down the hall. She thought it was her two-year-old son, so she shot out of bed and hurried after, but she found no one in sight. She made her way to her son's room and found him resting comfortably in a deep sleep. It's at that point that the innkeeper began to believe there were spirits in her house.

Accommodations: The Quill and Quilt Bed & Breakfast has 5 beautiful guest rooms, four of them with Jacuzzi tubs; the Suite also has a fireplace. Within 20 minutes, Nerstrand Woods offers premium hiking, and the Cannon Valley Bike Trail runs from the inn to Red Wing. Visitors can also enjoy canoeing, golfing, antiquing, shopping, and fine dining. The Mall of America is 40 minutes away, and in the winter, guests can enjoy cross-country and downhill skiing at Welch Village, which is 15 miles from the Quill and Quilt. Guests will enjoy a morning breakfast of hot egg-dish entrees with breakfast meats and breads.

Chatsworth Bed & Breakfast

984 Ashland Avenue • St. Paul, MN 55104
(877) 978-4837, (651) 227-4288 • www.chatsworth-bb.com
Room rates: $99-$169 • All major credit cards

History: The Chatsworth Bed & Breakfast is a spacious 1902 Victorian inn, located in a serene wooded setting. The previous owners lived at the home for 24 years, and they raised eight children. After the children had grown, the home was converted in 1985 to a bed and breakfast.

Today, innkeepers Neelie Forrester and Casey Peterson welcome guests to a romantic getaway far from the hustle and bustle of daily life.

Activity: The ghost of Chatsworth is a playful one. The staff feels it is a female spirit that resides in the home, and on one occasion Casey has even seen her misty outline. The ghost likes to lock the first-floor bathroom door when there's no one in there. She has also locked the doors on the third floor, as well. She keeps Casey busy bringing his tools out to unlock the doors. Another trick she likes to play is flushing toilets. When the owners' daughter was small, she would often go to the basement to talk to the ghost. The spirit's presence is often mischievous but never harmful.

Accommodations: The Chatsworth features 5 beautifully appointed rooms. Guests will enjoy a full gourmet breakfast served in the dining room or in the privacy of their room or on the porch in the summer. The Chatsworth is nestled in a quiet family neighborhood, only two blocks from the governor's mansion on historic Summit Avenue and three blocks from many excellent restaurants and unique shops. Within minutes of the Chatsworth is the Twin Cities' International Airport, the Mall of America, and downtown St. Paul and Minneapolis.

— MISSOURI —

Grand Avenue Bed & Breakfast

1615 Grand Avenue • Carthage, MO 64836
(417) 358-7265, (888) 380-6786 • www.grand-avenue.com
Room rates: $69-$99 • All major credit cards

History: Carthage, Missouri is a beautiful Victorian town located on historic Route 66 in the heart of the Ozarks. It was on this very ground where brothers fought and died in the first land battle of the Civil War. Later, stone mining created the wealth used to build the grand houses that stand today as a testament to an era long gone. Carthage was once able to boast the highest number of millionaires per capita in the United States.

Carthage retained a heritage of historic homes situated on maple-lined avenues. From its perch at the top of the Ozarks, Carthage is a wonderful place. Visitors can tour the Precious Moments Chapel or play a challenging round of golf. For a dose of the past, visit the Civil War museum or catch the flavor of a historic general store at the Main Street Mercantile.

Grand Avenue Bed & Breakfast, a historic Queen Anne Victorian, was built in 1893, and is filled with antiques and reproductions. Nestled in Historic Carthage, Grand Avenue has built a reputation over the last decade as a generous and comfortable retreat. Carthage has many diversions, including the Precious Moments Chapel, Civil War Battlefield and Museum, historic homes tour, antique shopping, and a thriving city square. Nearby there is the George Washington Carver National Monument and Harry S. Truman's birthplace.

Activity: Legend has it that past owner, Albert Carmean loved the house so much that his spirit still resides at Grand Avenue. On weekends in the fall, his trademark cigar scent can sometimes be detected in the house. He once loved to sit and drink cognac and smoke his stogie, and the current owners, Michael and Jeanne Goolsby, say that the smell of cigar smoke is occasionally present whether you're in the rooms or walking down the hall. One night, Michael was out of town, and Jeanne came across the cigar smell. The next day, guests reported some strange experiences. One guest was in the bathroom brushing her hair when she saw a figure of a person with dark hair walk by. She naturally thought it was one of her friends, but when she asked them if they had walked by, both said they had not. The same person also said the lights in her room flashed on and off during the night.

For those adventurers interested in further paranormal study, we recommend you travel to an area south of Joplin, about thirty minutes from the Grand Avenue Bed & Breakfast. There you'll find the Joplin Spook Lights, a well-documented occurrence of unexplained balls of light that appear in the countryside. Contact the Joplin Chamber of Commerce for directions and best times to witness the Spook Lights.

Accommodations: The Grand Avenue Bed & Breakfast is famous for its relaxed atmosphere and attention to guests. The inn has 5 well-appointed rooms that offer comfort and convenience, and a full complimentary breakfast is served each morning.

The Lemp Mansion

🚶 🚶 🚶 🚶 🚶

3322 DeMenil Place
St. Louis, MO 63118
(314) 664-8024 • www.lempmansion.com
Room rates: $85-$225
All major credit cards

Courtesy of Lemp Mansion

History: John Adam Lemp arrived in St. Louis from Eschwege, Germany, in 1838. He was a grocer by trade, and his new store was unique for its sales of lager beer. Lemp had learned the art of brewing lager from his father in Eschwege, and the natural cave system under St. Louis allowed the exact temperature needed for aging the beer. Lemp soon realized that his fortune was in his lager beer, so he abandoned the grocery business and built a brewery. Thus, a new St. Louis industry was born.

The Lemp Mansion was built in the early 1860s and was subsequently purchased by Lemp's son, William J. Lemp, as a residence and auxiliary brewery office. The 33-room mansion became a Victorian showplace.

In 1901, the first of many tragedies befell the Lemp family when Frederick Lemp, William's favorite son, was found dead under mysterious circumstances. Three years later, William Lemp, still grieving over the loss of his precious son, shot himself in the head in a bedroom at the family mansion. William J. Lemp, Jr., succeeded his father as president of the brewery.

The brewery's fortunes declined until Prohibition in 1919 closed the plant permanently. William Jr.' s sister Elsa, considered the wealthiest heiress in St. Louis, committed suicide in 1920. The magnificent Lemp brewery—once valued at $7 million and covering 10 city blocks—was sold at auction for $588,500.

William Lemp, Jr. shot himself in the same building where his father died 18 years earlier. William Jr.'s brother, Charles, continued to live in the house after his brother's suicide. Charles was a recluse, living alone until he also died of a self-inflicted gunshot wound. In all, four members of the Lemp family took their own lives, and one died of mysterious causes.

The Lemp Mansion still stands, welcoming all that bravely visit—for lager beer is not the only spirit you will find in the stately mansion.

Activity: In 1980, *Life* magazine recognized the Lemp Mansion as one of the ten most haunted places in America.

Witnesses believe the mysterious activity in the home is caused by the tragic deaths of the Lemp family. During renovations on the Mansion in the 1970s, tools were constantly disappearing, and strange noises were heard. Workmen felt a constant presence of someone watching them, and many workmen left the premises and never returned.

Today, eyewitnesses have seen drinking glasses lift off of the bar and fly through the air. Doors will also lock and unlock on their own, and a piano in the bar will occasionally play on its own accord. Guests and employees have witnessed an apparition throughout the Mansion who is referred to as the "Lavender Lady."

Accommodations: The Lemp Mansion offers four guest rooms. The huge kitchen that once served the elite of St. Louis society now serves honored guests of the historic Lemp Mansion Restaurant. A continental breakfast is included each morning, and a Mystery Dinner Theatre is available on Friday and Saturday.

— NEBRASKA —

Olde Main Street Inn

拃 拃 拃

115 Main Street • Chadron, NE 69337
(308) 432-3380
www.chadron.com/oldemain/
Room rates: $30-$72
All major credit cards

By Josephine Nielson. Courtesy of Olde Main Street Inn

History: The Olde Main Street Inn (formerly the Hotel Chadron) is located in the Pine Ridge section of Nebraska's panhandle, an area filled with steep, pine-covered bluffs and hill formations crossed by rolling rivers and creeks.

Peter and Margaret O'Hanlon built the elegant hotel in 1890 on the site of the old Chadron House that had been destroyed by fire. Four months after the hotel opened, a band of Miniconjou and Hunkpapa Sioux, led by Chief Big Foot, left the Pine Ridge Indian agency, northeast of Chadron. Though mostly unarmed, the band was considered hostile, and they were intercepted by the U.S. Army on December 29, 1890. Nearly 300 of Big Foot's band, including women and children, were massacred at Wounded Knee Creek. After the Wounded Knee uprising, the Hotel Chadron became the military headquarters of General Nelson Miles, who led the investigation of the tragedy.

Over the years, the hotel changed hands until Evva Gore-Bracken purchased it in 1969. The hotel has been handed down through the family ever since. Today, the four-generation family business is steeped in the traditions of the Old West. Innkeeper Jeanne Goetzinger, Evva's daughter, helped to transform the 100-year-old building into a showplace, and it has been nominated by the Nebraska State Historical Society to the National Register of Historic Places.

Activity: The spirits that inhabit the Olde Main Street Inn have been called historical ghosts, although they often border on the hysterical. There names of two people are scratched on the exterior of the building: Jack, the original builder, and Anna, his sister. The two most prominent ghosts have been nicknamed in honor of these two people. Jack, an Irish prankster ghost, has made himself known to staff and guests with one of his best pranks taking place on St. Patrick's Day. In the bar, a beer tap poured out green beer. Funny thing is, prior to that moment, there was no green beer in that beer tap. A luncheon guest saw the ghost of Anna on the steps. She was described as being a woman in a red satin dress with long dark hair.

Two Native Americans were once talking to the inn's bartender, who is Irish. He was talking to them about his Irish heritage when a glass on the bar cracked all around and then shattered. The bartender felt Jack must have been at the bar also.

Accommodations: The bed and breakfast offers 3 suites and 6 overnight rooms, all with private baths. The dining room features a beautiful stone fireplace and an original 1890s well. Guests will enjoy a delicious breakfast that is included in the rates. Lunch and dinner are also available from a diverse menu including prime rib, buffalo, and homemade chili. Visitors can dine as water cascades over the hand-laid stones of the 25-foot well.

The Cornerstone Mansion

140 North 39th Street • Omaha, NE 68131
(888) 883-7745, (402) 558-7600
www.cornerstonemansion.com
Room rates: $85-$125 • All major credit cards

History: Casper and Anna Yost built this mansion in 1894 as a wedding present for their daughter Bertha and her fiancée Charles Offutt. The Cornerstone Mansion was originally known as the Offutt House. No expense was spared when the 10,200-square-foot home was built. The mansion took two years to complete, and it reflects the opulence of another era. The mansion became the cornerstone of Omaha's historic Gold Coast, and it was a popular place for the wealthy of Omaha at the turn of the 19th century.

In the mid 1980s, the mansion began serving as a bed and breakfast. Owners Mark O'Leary and Julie Mierau named the home the Cornerstone Mansion in honor of its place as the first mansion in the area.

Activity: Back in the 1920s, a young couple living in the carriage house got into a bitter argument. The wife and her husband, who was the chauffeur, both worked for the Offutt family. Records show that the husband went into a rage and chased his wife down the stairs, then murdered her on the first floor.

After all these years, the spirit of the murdered young woman fills the carriage house with a heaviness of a love gone bad. It begins on the second floor and grows heavier as you walk down the stairs. The bedroom in particular has an extremely sad presence that makes one feel as though they cannot breathe.

Accommodations: The Cornerstone Mansion offers 6 guest rooms, each with antique furnishings and a private bath. Some have the original claw-foot tubs, and one room includes a sun porch. There is ample space for events from weddings to board meetings. Guests are encouraged to visit the large library, which features a mahogany-and-onyx fireplace and a 120-year-old Weber box grand piano. The Cornerstone Mansion also has a spacious sun porch. Each morning, breakfast is served in the formal dining room, which is furnished in ornately carved woodwork and a beautiful mosaic-tile fireplace.

— NORTH DAKOTA —

Chez Susanne Bed & Breakfast

🕈🕈🕈

1100 Third Avenue South
Fargo, ND 58103
(701) 293-9023, 866-SUSANNE
www.chezsusanne.com.
Room rates: $55-$100
Visa, Master Card

Courtesy of Chez Susanne B&B

History: Originally built in 1899, the three-story structure was historically known as the Lewis House after its original owner, Robert S. Lewis, a prominent business and political leader. Lewis' areas of interest included banking, farming, and politics, and he is remembered for starting the first Red Cross chapter in Cass County. President Teddy Roosevelt once traveled to Fargo, and while there he visited Lewis and stayed at the Lewis House.

Lewis was married twice and had three children. After his death, the home was willed to the Red Cross. The home was opened to the public as a bed and breakfast in 1998.

The Chez Susanne is an early Victorian structure with neoclassical elements. The building includes stained-glass windows, hand-carved oak and cherry wood paneling, inlaid mahogany floors, and decorative wall frescoes. Guests can enjoy a music room, a library, a formal living and dining room, a smoking room, a ballroom, and a billiard room.

Activity: Robert S. Lewis died on the grand staircase of the house, in front of the massive stained-glass window, just shy of his 100th birthday. He had outlived both his wives and two of his three children.

Legend has it that Lewis may still inhabit the home that he loved so dearly. When the present owners were considering the purchase of the home, a woman pulled them aside and quietly told them the house was haunted. She went on to tell the couple that while she had worked in the Lewis House, she would often hear footsteps on the staircase, and the door leading to the staircase would open, then close, and then open and close again. She believed it was the ghost of Lewis that walks the stairs.

After the home was opened to the public, the owners' cousin and his wife were asked to house-sit one night. Early in the morning, they awoke to hear doors opening and closing and footsteps. They called out to the chef, thinking she had arrived early, but they received no response. The next day, the cousin was preparing to leave and packing the car. He sat behind the wheel waiting for his wife to lock up. To the cousin's surprise, he watched as his wife walked out the front door with the ghost of Robert Lewis walking directly behind her. Apparently, the spirit of Lewis had followed her down the stairs.

Accommodations: The pride of Fargo, the Chez Susanne offers two floors dedicated to 4 spacious guest rooms and elegant suites, each with goose down pillows and blankets. All suites have multiple rooms with a full bath, a large bedroom, and an office/sitting room. As a treat to their guests, the suites offer complimentary Belgian truffles, imported coffees, and tea facilities. The suites are provided with down pillows and comforters and clock/radio/compact disc players with a variety of music available. Breakfast is also included with all suites.

— OHIO —

The Guest House Bed & Breakfast

🕊️ 🕊️

57 West Fifth Street • Chillicothe, OH 45601 Near Columbus, OH
(740) 772-2204 • www.theguesthousebb.com
Room rates: $70-$80 • All major credit cards

History: This Greek Revival home was built in 1826 by Governor Tiffin, the first governor of Ohio, as a wedding gift for his daughter.

The interior of the main house has been restored and furnished with period antiques. Two fireplaces are located downstairs, and the parquet floors in the hall and dining room were added in 1880 during a "modernization" to transform the home to Victorian. At the same time, the ornate staircase was added, along with the second story over the east wing of the home.

Edward Tiffin Cook, an athlete who won a gold medal in the pole vault in the 1908 Olympics, once lived in the home. The old guest house has now been converted into a two-unit bed and breakfast, while weddings, rehearsal dinners, and receptions take place in the main house.

Activity: The Guest House Bed & Breakfast features a guest that has decided not to leave. Apparently, the ghost of a Confederate soldier has been seen at the inn. He has been described as having dark hair and a beard, and he wears a topcoat. His footsteps have been heard emanating from the brick walls, and occasionally he has awakened guests.

Innkeepers Tom and Kay Binns describe the soldier as a friendly, quiet spirit that has never caused anyone to be scared. Some believe he may have been one of Governor Tiffin's sons who fought in the Civil War.

Accommodations: The Guest House Bed & Breakfast is located only one block from downtown and was added in 1987 to the National Register of Historic Places.

The guest house, a two-story brick building, features a guest unit on each floor with a separate entrance to both. Both units feature beautiful European décor, private baths, and a view of the Old English garden. The upstairs unit features an antique brass bed, and an old-fashioned canopy bed is in the unit downstairs.

The main house features two main units, with a queen-sized canopy bed upstairs and a queen-sized bed and fireplace downstairs. Both units have private baths. A full breakfast is served each morning.

The Buxton Inn

313 East Broadway • Granville, OH 43023
(740) 587-0001 • www.buxtoninn.com
Room rates: $70-$90 • All major credit cards

History: The home was built in 1812 by Orrin Granger. It was a stagecoach rest stop and mail delivery depot. Over the years, notable personalities like Henry Ford and Charles Dickens both stayed at the inn.

Major Buxton owned the inn from 1865 to 1905, and Bonnie Bounell operated the inn from 1934 to 1960. Known as "the Lady in Blue," Bounell always wore blue and died in Room 9. In 1972, Orville and Audrey Orr purchased the Buxton Inn and a restoration project immediately began. After two years of restoration, the Buxton Inn opened to the public on Friday the 13th of September 1974.

Activity: The ghost of "the Lady in Blue" has reportedly been seen at different ages at the inn and in different attire, but ordinarily she is dressed in her signature blue dress.

During the two-year restoration of the house, Orville Orr was on the second floor one day when he heard the heavy front doors open and close. Footsteps were heard as if someone was walking up the stairway and back down again. The front door once again opened and closed on its own.

Audrey Orr was painting the kitchen when she saw a man standing to her right. She naturally thought it was Orville. When he turned and walked away without saying anything, she became annoyed. She stopped painting and found Orville in the lobby. She asked if he'd been watching her. He said no, so she went back to her painting, and it happened again. It was beginning to scare her when the door suddenly opened and closed, but she hasn't been bothered since.

A sweet fragrance of perfume is occasionally noticed in the office across from Bonnie Bounell's room. Reportedly, in life, Bounell was known for her gardenia perfume.

On one occasion, a group of employees had been snowed in, and the head chef of the inn was staying the night in Room 7. He went to bed and got under the covers only to find a woman lying there. She kicked him in the hip. He jumped out of bed and collected his things to leave the room. When he turned around, she was gone.

Accommodations: The Buxton Inn offers 25 guest rooms, a gift shop, two porches, and beautiful gardens and fountains. There are dining and meeting rooms that can accommodate from 12 to 60 people.

Breakfast, lunch, dinner, and Sunday brunch are available year-round, offering fine American and French cuisine. The Tavern is open evenings Monday through Saturday, offering light fare and liquid spirits.

The Golden Lamb

27 South Broadway • Lebanon, OH 45036
(513) 932-5065 • www.goldenlamb.com
Room rates: $87-$113 • All major credit cards

History: Opened to the public in 1803, the Golden Lamb is Ohio's oldest inn and restaurant still in operation. Throughout its history, ten U.S. presidents and other notable personalities like Charles Dickens and Mark Twain have enjoyed dinner and lodging at the inn. Reportedly, Charles Dickens was planning to bed down, but refused to stay overnight when he couldn't get a drink at the bar.

Activity: Guests occasionally complain that, while in bed, they will get the feeling someone or something is playing with their toes. So far, no one has found the cause of this annoyance. Nevertheless, most of the mysterious activity at the Golden Lamb centers on Room 2.

Recently a gentleman was hired by a local corporation to transfer to Lebanon. He came in from out of town, and the company paid for him to stay at the Golden Lamb for three months. He stayed in Room 2. This guest room was created to commemorate a little girl named Sara, whose parents owned the hotel in the 1800s. It is set up to look like a little girl's bedroom. During the guest's stay, he reported several mysterious events. Every night, he would take off his glasses and place them on the nightstand by his bed. He would wake up the next morning to find the glasses placed neatly on the floor underneath the nightstand on the other side of the bed.

One night, he left his day planner by his wallet on the nightstand nearest his side of the bed. The next morning, it was gone. He looked, and the day planner was lying under the nightstand on the opposite side of the bed, just where his glasses had been.

On another occasion in Room 2, a guest wore house slippers to bed and left them by his side of the bed before turning in. The guest woke up the next morning to find the slippers were not by his side of the bed. He looked around and saw the house slippers were by the door to the room, facing toward the doorway, as if someone had worn them to the door and left them in the room as they were leaving.

Accommodations: The Golden Lamb has 4 floors, a lobby, 4 large public and 4 private dining rooms, a gift shop and 40 guest rooms. The Golden Lamb really goes all out for the holidays, decorating its rooms with garlands and ribbons, and special Christmas menus are featured each week. Special treats include Golden Lamb eggnog pie and frozen cranberry daiquiris. Guests can enjoy listening to holiday carolers that make periodic visits during December.

Old Stone House Bed & Breakfast

🎄 🎄 🎄 🎄

133 Clemons • Marblehead, OH 43440
(419) 798-5922
www.oldstonehousebandb.com
Room rates: $79-$150 • Visa, Master Card, Discover

History: The Old Stone House Bed & Breakfast was completed in 1861. The house was built as a private residence for Alexander Clemons and his 14 children. Clemons was the owner and founder of a quarry occupying most of the center of the Marblehead peninsula. Fortunately, Clemons had an abundant supply of material and talent to build his home. The four-story mansion is 8,700 square feet of Federal-style architecture, with walls made of 20-inch limestone blocks. Two main ornate entrances with nine-foot limestone pillars are located on the front of the house.

Clemons offered lodging to his quarry supervisors on the third floor. That floor has six bedrooms surrounding a large common area with a fireplace. The porches outside are giant, 137-year-old slabs of limestone. Even the sidewalks are 12-inch-thick limestone pavings.

Activity: In the 1890s, a little girl fell out of the window of Room 11 on the third floor, which was then the nursery. Today, the spirit of the little girl has been witnessed by as many as a dozen guests each year, with most of the occurrences being in Room 11. She has been described as having dark, bowl-cut hair and a little white dress. One guest awoke at 1 A.M. to find the girl standing by her bed, staring at her. The girl will often play mischievous pranks, like hiding things in the guest rooms. Occasionally, when a photograph is taken of the exterior of the building, the girl's image will appear on the photograph, sitting in the window of Room 11.

The girl will also move the figurines on the fireplace mantle in the common area of the third floor. The staff will point the figurines in one direction, only to find the same figurines pointed in the opposite direction a few hours later.

During the Civil War, a Union prison was located on Johnson's Island, a mile from the inn. While the Confederate soldiers were held captive, Union soldiers occupied the guest rooms of the inn. The ghost of a soldier dressed in a Confederate uniform has been seen in Room 8. Witnesses have reported that he paces back and forth across the floor and looks out the window.

Accommodations: The Old Stone House Bed & Breakfast offers 13 guest rooms and a beautiful view of Lake Erie. Seven of the rooms include private baths, and some have whirlpool bathtubs. Each morning, a full breakfast is provided with a hot entrée.

A 150-foot lakefront patio with tables is available for waterfront breakfast dining, with a panoramic view of Kelley's Island and South Bass Island. On the third floor, the common area with fireplace and library features oversized chairs for reading and relaxing. Guests can enjoy shopping, fine restaurants, swimming, fishing, and the Marblehead Lighthouse, all within walking distance.

Rider's Inn

🐦 🐦 🐦 🐦

792 Mentor Avenue
Painesville, OH 44077
Near Cleveland, OH
(440) 942-2742 • www.ridersinn.com
Room rates: $75-$99
All major credit cards

Courtesy of Rider's Inn

History: Joseph Rider, a sergeant in the American Revolutionary war, opened Rider's Inn in 1812 to provide a shelter to weary travelers en route to the west by way of the Oregon Trail. The Rider family operated the hotel until it fell on hard times in 1902.

George Randall of New York bought the inn in 1922 after a short-lived hot spring was found on the property. He added a dining room and speakeasy and expanded the north wing. From 1940 to 1979, the Lutz brothers operated the inn and added the Sunday Stagecoach Breakfast, a tradition that continues today. Upon the brothers' retirement, the inn went through difficult times until 1988, when Elaine Crane and her mother Elizabeth Roemisch purchased and thoroughly refurbished the establishment into a beautiful country inn.

Activity: One day, an elderly relative of the Rider family visited the inn and told innkeeper Elaine Crane that her whole family lived with the Rider Inn ghost; the relative claimed the ghost's name is Suzanne Rider. She was an original owner, and Joseph Rider's third wife.

Shortly after Crane and her family purchased the inn, she was in the process of remodeling when she found an odd-shaped room that was sealed off without a door. It's now Room 7 of the inn. One day, in comfortable clothes and flip-flop shoes, Crane was tapping at some tile on the wall while the rest of her family was away. She hit it too hard, and the entire wall fell down on top of her. She received a 16-inch gash across her chest, and she was knocked backwards and pinned to the floor. She screamed and yelled and she tried to get her arms out, but could not. After a few minutes, Crane felt something brush her hair, and as it did, the wall lifted enough for her to get her right arm out. She was then able to push her body out from under the wall. She walked to her car and drove to the emergency room. After five hours in surgery, her husband brought Crane back to the inn. When they looked at the collapsed wall, they saw her flip-flop shoes sitting atop a footprint of a woman's high-heeled shoe.

Suzanne is thought to be responsible for many other supernatural events, from harmless pranks and thievery to actually impersonating the innkeeper to fool unsuspecting guests.

Accommodations: Rider's Inn features 10 guest rooms, each beautifully furnished with antiques reflecting the Victorian era through the Early American periods of the inn's history. The rooms include private baths and a special continental breakfast served in bed. One suite is available for monthly occupancy, and a Romantic Tour Surprise Package is available for lovers. Warmed by the glow of the old stone fireplace, Joseph's English Pub is the perfect place for visitors to play a game of darts or chess, take part in lively conversation, or simply kick back and relax over a whole different spirit.

— OKLAHOMA —

The Stone Lion Inn

1016 West Warner • Guthrie, OK 73044 Near Oklahoma City, OK
(405) 282-0012 • www.stonelioninn.com
Room rates: $77-$125 • Visa, Master Card

History: A wealthy businessman named F. E. Houghton built the Stone Lion Inn in 1907 to accommodate his expanding family. The Houghtons proceeded to have six more children, totaling 12 in all (though the first six were from Houghton's first wife, who had died). All of the children survived childhood, except for a daughter, Augusta. It's believed that the maid overmedicated the young daughter for whooping cough, and she died. In 1986, Rebecca Luker and her two sons purchased the house and converted it into a bed and breakfast inn.

Activity: The spirit who apparently still resides at the Stone Lion Inn is that of the child Augusta. Apparently, between 2–2:30 A.M., guests in the Cora Diehl Suite will be awakened by a small child patting them on the cheek. As their eyes open, she quickly disappears. On another occasion, a woman was so surprised by the appearance of the child that afterward she woke up every guest in the hotel, asking them to assist in looking for her.

Rebecca Luker's younger son once had a close encounter with Augusta. One night, her son walked up to the third floor while Rebecca was checking in guests downstairs. He decided to go to bed, so he got under the covers to watch some TV. He felt someone rub his back the way Rebecca usually did. The son rolled over, and to his surprise, no one was there. Rebecca tells us he quickly came downstairs and spent the rest of the evening in the kitchen with the maid learning how to play poker.

The Stone Lion Inn also has a gentleman apparition that tends to smoke in the front room. Guests will notice the pungent smell of tobacco, and as they look to see who's cheating on the inn's no-smoking policy, they will find no one there (except the occasional curl of smoke fading over an empty chair). One guest even claimed to see smoke rings appearing from thin air.

Accommodations: The Stone Lion Inn offers luxurious accommodations with 6 suites and a parlor, fine dining in the evening, and even murder mystery weekends. Each morning guests will awake to a full breakfast with french pressed coffee, fresh blueberries and strawberries in rum cream sauce, and the quiche of the day.

Meadowlake Ranch

3750 South 137th Avenue • Tulsa, OK 74136
(800) 256-5323, (918) 494-6000 • www.meadowlakeranch.com
Room rates: $149-$169 • All major credit cards

History: Meadowlake Ranch literally grew out of the fertile soil of Oklahoma. The ranch is located in Indian territory near Tulsa. Once a thriving cattle ranch, things changed when oil was discovered on the property in the 1920s. After the oil played out, a rock quarry was established for a Corps of Engineers' project called Keystone Lake.

Following the completion of the Keystone Dam, the ranch sat idle for almost 20 years. In 1999, innkeepers Dr. Tom and Sue Lynn Warren purchased the property. Dr. Tom Warren recently led a team of modern-day explorers in the first-ever, 4,000-mile transcontinental retrace of the Lewis & Clark Trail, so he knows a little about ranching.

Since their purchase, the Warrens have built two miles of road, cleared 18 acres of pasture, built a 4,200-square-foot welding and carpentry shop, and constructed an 1,800-square-foot cabin duplex which they operate as a bed and breakfast.

With its wondrous natural beauty of open prairie meadows and spring-fed lakes, Meadowlake Ranch offers visitors the perfect getaway.

Activity: This beautiful bed and breakfast was built amidst picturesque meadows, crystal clear lakes, towering trees, and a graveyard. Yes, you heard right—Sparky's Graveyard is located on the property, and it seems there's a story or two about this old cemetery.

This National Historic Gravesite is where a man by the name of Sparky is buried along with his parents. Legend has it that the ghost of

Sparky is a restless murderer, and he likes to walk through the woods carrying a hatchet and a bucket of blood from his victims. Some say Sparky walks through the woods searching for new victims to behead. Many of the local townspeople believe this tale, and they have their own stories about Sparky and their encounters with him.

Whether it's factual or an urban (make that rural) legend, sometime around midnight, the ghost of Sparky haunts the graveyard. Kids who venture forth have been chased out of the cemetery in fear that Sparky will chop their heads off.

Accommodations: Meadowlake Ranch offers premium bed and breakfast accommodations of 4 guest rooms in private log cabins or authentic Indian tepees. Guest services include bass fishing, hunting, canoeing, and hiking. A planned expansion will add eight log cabins, an outdoor pavilion with amphitheater, a meeting center, and horse stables. A full breakfast is available, as well as lunch and dinner.

— SOUTH DAKOTA —

The Bullock Hotel

633 Main Street • Deadwood, SD 57732 Near Rapid City , SD
(800) 336-1876 • bullock.casinocity.com
Room rates: $60-$130 • All major credit cards

History: In 1876, following the death of Wild Bill Hickok, a movement to bring law and order to Deadwood resulted in the hiring of Seth Bullock as the first sheriff of Deadwood. Bullock, a pioneer law officer, businessman, politician, and soldier, earned the respect and admiration of a young Theodore Roosevelt. He later described Bullock as "my ideal typical American." Seth Bullock's influence upon Deadwood is evident today at the Bullock Hotel. Deadwood was full of bordellos and flophouses until Bullock replaced his burned-down hardware store with a luxurious hotel in 1895. The Bullock Hotel appealed to the "sophisticated traveler" and was known as one of the finest hotels between Minneapolis and San Francisco. After a meticulous restoration inside and out, the Bullock Hotel is unbelievably beautiful. It's turn-of-the-19th-century surroundings pack 100 years into every restful night.

Activity: It is common knowledge that the ghost of Seth Bullock has haunted the hotel for a long time. The original owner called him "Old Seth," and his appearances were frequent.

One evening, there was a sheriff staying in one room, and he was having an argument with his wife when he felt something hit his leg. He looked down and found a rifle shell casing on the floor. He thought that was odd, so he took it back and had his forensic team look it over. They determined the shell casing was from the late 1880s. The hotel has offered several times to buy the shell from the sheriff, but he has refused to sell it, for he felt it was a reminder for him not to argue with his wife.

A photographer was taking pictures on the third floor after the renovation was completed. Before he began, he opened all of the doors to the rooms down the hallway. He bent down to plug in his lights, when all of the doors shut one by one on their own. This happened twice. The photographer asked a couple of people to stand at the end of the hallway and watch for someone who was obviously playing tricks on him. Once again, he went to plug his lights in, and all of the doors shut again. He promptly packed up his equipment and left.

The hotel staff feels Seth Bullock is still present at the hotel in spirit so that he can watch over his property and investment.

Accommodations: The Bullock Hotel offers 28 luxurious guest rooms. Notable personalities often visit; Kevin Costner reportedly stays at the Bullock every time he's in town.

The spirit of the old mining town is alive and well at the Bullock Hotel, and the amenities of today are combined with the elegance of the past. Rooms offer king-size beds, hospitality bars and Jacuzzi tubs. In the evenings, guests can relax by a crackling fire while they're served the thickest cuts of steak and the freshest seafood on Main Street. To complement your meal, drinks are available in Bully's Lounge and the Gentlemen's Bar.

The Toal House Bed & Breakfast

🕯️🕯️🕯️

801 Almond Street
Hot Springs, SD 57747
(888) 881-4633, (605) 745-4633
www.blackhillsguesthouse.com
Room rates: $95-$135
All major credit cards

Courtesy of The Toal House B&B

History: The property was originally a sacred Sioux Indian site that was taken over by Americans. In 1891, it became the location of the "Sioux City Club," a gaming establishment that provided men the chance to gamble, along with some female companionship. The exclusive club had several elegant suites and featured a two-story octagonal gaming room topped with a special poker room.

In the 1920s, Chicago multimillionaire F. O. Butler purchased the property and converted it into a guesthouse for his affluent friends. Once known as the Black Hills Guest House, the Toal House Bed & Breakfast is located by parks and attractions and is a perfect getaway for guests seeking adventure.

Activity: When the current owners were looking to purchase the Toal House, they soon found that ghost stories about the inn were widespread. The owners don't usually mention the ghost stories; even so, quite a few guests have witnessed odd occurrences.

A couple was once staying in a suite downstairs, and the wife was taking a shower when she heard a man's voice that she thought was her husband's. However, her husband was in the other room unpacking and told her he hadn't called out. They promptly changed rooms. The room in which they were staying has been known to have a very supernatural presence. Apparently, a couple of the spirits that inhabit the Toal House are two ladies of the evening that worked there when it was a men's club. The smell of their perfume has been sensed just outside the doors of two particular guest rooms.

One evening, the Toal House hosted a private group of influential people from town. All night long, the chandelier acted strangely—it would shine brightly, then dim down, and then back up, and down again. Several guests noticed it and asked the innkeeper if he was playing with the light switch. He responded "No, but I'm having a ball watching it." After they left, the chandelier stopped.

Accommodations: The Toal House Bed & Breakfast offers 8 guest rooms. Breakfast is served each morning in the formal dining room. The inn sits on a bluff overlooking historic Hot Springs. Since the 1890s, Hot Springs has drawn people to this little town to experience the mineral-water hot springs. Nearby are several attractions, including a top-rated nine-hole golf course at Southern Hills Golf Course. Plans are underway to add the back nine.

— WISCONSIN —

Karsten Inn

🕆🕆🕆

122 Ellis Street • Kewaunee, WI 54216
(800) 277-2132 • www.karsteninn.com
Room rates: $59-$159 • All major credit cards

History: In 1836, John Jacob Astor chose Kewaunee, a Potowotami village, at the mouth of the Kewaunee River, as the site for a trading post. There he plotted to create a city larger than Chicago.

By 1858, it was a center for lumber and commerce with up to 20 schooners arriving daily. That year, Charles Brandes built the Steamboat House, the county's largest hotel. In 1876, it was purchased by John Karel and renamed the Erichsen Hotel.

After Karel's death in 1911, William Karsten bought the hostelry. Unfortunately, on the night of February 15, 1912, a fire started in an outside kitchen wall and blazed quickly through the wooden hotel. Though the hotel was crowded that night, all guests escaped unharmed. Karsten rebuilt and opened the three-story hotel in December 1912. At the time, the hotel had 52 rooms.

In the mid 1990s, the hotel was restored to its former glory, with the rooms on the second and third floor increased in size, changing the total number to 23 guest rooms.

Activity: A ghost maintains residence in Room 310. This was and still is Agatha's room. Agatha was the third-floor housekeeper who was reputedly in love with William Karsten. Some say she hanged herself because her love was unrequited. Whether this is true or not, it is apparent that her spirit haunts the third floor. Witnesses have observed doors opening and closing during the night. To tease the kitchen staff, Agatha has tipped over sugar bowls and salt shakers. Guests have seen the apparition of Agatha in Room 310 and in the lobby. The third-floor guests' eyewitness accounts have been well documented in the diaries in their room.

Accommodations: On the shores of Lake Michigan, the Historic Karsten Inn is located just 22 miles east of Green Bay. The inn has something for everyone with 23 theme rooms, including 15 Jacuzzi rooms with king, queen or double beds. Lunch is available at Karsten's Zum Engel Restaurant, or guests can enjoy dinner at the historic Karsten Inn Restaurant, where an authentic German buffet is served each Saturday night.

The Pfister Hotel

424 East Wisconsin Avenue
Milwaukee, WI 53202
(800) 558-8222, (414) 273-8222
www.pfister-hotel.com
Room rates: $139-450
All major credit cards

Courtesy of The Pfister Hotel

History: Built in 1893 by Guido Pfister, a tanner and local community leader, the Pfister Hotel is the pride of Milwaukee. Pfister's vision was to build a hotel that would be a showcase for the city. Building costs skyrocketed due in large part to the fact that the eight-story structure was one of America's first all-electric hotels, as well as the first hotel to have its own thermostat in every room. Under the leadership of Guido's son, Charles Pfister, the hotel became world famous for its superb service and accommodations. It was a popular haven during the Roaring Twenties, and during World War II the hotel hosted European immigrants who came to Milwaukee in search of a better life. The hotel saw hard times in the 1950s as a result of increased competition. In 1962, the building was sold at auction to a group of businessmen, led by Ben Marcus and his son Steve, who developed a plan to renovate and remodel the hotel to its former glory. An additional tower was constructed that allowed for convention facilities, a pool, nightclub, and additional guest rooms. Today, the 307-room hotel is back to its original elegance, and as a result the hotel plays host to visiting major-league sports teams and celebrities like Aretha Franklin, Luciano Pavarotti, and Jay Leno. The Pfister Hotel once again lives up to Guido's dream of being Milwaukee's very own grand palace.

Activity: Guido Pfister loved his hotel, and it became a dream realized. It's no wonder that guests will occasionally still see the spirit of Guido riding the hotel elevator or strolling around the hallway. Reportedly, the apparition of Guido is seen wearing turn-of-the-19th-century clothing. The hotel concierge, who witnessed his appearance, reports that the meeting was not a frightful one. He simply feels that Guido Pfister is proud of his hotel.

Accommodations: The Pfister Hotel offers 307 guest rooms; 82 of which are elegantly appointed suites that include modern conveniences like air conditioning, data ports, voicemail, radios, and minibars. The elegant suites at the Pfister offer a variety of personal amenities, such as a sitting room and large windows with views of Milwaukee and Lake Michigan. A collection of priceless Victorian artwork is on permanent display and is the largest such collection in any hotel worldwide. Guests can enjoy two wonderful restaurants, as well as the Lobby Lounge and Blu, the Pfister's new 23rd-floor lounge.

SOUTHWEST

— ARIZONA —

Hotel LaMore/Bisbee Inn

45 OK Street • Bisbee, Cochise County, AZ 85603-2855
(888) 432-5131 • www.bisbeeinn.com
Room rates: $60-$175 • All major credit cards

History: The United States acquired a section of Arizona from Mexico
in 1853 as part of the Gadsden Purchase. In 1904, the U.S. deeded the
townsite known today as Bisbee. The town prospered and grew, and in
1916, Mrs. S. P. Bedford commissioned the building of a 24-room
hotel. The hotel was later leased to Mrs. Kate LaMore in 1917.
Advertised as "the most modern hotel in Bisbee," the Hotel LaMore
flourished. It traded hands several times over the years, changing from
the LaMore to the Waters Hotel, and in the 1970s, it became a rooming
house with 12 efficiency apartments. Afterwards, the property became a
Peace Corps training facility and dormitory. In 1996, Al and Elissa
Strati purchased the inn and began a complete renovation. They brought
back the original name, and today the Hotel LaMore/Bisbee Inn blends
the best of yesterday with the conveniences of today.

Activity: No deaths have ever been recorded at the Hotel LaMore;
however, the second floor experiences a great deal of paranormal
activity. Guests have reported seeing the spirit of a lady drifting upstairs
late at night. She always leaves the unmistakable scent of lilacs in her
wake. A housekeeper was having sinus problems caused by odors from
the cleaning materials she used. The owner decided to help, and she
switched out products several times. After a while, the housekeeper
stopped complaining, so the owner asked if the change in supplies fixed
the problem. The housekeeper replied that she no longer had any reason
to complain, since "all I smell now in the bathrooms is the fragrance of
lilacs." The scent travels around the hotel to this day. Other visitors
have reported the ghost of a miner who has a playful nature and likes to
push chairs out of the rooms and into the hallway. Also, imprints are
often seen on the beds, giving the appearance that a person has laid on
the covers. The bedspreads can be straightened out, only to find the
same imprints minutes later.

Accommodations: Located in the downtown historic district, the Hotel LaMore has 20 rooms and 3 stand-alone suites with fully furnished kitchens, living rooms, and bedrooms. Each room has hand-sewn quilts, antique furnishings (many of which are from the original hotel), and a pictorial history of Bisbee. A full country breakfast is included with your room.

Hotel Monte Vista

🚶 🚶 🚶 🚶

100 N. San Francisco Street
Flagstaff, AZ 86001 • (800) 545-3068
www.hotelmontevista.com
Room rates: $50-$100
All major credit cards

Courtesy of Hotel Monte Vista

History: Listed on the National Register of Historic Places, the Hotel Monte Vista opened its doors on New Year's Day 1927. Slot machines were located in the hotel at one time, and when a major bootlegging operation was put to an end by local officials, it was revealed that the main speakeasy was the lounge at the Hotel Monte Vista. In the 1940s and 1950s, over 100 movies were filmed in and around Sedona. With no accommodations around for the actors in Sedona, they came to Flagstaff and called the Hotel Monte Vista their home away from home. Many of the rooms are named for the famous guests who stayed there, which reads like a who's who of Hollywood: John Wayne, Clark Gable, Bing Crosby, Jane Russell, Gary Cooper, Spencer Tracy, and Humphrey Bogart to name a few. A scene from Casablanca was even filmed in one of the rooms. Recently, Jon Bon Jovi, and R.E.M.'s Michael Stipe have stayed at the Hotel Monte Vista. In the early 1990s, hotel owner Jim Craven restored the hotel to its original magnificence.

Activity: In the late 1950s, actor John Wayne reported seeing a friendly ghost in his hotel room. The story quickly spread, and today over fifty different accounts of paranormal activity have been reported at the Hotel Monte Vista.

A maintenance worker once turned off the light in Room 220 and proceeded to lock the door. He returned only five minutes later to find the light was back on, the television was on with the volume blaring, and the linens were stripped from the bed.

Other occurrences have involved the sightings of phantom bellboys that walk the halls and the ringing of the lobby telephone late at night. An image of a woman has been seen outside of the Zane Grey Room, and in that room there has also been a report of a lamp that slid across the mantle by itself.

Legend has it that in Room 216, nicknamed the "hooker room," two prostitutes were reportedly murdered, and their spirits still maintain residence in the hotel. Guests, especially males, have reported having the feeling that someone was watching them.

In 1972, a bank robber was shot during a holdup. To celebrate the heist, he came to the hotel bar for a drink with his four accomplices. He died in the bar. To this day, a barstool in the lounge sometimes sails past guests as it moves across the room. It gives the appearance of being kicked across the floor by some invisible force.

A rocking chair in Room 305 is often found facing the window. No matter how many times it is turned around, the chair will be found again turned toward the window.

Accommodations: Convenient to the Grand Canyon, the Painted Desert, and Sedona, the Hotel Monte Vista is a delight. There are 50 rooms and suites, conference and banquet rooms, and custom tours leave daily to several southwestern scenic wonders. Eat lunch at the coffee shop or listen to live regional music nightly at the Monte Vista Lounge.

Connor Hotel

64 Main Street • Jerome, AZ 86331
(800) 523-3554, (928) 634-5006
www.connorhotel.com
Room rates: $90-$115
Visa, Master Card, American Express

Courtesy of Connor Hotel

History: Built in 1898 by David Connor, the hotel was originally designed with 20 rooms upstairs, including a barroom, card rooms, and billiard tables. The stone foundation of the structure was quarried from the hills around Jerome. Before the turn of the century, the first-class Connor Hotel burned to the ground twice, along with many of the other structures in town. Fortunately, Connor was one of the only two business owners in Jerome to carry insurance. As a result, he could rebuild quickly. When the Connor Hotel reopened in 1899, the hotel enjoyed a heyday as one of the finest lodging establishments in the booming towns of the West. It was one of the earliest buildings in Jerome to be fully wired for electricity, and each room had a call bell for service. As the riches of the nearby mines dwindled, so did the fortunes of the Connor Hotel. The establishment closed in 1931, though Connor's sons continued to rent the shops downstairs. Jerome was turning into a ghost town, until counter-culture folks and sightseers in the 1960s and 1970s helped the town and hotel to prosper again. The hotel opened and closed several times throughout the years, but today it thrives as one of the most comfortable pieces of history in the West.

Activity: Many of the tales from the Connor Hotel's 104-year history have gone unrecorded. However, since the renovation in 2000, ghost stories have flourished. Apparently the bulk of the activity has centered on Room 5. On several occasions, couples have reported seeing the shape of women in the room. And electronic gear will not function properly there. Palm computers will reprogram themselves, alarm clocks will come on when no one has occupied the room for several days, and the television in that room always gives the owners fits.

Even guests staying adjacent to Room 5 have reported hearing the sounds of a man coughing in the room, as well as a very large dog growling and barking under the doorway at visitors as they walked down the hall. The owners would always check the room after these reports, only to find it unoccupied.

A television technician staying in Room 1 was awakened in the middle of the night to sounds of women whispering. He decided to turn the light on and read. The voices continued and he felt a cold wave of air.

Accommodations: Perched high in the hills overlooking the spectacular Verde Valley, Jerome offers visitors a glimpse of the Old West. As you step out the front door of the Connor Hotel, you'll find a plethora of eateries, saloons, and unique shops. Located in the West's most delightful former ghost town, the Connor Hotel offers 11 historic rooms decorated with authentic antiques, as well as modern conveniences and private baths.

Ghost City Inn

☆☆☆

541 Main Street • Jerome, AZ 86331
(928) 63-GHOST, (888) 63-GHOST • www.ghostcityinn.com
Room rates: $90-$135 • All major credit cards

History: The city of Jerome was founded in the late 1800s. Once a booming mining town, the last of the mines was shut down in the 1950s, and Jerome became one of America's largest ghost towns. The inn was originally built in 1898 as a boarding house for mine employees. It later was converted into a funeral home, then it was acquired by a family and became a private residence. In 1994, owners Allen and Jackie Muma converted it into a bed and breakfast and named it the Ghost City Inn. From the front veranda, guests can take in the surrounding splendor of old Jerome, the breathtaking views of the terraced red rocks of Sedona, or kick back and watch the sun rise over the VerdeValley while sipping a cup of freshly brewed coffee. Visitors can also check out the Harley-Davidson motorcycles available as part of a package for guests.

Activity: Visitors of the Ghost City Inn often get the feeling they are not alone. Apparently, one room on the first floor was originally used as a funeral home viewing room. Guests of the inn have reportedly been awakened in the middle of the night by something shaking their shoulders; however, none of the witnesses find it scary. Another guest claimed that he was awakened to find a female spirit floating above his bed. On another occasion, a figure of a man was seen in a bathroom on the second floor, walking from one end of the bathroom to the other. During its history as a funeral home, a plague of smallpox ravaged the town and took the lives of many children. The undertaker was accused of burying the children in mass graves, a charge he reportedly denied. Whatever the truth, the ghostly occurrences often seem like childish pranks. Doors will be locked when they were not locked before, and items will sometimes be moved from the dining room to the kitchen. On one occasion, a clock radio in one room turned on by itself. The owners enjoy the pranks and are not worried; in fact, the shenanigans often make them laugh.

Accommodations: Old West meets nouveaux western in the Ghost City Inn's 6 Victorian and Early American rooms. A full breakfast is served daily, and tea, cake, and cookies welcome visitors on arrival.

The Inn at Jerome

ᛨ ᛨ ᛨ ᛨ ᛨ

309 Main Street • Jerome, AZ 86331
(800) 634-5094 • www.innatjerome.com
Room rates: $55-$85 • All major credit cards

Courtesy of The Inn at Jerome

History: Once a refuge for "ladies of the night," Pancho Villa, gold seekers, gunslingers, and gamblers, Jerome is a delight. In its heyday, an oldtimer once proclaimed that there were 120 "ladies of the night" enjoying their profession to the fullest in Jerome. Some claim that Jennie Banters, the most prominent and prosperous madam in the red-light district, was possibly the richest woman in northern Arizona.

The Inn at Jerome has been elegantly restored to its original 1899 Victorian splendor. It is located on Cleopatra Hill above this once-booming copper-mining town. The Inn at Jerome has turned Madam Jennie's bordello into a turn-of-the-century Victorian inn. Even though Jennie's former home is no longer a brothel, she must be happy living at the inn, because she has never left.

Activity: The inn has several permanent residents that happen to be ghosts, and over the years guests have reported countless paranormal experiences.

A cherub statue that sits on a dividing wall between the parlor and stairway has been observed turning on its own with no one near it.

In the Victorian Rose Room, the manager has cleaned the furniture and placed a vase on a lace runner, only to see it sailing to the ground a few seconds later.

Guests staying in the Memories of the Heart Room have locked and bolted their doors only to find the doors slightly opened during the night. They will see the light from the parlor peeking through. A second later the door quietly closes. When they get up to check the door, it is still securely bolted.

In the Kiss and Tell Room, guests have observed the doors of the armoire opening, and on occasion, wall hangings and pictures rearrange themselves on the walls.

During the Jerome Homes Tour of 2000, the door between the parlor and the hallway slammed shut six times on its own. The manager was forced to prop the door open with a brick so as not to disturb the tour.

A ghost cat will often leave its footprints and "curled up" impressions on the bedspreads, and it will sometimes rub on the legs of the guests in the restaurant or run from room to room.

Finally, a female guest reported that she was taking a shower when she heard a man's loud laughter. Luckily for the owners, she thought the experience was funny and laughed it off.

Accommodations: The inn has 8 rooms. A large parlor in the inn has a cozy fireplace; it's a popular place to sit and reflect on the charm and feel of the past. The Jerome Grill offers registered-dietician-approved heart-healthy American cuisine. They serve breakfast, lunch, and dinner.

The Oatman Hotel

🍸🍸🍸🍸

181 N. Main Street, Route 66 • Oatman, AZ 86433
(928) 768-4408 • www.oatmanhotel.com
Room rates: $35-$55 • All major credit cards

History: The city of Oatman began over 90 years ago as a mining tent camp, and quickly grew to become a prosperous gold-mining center. Built in 1902, the Oatman Hotel was originally named the Durlin Hotel, and it's the oldest two-story adobe structure in the county. The hotel was rebuilt in 1920 after one of three major fires swept through the town. In the 1960s, the hotel became the Oatman Hotel.

Miners, politicians, and movie stars have all stayed at the Oatman. Famous guests include Clark Gable and Carole Lombard, who spent their wedding night at the hotel after being married on March 29, 1939, in Kingman, Arizona. The town of Oatman was used as the location for movies, including *Foxfire* and *How The West Was Won*.

Activity: Legend has it that a miner by the name of William Ray Flour traveled from his home in Ireland to America in search of gold. Flour ended up in Oatman, stayed at the hotel, and worked two mines in town. He prospered and was able to send for his wife and children to come and join him. Unfortunately, his entire family perished en route to America. Shortly after receiving the news of their demise, Flour himself died, apparently drinking himself to death. A hole was dug outside and the miner was buried there.

Since his death, the miner's spirit has earned the nickname of "Oatie," and he is quite active at the hotel. Reportedly, Oatie is a prankster and is often seen in photographs. Eyewitnesses have also seen his image around the hotel.

The mysterious sound of bagpipes is sometimes heard in the middle of the night, and guests have occasionally heard Oatie laugh.

The gift shop located in the hotel lobby had a life-size boy doll on display. If no one was around, the doll would often be kicked around the lobby or moved about the room. The bartender once observed the doll sailing across the room as if it had been dropkicked. The doll was finally sold, and the next morning, the gift shop was in total disarray— nothing broken, just a mess. After that, a life-size girl doll, which stayed in the gift shop, would be moved nightly around the shop.

The owner of the hotel has found that if Oatie's room is cleaned, the ghost will thank the staff by placing a crayon and a page from a coloring book under his bed.

Accommodations: The Oatman Hotel features 9 guest rooms. The hotel's restaurant is known for its Buffalo Burgers and Sweet Sally's Ice Cream Parlor. The hotel is full of memorabilia from its gold-mining days. The walls and ceiling of the bar and restaurant are covered with signed and dated dollar bills. The miners apparently started this tradition when they had money, so that when they were broke again, they would have at least one more drink coming.

Hotel Congress

311 E. Congress Street
Tucson, AZ 85701
(520) 622-8848
www.hotcong.com
Room rates: $39-$89
All major credit cards

By David Fox. Courtesy of Shana Oseran
and Hotel Congress

History: The Hotel Congress
was built in 1919. Perhaps one
of the most famous stories in Tucson history surrounds the arrest of
America's public enemy number one, John Dillinger. Not his final
arrest and shooting, which took place in Chicago, but rather the arrest
of the Dillinger gang following the 1934 Hotel Congress fire.

On January 22, 1934, an early morning fire blazed through the
building, sending the hotel's patrons onto the streets. Among the guests
were Dillinger and six of his gang members. Following two days of
sightings and tips, the Tucson police staked out the location where they
were reportedly held up and captured most of the gang, and within a
few hours, they captured John Dillinger, all without firing a single shot.
In bringing Dillinger to justice, the Tucson police were able to do what
the FBI and many other big city police forces were incapable of doing.
Visitors are welcome to visit the Tucson Police Station and see their
display on the arrest of Dillinger and his gang.

Activity: For the employees of the Hotel Congress, it's common
knowledge that ghosts are present, even though owner Shana Oseran
has never seen anything firsthand. The employees have described the
spirit to be a gentleman, dressed in a speckled suit with a ruffled
collar, goatee, and gray felt hat. He has been seen walking through the
hotel lobby.

Each year, the hotel holds a big Halloween event. Prior to
Halloween, a psychic visited Shana and offered to give her a free
reading. During the reading, the psychic predicted her hotel would soon
receive national recognition, and also that there was a spirit present and
seated next to them. He proceeded to describe the spirit, and it matched
exactly the description of the gentleman that her employees had seen
weeks before. Shana learned that the spirit was there because many
years ago he was shot in a card game that took place in the lobby. The
initials T.E. were mentioned, and those same initials are on a doorknob
in the hotel. Shana was told that a flask belonging to the Dillinger gang
would be found soon. Sure enough, a few weeks later, a flask was
found with the inscription "Sheffield, England 1919."

Employees have witnessed the appearance of another ghost in the hotel. They describe the spirit as a lady wearing a long black dress with a high collar and her hair pulled back in a bun. Though Shana has never seen that spirit either, she once smelled a scent at the top of the stairs; she described it as "quite pleasant." Days later, she smelled the same aroma in the lobby. Shana believes this aroma may indicate that the spirit of the lady is present. Finally, a third spirit has reportedly been seen on the second floor, and when the spirit is observed, it is always looking out the window.

Accommodations: As you approach the building you'll spot the distinctive red neon sign that adorns the roof. Located in the hotel is a café and The Club Congress. The Club Congress nightclub features dance nights including hip-hop, disco, and techno, and it's one of the best live music venues in town. The nightclub has been voted one of the top clubs in the country. The hotel also offers an artist-in-residence program. The interior of the hotel, refurbished after the 1934 fire, features elegant wooden floors, ornate columns, and high ceilings. With 40 guest rooms, Hotel Congress offers visitors the comfort and relaxation of yesteryear.

— NEVADA —

Gold Hill Hotel

1540 Main Street • Gold Hill, NV 89440
(775) 847-0111 • www.goldhillhotel.net
Room rates: $45-$225 • Visa, Master Card

History: Constructed around the early 1860s and known as the Riesen House, the hotel was acquired by H. M. Vesey. He added a wooden structure to the original stone building, and the hotel became an important part of the growing town of Gold Hill.

Located one mile south of Virginia City, the town grew to a population of nearly 40,000 people, and it became the largest city in the West. Schools, opera houses, newspaper offices, factories, and churches were all built, along with major mining operations that produced enormous amounts of gold and silver.

The mining boom continued throughout the 1870s, but after the gold played out, the population sank to a few hundred by the 1930s. The town was faced with complete ruin and, with no source of income, many abandoned their property and drifted away. The population that was left scrounged among the ruins. From the dust of a once-prosperous metropolis, a traveler's retreat has been recreated as guests come to Gold Hill fascinated by the history of the Comstock Lode.

Activity: Room 4 is reportedly haunted by the ghost of red-haired Rosie, a former housekeeper. Rosie wears a white blouse and a long skirt, and she appears in one of the bedrooms in the older portion of the hotel. When she is present, witnesses smell a fragrance of roses.

Room 5 is said to be haunted by the ghost of William, a dark-haired man who's believed to be the original owner of the hotel. He reportedly died in a fire that took place in the 1880s. William will occasionally leave the scent of cigar smoke when he has been near.

There has also been a sighting of a tall, thin man, dressed in 1860s clothing and carrying a violin.

Accommodations: Nestled in the hills around Virginia City only an hour's drive from Tahoe, the Gold Hill Hotel features 20 guest rooms and lodges located in a relaxed atmosphere surrounded by beautiful views—a perfect place for hiking and enjoying crisp, clean air. The guest rooms range from 4 small, but comfortable, rooms in the original hotel to 16 new, spacious and elegant rooms, all with private baths. The Crown Point Restaurant, located in the hotel, has been called one of the best restaurants in Nevada. With an award winning wine selection you can find a wine to accompany any of their exotic meals.

Silver Queen Hotel

☆☆☆☆

28 North C Street • Virginia City, NV 89440
(775) 847-0440
Room rates: $45-$125 • All major credit cards

History: Virginia City was one of the first industrial cities in the West when it began in the late 1850s. At the head of Six-Mile Canyon, gold was discovered in 1859 by two miners, Pat McLaughlin and Peter O'Reilly. A third miner, Henry Comstock, claimed it was his find, and the two original miners believed him. The giant lode was named after Comstock.

Virginia City was reportedly named after James Finney, whose nickname Old Virginny was given to him after his birthplace. Legend has it that during a drunken celebration, Finney dropped his bottle on the ground and named the newly founded tent town on the slopes of Mt. Davidson "Old Virginny Town." Virginia City at its peak had something happening 24 hours a day—both above and below the ground—and nearly 30,000 residents lived there.

The Silver Queen Hotel was built in 1876. The two-story hotel has an open banister, original doors, and 14- to 18-foot ceilings. The current owners restored the hotel and added private baths to each room.

Activity: The Silver Queen Hotel has an assortment of spirits that tend to occupy their own favorite rooms.

Starting in Room 5, an armoire was purchased and delivered that apparently brought the ghost of a young girl along with it. She has been called Anna Marie, and she appears to be around six years old. She resides in the armoire and likes to open the door. She will often push the door button so it pops up and open. A man, neatly dressed with a big hat, has been seen in the reflection of the mirror of the same armoire.

In Room 1, a ghost by the name of Dave is a practical joker. One guest staying in the room was pushed off the toilet, and while was lying in bed, someone pushed on his back. He was alone in the room.

In Room 9, guests have reported hearing noises in the middle of the night. Visitors often request to stay in Room 11, where the ghost of Sara Haggerty apparently resides. Sara was a pregnant woman who took her own life. She reportedly likes to be left alone and lets guests know it!

Accommodations: The Silver Queen Hotel features 29 comfortable guest rooms, and patrons can enjoy any of the haunted rooms. Each room is decorated with antiques, including claw-foot bathtubs. The hotel serves hot dogs and Polish sausage. A wedding chapel is a favorite spot for local residents wanting to tie the knot.

— NEW MEXICO —

Casa del Rio Bed & Breakfast

19946 Hwy 84 • Abiquiu, NM 87510
(505) 753-2035 • www.bbonline.com/nm/casadelrio
Room rates: $100-$125 • All major credit cards

History: The Casa del Rio is a modern bed and breakfast that captures the elegance of Old World Spanish culture. The traditional adobe haciendas are located within close proximity to Santa Fe and Taos, and it's perfectly situated for day trips to the Ghost Ranch Living Museum, Rio Grande Gorge, Chama Steam Train Trips, and the eight Northern Indian Pueblos. Mel Vigil, a native New Mexico cowboy who was born in Santa Fe, and Eileen Sopanen, a 30-year resident of Rio Arriba County, host your stay at their Chama Valley hacienda.

Activity: Reportedly, the Casa del Rio Bed & Breakfast was built on top of a much-traveled Indian route. This may be the reason there is a strong and frequent aroma of baked bread that will come and go, manifesting itself mostly at night. The smell will occur around the time everyone turns in for bed. It is at its strongest in the corner of a bedroom in the main house.

The innkeepers feel that the aroma may be occurring because an orno—a southwestern outdoor cone-shaped oven—may have been located where the bedroom is today.

Recently, the scent has gone from the smell of fresh baked bread to a sweet smell. The staff feels a very benevolent ghost inhabits their inn, and they are pleased that it's willing to share space with them.

Accommodations: The 2 adobe guesthouses are appointed with local handmade crafts, rugs, bed coverings, and furniture. Visitors will find traditionally designed viga and latilla ceilings that reflect the soft light of the kiva fireplaces. Each room has modern baths finished in handmade Mexican tile and a full breakfast is served each morning. Outside the patio window, guests can enjoy a magnificent view of the cliffs above Rio Chama. Visitors can take advantage of exciting day trips for skiing and bicycling, hiking and fishing, or whitewater rafting.

La Hacienda Grande Bed & Breakfast

21 Barros Lane • Bernalillo, NM 87004
(800) 353-1887, (505) 867-1887 • www.lahaciendagrande.com
Room rates: $109-$149 • All major credit cards

History: Nestled along a tree-lined country lane on the northern side of Albuquerque sits a 250-year-old destination for weary travelers. This buckskin-colored, buttressed building has been renovated and fashioned into La Hacienda Grande Bed & Breakfast. Said to be one of the oldest inns in the country, it served travelers even before it became a stagecoach stop in the 1800s. In fact, in 1711, the Spanish colonial government granted the Gallegos family a large section of land (encompassing 100 square miles of present-day Bernalillo) to be used as a farm and ranch.

Between 1711 and 1750, the original structure of La Hacienda Grande was built on the ranch. The estate served as the economic, cultural, and political center for the surrounding community. Since that time, it has served as a comfortable resting place for travelers along the Rio Grande.

Legend has it that Spanish gold and treasures were once stored under the floors of the La Hacienda Grande. The building served as a chapel before Our Lady of Sorrows Catholic Church was built in Bernalillo. Long before the Spanish arrived, the site was known as sacred land to the nearby Tiguex Pueblo tribe. During the Civil War, Confederate soldiers ransacked churches in New Mexico. For protection, Our Lady of Sorrows Church in Bernalillo brought their Spanish gold and other sacred icons and treasures to the Montoya chapel and buried them under the floor of what is now La Hacienda Grande. For whatever reason, after Our Lady of Sorrows Church was spared, the gold was left in the chapel and its exact location was lost. Though many have tried, no one has ever discovered the whereabouts of the Spanish gold.

Activity: Someone was supposedly murdered long ago in the archway between the kitchen and the San Felipe Room. Witnesses claim there is a ghost that now haunts the kitchen.

Also, the tree in the center of the courtyard is said to give off certain energy, and locals talk about the spirit of an Indian who sits on the front of the roof of the La Hacienda.

Accommodations: La Hacienda Grande features 6 spacious suites, complete with beamed cathedral ceilings, cozy sitting/reading areas, an intimate dining room, and a huge, 40' x 60' open-air center courtyard with a covered portico. The restaurant's daily menu features fresh homemade foods with a southwestern flair.

The Madeleine

☆☆☆

106 Faithway Street
Santa Fe, NM 87501
(888) 321-5123, (505) 986-1431
www.madeleineinn.com
Room rates: $70-$180
All major credit cards

Courtesy of The Madeleine

History: Built in 1886 by railroad tycoon George Cutler Preston, the Madeleine is one of Santa Fe's oldest and grandest estates, as well as the first bed and breakfast in town. It's not difficult to imagine gentle ladies bustling around in their hoop skirts of silk and velvet while Preston conducted business over whiskey and cigars in the parlor. Formerly the Preston House, the inn has been renamed for owner Carolyn Lee's daughter, Madeleine.

Activity: The Ivy Room ison the third floor of the Madeleine, in what used to be the attic. It is now divided into two rooms— a bedroom and a sitting room. Most of the activity has occurred in the sitting room.

One morning, a guest came downstairs with a strange look on her face. She told the management she normally did not believe in ghosts, but the previous night changed her mind. Her friend was asleep in the bedroom, and she was sitting on the sofa in the sitting room. Suddenly, the room filled with all sorts of people who stood around talking to one another. They finally all left, leaving one woman, dressed in Victorian clothing and sitting at the foot of her bed. The guest reported having a very long conversation with the spirit, none of which was frightening, and then the woman vanished.

Honeymooners were staying in the Ivy Room one evening. They had been given complimentary champagne and truffles. While they were on the sitting-room sofa (across the room from the table holding the champagne), the champagne glasses suddenly shattered. Neither guest was anywhere near them at the time.

Accommodations: Tucked away on a quiet street on Santa Fe's famous East Side, the Madeleine offers 8 beautifully appointed guest rooms. The property features stained-glass windows, ornate wood molding, brick and tile fireplaces, window seats, and a large front porch with wooden rocking chairs. The interior is filled with period antiques and is painted in warm and sunny hues. In the morning guests wake to the enticing aroma of gourmet, freshly-brewed coffee and unforgettable just-baked muffins. Their generous breakfasts feature a hot entree of breakfast enchiladas, southwestern frittatas, pancakes, waffles, and other delights that change daily. The inn is located only blocks away from the historic Plaza and the galleries of Canyon Road.

The Laughing Horse Inn

729 Paseo del Pueblo Norte • Taos, NM 87571
(800) 776-0161 • www.laughinghorseinn.com
Room rates: $47-$150 • All major credit cards

History: In 1924, William Willard "Spud" Johnson came to Taos with his magazine and hand-letter press to join his friend, author D. H. Lawrence. Johnson remained long after Lawrence left town, enchanted by the city and its culture.

Johnson published *The Laughing Horse*, a literary journal with 21 issues published over 18 years—basically, the journal was published whenever Johnson felt like it. Regardless of his sporadic publication, local historians called Johnson "the intellectual conscience of Taos."

The adobe hacienda that is now the Laughing Horse Inn was built in 1887 and was Johnson's home for 45 years. Spud used the bedroom as his print shop and library, sleeping in the living room until he added a bedroom area between the original house and the tool shed. Spud probably would have been satisfied with sleeping in the living room; however, the bedroom was most likely added to accommodate a regular visitor, artist Georgia O'Keeffe.

Activity: There have been various reports of ghosts over the years, and most assume the prankster spirit is that of Spud Johnson. The ghost tends to plays little tricks, as if he wants everyone to know he's still there.

On one occasion a few years back, a housekeeper was the only person in the inn. She was in the penthouse cleaning. Apparently the ghost had moved upstairs to the penthouse when the previous owner had remodeled one of the ground-floor rooms. The ghost must have become disgusted when they tampered with his space.

The housekeeper walked downstairs to retrieve supplies; upon her return she could not open the door at the foot of the stairs leading to the penthouse. The owner had to break into an upstairs window and come down the stairs, and there he found the door securely locked. It had a hook latch, and it was impossible for the latch to lock on its own.

Accommodations: The inn is built on the banks of the Rio Pueblo, the sacred river of the Taos Pueblo Indians, and is adjacent to Pueblo land. Visitors can relax and mellow out within the 114 year-old adobe walls of the Spanish hacienda. The Laughing Horse Inn offers 10 eclectic guest rooms that share 3 bathrooms. There are also 2 suites with private baths. Breakfast is included with each room. Some of the rooms were uniquely crafted by "hippie" carpenters in the early 1970s. Instead of crackerbox-motel squareness, this historic hotel blooms with curved and rounded shapes of Mother Earth. Guests are graciously welcomed into a setting that once hosted D. H. Lawrence, Gertrude Stein, Georgia O'Keeffe, and Alice B. Toklas.

Old Taos Guesthouse Bed & Breakfast

☆☆☆

1028 Witt Road • Taos, NM 87571
(800) 758-5448, (505) 758-5448
www.oldtaos.com

Courtesy of Old Taos Guesthouse B&B

Room rates: $80-$160 • Visa, Master Card, or personal check

History: This inn began as a humble adobe hacienda built over 180 years ago. Nestled amid a grove of stately old cottonwoods and spruce, the property is situated on 7 ½ fertile acres on a rise that overlooks Taos. The small farmer's home eventually grew into an artists' estate, and then into a guesthouse in the 1940s. The building was rescued from dilapidation almost 50 years later, and today it has been lovingly restored in the southwestern tradition and opened to the public as a bed and breakfast.

Activity: There is an old Mexican legend about a woman named La Lorna, or "the wailing woman" as she is often called. As the story goes, La Lorna lived during the 18th century and, with her husband, had a large number of children. They lived near Santa Fe in the mountain countryside. La Lorna supposedly drowned her children, either because her husband left or because a new man in her life did not want a family. In another version of the story, La Lorna's children were brutally killed by renegade marauders.

Whatever the cause of the children's death, the legend says the tortured soul of La Lorna still walks the hillsides to this day, wailing in mournful torment. Sightings of her ghostly figure have been reported all over Santa Fe.

Similar sightings at the Old Taos Guesthouse Bed & Breakfast have led the innkeeper to believe that La Lorna and Maria, as their ghost is called, may be one and the same. Local legend says that Maria also drowned her children in one of the irrigation systems in town. The strange thing is that the only occasions the innkeeper or guests have seen the ghost of Maria is during irrigation time. The whole community is very fertile and is irrigated at certain times by an old system of irrigation ditches called acequias. Mysteriously, when the river flows on the property, this brings the spirit of Maria out.

The apparition of Maria has visited guests on two separate occasions, in two different rooms. Each time, she sat at the edge of their bed and talked with the guests. The innkeeper has had his own personal sighting of Maria as well. It was raining once, and he and four other people were looking out at the property that was being irrigated at the time. Out in the fields, they could see the misty image of someone in a long-flowing white dress walking through the rain. They didn't sense anything odd until the bells of an old church nearby started to ring, and the woman in white abruptly disappeared.

Accommodations: The Old Taos Guesthouse Bed & Breakfast offers 9 guest rooms, all with outdoor entrances, private baths with Mexican hand-painted tiles, and hand-carved doors and furniture. A few of the guest rooms have large skylights and kiva fireplaces, and all rooms have the spice of the Southwest. All rooms include a healthy continental breakfast.

— TEXAS —

The Driskill Hotel

604 Brazos Street • Austin, TX 78701
(800) 252-9367, (512) 474-5911 • www.driskillhotel.com
Room rates: $100-$300 • All major credit cards

History: Colonel Jesse Driskill, a wealthy cattle baron and civic leader, built the luxurious Driskill Hotel in 1886. His goal was to rival the palaces of New York, Chicago, St. Louis, and San Francisco. A life-size portrait of the Colonel still resides in the lobby.

In 1934, a young Texas politician by the name of Lyndon Baines Johnson had his first date with his future wife LadyBird—they dined in the Driskill dining room. Fifteen years later, Johnson stayed in the Jim Hogg Suite of the Driskill, awaiting the results of his U.S. Senate race against Coke Stevenson. In 1960, Johnson once again stayed in the hotel while awaiting the results of his race for Vice President on John F. Kennedy's presidential ticket.

In 1996, a multi-million dollar renovation of the property began, restoring the hotel to its original grandeur and elegance.

Activity: At least six ghosts supposedly inhabit the Driskill Hotel. Leading the pack is the builder himself, Colonel Driskill. The Colonel occasionally smokes his cigar in the guest rooms, and he turns the bathroom lights on and off.

Reportedly, the four-year-old daughter of a U.S. Senator was playing too close to the grand staircase when she fell to her death. Her spirit is still heard in the hotel, bouncing a ball and laughing.

A Mrs. Bridges worked the front desk during the early 1900s and was a long-time employee of the hotel. Today, guests have seen her image, wearing Victorian clothing and walking from the original hotel vault to the front desk where she once worked.

Peter J. Lawless lived in the hotel from 1886 to 1916, and his spirit is also seen. He has been found near the elevator on the fifth floor, standing and checking his pocket watch.

Reportedly, two brides died tragically in the hotel, and they have been seen on the fourth floor and in the ladies' rooms dressed in full bridal attire.

Accommodations: The Driskill Hotel has returned to a haven of opulence and comfort—everything you would expect from a luxury hotel. The hotel offers 110 guest rooms; each with Romanesque furnishings inspired by the original 1886 décor. The guest rooms are located in the Driskill Tower that was originally built in 1929. The Driskill also has 12 luxury suites, each exquisitely decorated. Adjoining the hotel's piano bar, the Driskill Grill is an excellent Texas dining room serving southwestern fare.

Miss Molly's Hotel

☆ ☆ ☆

109 ½ W. Exchange Avenue
Fort Worth, TX 76106
(800) 99MOLLY, (817) 626-1522
www.missmollys.com
Room rates: $125-$200
All major credit cards

Courtesy of Miss Molly's Hotel

History: Built in 1910, Miss Molly's Hotel was originally a prim and proper boarding house, catering to cattle barons, ranchers, and cowboys. The boarding house later became a "bawdy house," or bordello. In the 1940s, a Miss Josie managed the "sporting house" and called it the Gayette Hotel. Her "ladies" entertained clients in any of the nine rooms. Cowboys, meat packers, businessmen, and a politician or two frequented the hotel in search of ... well, you know.

When the hotel was transformed into a bed and breakfast in 1989, the new owners renamed it Miss Molly's after the famous lead cow on the Goodnight-Loving Cattle Drives. The new proprietress, Dawn Street, greets her guests in authentic1800s madam/saloon girl attire as she entertains visitors with stories and history of old Fort Worth. All of the ladies who stay at Miss Molly's are given a special souvenir: an authentic 1800s license of prostitution (only valid at Miss Molly's) complete with their name, room, and official seal.

Activity: Dawn Street reports that on numerous occasions a presence has been felt at Miss Molly's Hotel, but each time it has been a benevolent, watchful presence. An English gentleman once stayed in the Cattlemen's Room. He awoke to see the dim figure of an elderly woman standing at the foot of his bed. She was dressed in old-fashioned clothing and was wearing a sun bonnet. The guest and management felt it might have been Amelia Eimer, a prim, proper, and sedate lady who ran the boarding house in the 1920s.

A local journalist was staying in the Cowboy Room one night when he awoke from a deep sleep to find the image of a blond woman floating above him. After a few seconds, the spirit was gone. The witness described her as beautiful.

Accommodations: Located in the heart of the Stockyards National Historic District, each of Miss Molly's 6 guest rooms is furnished in Old West antiques and turn-of-the-19th-century Texas style. Shutters, lace curtains, iron beds, quilts, and oak furniture are found in every room. Guests share the 3 bathrooms down the hall. All have claw-foot tubs and pull-chain toilets. Robes are provided to guests during their stay.

Miss Josie's Room, Miss Molly's premier suite, was originally the madam's quarters in the 1940s when the girls were rented along with the rooms. It features elegant Victorian décor and a private bathroom.

Nearby attractions include the 1880 Tarantula Steam Excursion Train; the world's largest honky-tonk, Billy Bob's Texas; Cowtown Coliseum, where the first indoor rodeo was held in 1918; the Livestock Exchange Building & Museum; and several shops and fine restaurants.

The Texas White House Bed & Breakfast

🕆 🕆 🕆

1417 Eighth Avenue
Fort Worth, Texas 76104
(800) 279-6491, (817) 923-3597
www.texaswhitehouse.com
Room rates: $105-$185
All major credit cards

By Mark Jean. Courtesy of
The Texas White House

History: The home was built in 1910 by a gentleman named Mr. Bishop. The structure has been called the Bishop-Newkirk house, and it is a classic example of a hipped cottage, known later as an Open Plan, a popular house design between 1870 and 1940. The home was sold to the William Newkirk family—the only family to occupy it as a residence. The Newkirks raised four sons, and all four joined the service to fight in World War II. All four survived to return home and follow their individual careers. They later brought their children and grandchildren back to live in the home. Both William Newkirk and his wife died there. After his death the Newkirk family sold the home, but all five generations returned in 1994 for a Newkirk family reunion. That same year, the house was designated a Fort Worth Landmark.

Activity: Innkeeper Grover McMains reports that they've experienced three encounters with ghosts at the inn and they believe it is the spirit of William Newkirk who died in the home at the age of 97. In each occurrence, only one female guest was staying in the room.

The first time, a female guest awoke in the middle of the night to a feeling that someone was lying on the bed beside her, back to back. She lay there motionless and then she felt the person start to move off the bed. She turned over very fast to see who it was and no one was there. Then the overhead light turned on by itself.

In the second occurrence, a woman awoke when she had the feeling someone was getting into bed with her. She turned over immediately to see who is was, but again no one was there. Her cell phone, which was plugged into the wall several feet away, began to beep and would not stop for several seconds. The phone had never done that before.

In the third and most recent occurrence, a lady was returning to her room when she felt a presence in the corner of the room. Later that night she experienced the same presence on the other side of her bed. Prior to her encounter, she was unaware of the two previous encounters in the room. Upon checking out she thanked the innkeeper and said she enjoyed the "friendly presence" in her room.

Accommodations: The Texas White House features 5 guest rooms, Jacuzzi tubs, a sauna, luxurious beds, and a bountiful breakfast.

Located in the heart of Fort Worth, the culture of The Modern Art Museum of Fort Worth, the Bass Performance Hall, and the Cowgirl Hall of Fame are all within a short drive from the inn. Business guests will appreciate being a short distance to downtown Fort Worth and the Medical District.

Rose Hall Bed & Breakfast

✩✩✩✩

2314 Avenue M
Galveston, TX 77550
(409) 763-1577
www.rosemansion.com
Room rates: $89
All major credit cards

Courtesy of Rose Hall B&B

History: A man by the name of Charles Adams arrived on Galveston Island in 1839 to sell his cargo. Adams fell in love with Galveston and with Texas. He opened the first flour mill in Texas and started a coffee trade between Rio de Janeiro and Galveston, which was the only Confederate port still in operation at the close of the war.

Around 1860, Adams built Rose Hall, completing it just before the Civil War. After surviving the Great 1900 Hurricane, the house was rotated to its current position, facing the Gulf of Mexico. Now restored to its former glory, Rose Hall stands proudly as a survivor of both the Civil War and the Great Hurricane.

The horrific 1900 Hurricane that hit Galveston Island took the lives of 6,000 people in one day. It's no surprise that there still may be some spirits that have stayed behind.

Activity: We spoke to innkeeper Barbara Souza, and she told us that within the past five years, over 100 paranormal experiences have occurred at Rose Hall. However, it's the spirit of a small child that causes the most mischief. The boy, who looks to be seven or eight years old, will rattle the curtains to get attention and tug on the bedspreads. On one occasion, a couple looked out their third-floor window, and the boy was there looking back at them.

Another time, a couple was staying in the guest room on the second floor of the Carriage House. They brushed their teeth before bed, and awoke the next morning to find their toothbrushes missing. A few days later, the innkeeper found the toothbrushes in the toilet. To add to the mystery, that night, there was a knock on the guests' door. When they answered, no one was there. They closed the door, but suddenly the doors of the room's armoire flew open, and a vase inside levitated out and then hit the ground without shattering. The next couple to stay in the room had the very same experience. To end the complaints, the innkeeper stopped renting out that room.

A Miss Kinkler was a resident of the inn when it was a boarding house in the 1940s. She was a wealthy lady and was the only female allowed to stay at the boarding house. Visitors have seen her spirit often. One guest awoke in the middle of the night to find a little old lady standing at the foot of her bed. The guest said she did not feel scared at the time—however she'd prefer never to see Miss Kinkler again.

Accommodations: Rose Hall Bed & Breakfast offers 7 guest rooms, each with private bath and most with antique claw-foot tubs and showers. The Victoria and Rose Rooms each have Jacuzzi tubs. The inn features 16 crystal chandeliers, a winding staircase to the third floor, and a large, breezy veranda. The interior includes an 1860 parlor, gift shop, library, and intimate "Tables for Two" breakfast dining in the Grand Salon.

The Jefferson Hotel

🕆 🕆 🕆 🕆 🕆

By Mark Jean. Courtesy of
The Jefferson Hotel

124 W. Austin Street
Jefferson, TX 75657
(866) 33HOTEL
www.historicjeffersonhotel.com
Room rates: $60-$125
All major credit cards

History: Built in 1851, in a time when steamboats plied the Big
Cypress River from New Orleans, the Jefferson Hotel stands today as one
of the oldest buildings in town. The stately structure, once a cotton
warehouse, is located in the heart of Jefferson's Riverfront District.
Around the turn of the 19th century, it was transformed into a hotel; by
1920, the hotel was known as the Crystal Palace. Today, innkeepers
Michael and Elise Lakey welcome you to the Victorian charm of the past.

Activity: The Jefferson Hotel is such a popular haunt that guests don't
want to leave. One spirit in particular might be Mrs. Schluter, innkeeper
from the 1890s through the Roaring 20s.

A few years ago, the hotel was empty one night and a desk clerk
walked to the second floor to make his rounds. As he turned off lights
and locked doors, he reached the last door in the hallway, and all of the
doors started opening and slamming shut by themselves. Lights then
began turning on and off as he rushed downstairs. He could hear
footsteps coming from the second floor and the sound of someone
dragging furniture. The desk clerk quickly phoned a friend, screaming
"all heck is breaking loose upstairs." Other encounters involve the
sighting of a man in a long coat and high boots in Room 5, as well as a
long-haired blond that apparently has an attachment to the bed that was
moved from Room 12 to 14. This woman is often seen in Room 14 and
occasionally floats down the stairs, only to disappear once she reaches
the bottom. The sound of splashing, running water has been heard in
Rooms 19 and 20.

The sounds of children laughing and romping throughout the hotel in
the middle of the night are often heard when no children are present,
and footsteps on a hardwood floor are heard in areas where the floors
are carpeted.

One morning a woman awoke to see a nice-looking man dressed in
western clothes walk into the entrance of rooms 20 and 21. She thought
that was odd, so she followed, only to find both doors open and the
rooms empty.

Finally, even investigators should "beware." Many local news
reporters have stayed in the hotel while conducting their own

investigations, only to find their video cameras not working in certain areas of the hotel and tape recorders turning themselves off and on.

Accommodations: Entering through the front door, you feel an aura of timelessness. Each of the Jefferson Hotel's 25 rooms boasts its own theme and décor, and all are impeccably decorated with antique furnishings. During your stay, visit the award-winning Lamache's Italian Restaurant for authentic Italian cuisine.

Maison Bayou Bed & Breakfast Plantation

300 Bayou Street • Jefferson, TX 75657 • (903) 665-7600
www.maisonbayou.com • Room rates: $85-$145
Visa, MasterCard, Discover

History: Within Jefferson, nestled on 55 wooded acres and overlooking Big Cypress Bayou, is the Maison Bayou Bed & Breakfast. An authentic recreation of an 1850s Creole plantation, the Maison Bayou is a wonderful inn with a few unsolved mysteries.

The Maison Bayou has something of a notorious past. A well-to-do couple, "Diamond Bessie" Moore (a former lady of the evening) and Abe Rothschild visited Jefferson in 1877. After they were seen arguing, the two went on a picnic, and Moore was later found dead on what is now the property of the Maison Bayou. She had been shot and all of her jewelry was missing. Rothschild fled, but he was captured and put on trial for the murder. Though convicted, the case was overturned on appeal, and Rothschild went free. To this day, no one is really sure who killed Diamond Bessie.

Activity: The spirit of Diamond Bessie may still be present in the historic town of Jefferson. When the Maison Bayou Overseer's House was being constructed in 1991, the plumber was working under the house on a hot day when he decided to take a break and lie down for a couple of minutes. His head tilted over to a strand of chicken wire wrapped around some insulation on the ground. When his cheek touched the wire, it sent an electric shock through his face. He shot up and reported the incident to innkeepers Jan and Pete Hochenedel. Concerned that there may be an old line buried underground, the Hochenedels called the power company, which informed them that no cables were located there. After tests by the local utility company, it appeared that an AC voltage on the ground was present that measured between 3 and 18 volts AC. To this day, no one has been able to explain why this is present.

A couple retreated to Cabin 2 one night after a day of shopping in

Jefferson. As they lay in bed, the woman awoke to hear a rocking chair creaking back and forth on the wooden floor. She assumed it was her husband because he occasionally experienced back pains and would get up in the night. The next day, the wife asked her husband how he slept. He replied that he slept like a rock. Upon telling her husband about the rocking chair sounds, they discovered that not only was the rocking chair located away from the air conditioner or any air source, but it was also sitting atop a hoop rug, which would have made no sound when rocking.

Accommodations: Each building on the plantation has been painstakingly recreated with materials from the 19th century. The main house is an authentic reproduction of a plantation overseer's home, which features pine floors, walls, and ceilings, natural gas–burning lanterns in each room, and period antiques and fabrics. During their stay at the plantation, guests may stay in a room in the main house, 4 individual cabins, 4 poolside cabanas, a replica of a paddlewheel steamboat, or 2 railroad cars. Each morning a full breakfast is served.

The Badu House

ゲ ゲ ゲ ゲ

601 Bessemer Road
Llano, TX 78643
(915) 247-1207
www.baduhouse.com
Room rates: $70–$100
All major credit cards

Courtesy of The Badu House

History: Built to house the First National Bank of Llano in 1823, this Italian Renaissance–style structure is on the National Register of Historic Places. When the bank closed in 1898, the building was sold at auction to Professor N. J. Badu. Professor Badu, his wife Charlie Neal, and their two girls, Tillie and Kittie, were prominent Llano citizens and enjoyed entertaining guests with elegant dinner parties. Charlie Neal Badu died in 1909, and the Professor gave the home to his children. In 1913, when Tillie got married, the downstairs floor of the house was remodeled into living quarters for the newlyweds. Professor Badu continued to live on the second floor until his death in 1936.

Activity: Legend has it that a male and female spirit visit on a regular basis. The male apparition is believed to be that of Professor Badu, and the female entity may either be Tillie, who died in the home, or a third daughter who may have died at an early age. Whatever the reason, over the years, many guests have experienced something out of the ordinary.

Footsteps are often heard in the building and, on one occasion, a couple was coming down the stairs for dinner and another couple was seated at the table when a large crash was heard from the stairway. It sounded as if someone had fallen down the stairs. The seated couple rushed from the table to see who had fallen, while the couple already traveling down the stairs turned to see what caused the noise. To everyone's surprise, no one was there.

Accommodations: The Badu House offers 6 guest rooms and one suite, furnished with antiques and private baths. A country breakfast is complimentary. Less than a block away are the Llano River and the shops and antique stores of downtown Llano.

The Faust Hotel

🍤 🍤 🍤

240 S. Seguin Street • New Braunfels, TX 78130
(830) 625-7791 • www.fausthotel.com
Room rates: $79-$400 • All major credit cards

History: Walter Faust Sr., President of the First National Bank of new Braunfels, played a big part in the construction of the hotel. He joined leading citizens who believed a new hotel was needed in town. Named originally The Traveler's Hotel and later The Hotel Faust after its founder, it has also been called The Honeymoon Hotel. Today, the lobby contains many of the original furnishings, including the cash register, built especially for The Faust Hotel. In the small Texas town of New Braunfels, you'll find a multitude of attractions, like the world-famous Schlitterbahn Water Park (say that ten times fast!). The Schlitterbahn is one of the best water parks in the country. Along with swimming and tubing in the park and in the nearby Guadelupe River, visitors can pick from a vast array of antique shops and designer outlet stores, or they can pan for minerals and dig for dinosaur bones before journeying into the Natural Bridge Caverns.

Activity: It appears that Walter Faust Jr. enjoyed his fine hotel so much that he has chosen not to leave. Guests of the historic Faust Hotel occasionally report the sighting a stately gentleman standing at the foot of their bed in the very room Walter once occupied. Walter apparently also tends to lock guests out of their rooms and turns the majestic wrought-iron ceiling fans on at random. Doorknobs will also turn and shake on their own accord.

A chilling incident occurred one evening after a couple had checked into the hotel. They loaded their belongings onto one of the luggage caddies, placed it next to the elevator, then walked over to the front desk to check in. When they completed the check-in and turned to go upstairs, the caddy and their luggage were missing. The elevator was taking a long time to reach the first floor, so they walked up the stairs to their room. When they came down the hall, their luggage had been placed outside of their room. As they were looking for the key to go in, a bellboy, who was standing in the elevator door, told them that the door was open and the keys were inside. Then the elevator doors closed, and he was gone. The man failed to tip the bellboy, so he called downstairs and asked if the bellboy could come back up for his tip. The front desk informed the guest that they had not had a bellboy working at the hotel for over 30 years.

Accommodations: The 70 year-old, 4-story Faust Hotel has 61 rooms, including the Honeymoon Suite. In 1990, a microbrewery was added near the elegant gourmet dining room. The Faust Hotel is listed on the National Register of Historic Places.

Menger Hotel

☆☆☆☆☆

204 Alamo Plaza • San Antonio, TX 78205
(201) 223-4361 • www.historicmenger.com
Room rates: $195-$275 • All major credit cards

History: The Menger Hotel was constructed in 1859, 23 years after the fall of the Alamo. Under the direction of owner William A. Menger and architect John Fries, the hotel was originally built as a two-story building. Located downtown, the Menger, the oldest continuously operating hotel west of the Mississippi, is only 100 yards from the site of the Alamo.

Famous individuals like Theodore Roosevelt, Babe Ruth, Mae West, Robert E. Lee, and Ulysses S. Grant have all stayed at the Menger. Guests are welcome to experience the history and charm of a national landmark while enjoying the comfort of a high-class hotel.

Activity: The Menger Hotel is said to have no less than 32 different apparitions that haunt the property. Stories have included bumps in the night, kitchen utensils moving by themselves, and the presence of spirits.

A maid named Sallie White, who was murdered by her husband, has reportedly been seen walking the corridors at night. She wears an old gray skirt with a bandanna around her forehead, and she is usually carrying towels that are never delivered.

Captain Richard King, founder of the King Ranch, makes his appearance by entering his room, the King Suite, by walking through the wall. It's interesting to note that there was a door in that location many years ago. Many guests and employees have seen him.

On one occasion, a guest stepped out of the shower and walked into the bedroom. To his surprise, he witnessed the figure of a man dressed in a buckskin jacket and gray trousers. He was seen talking to someone else in the room who was not visible. The apparition asked the question, "Are you gonna stay or are you gonna go?" three times.

The ghost of a lady has been seen knitting in the original lobby of the hotel. She was seen wearing an old-fashioned blue dress and a beret with a tassel. Her glasses are metal-frame and small in size. When an employee asked her, "Are you comfortable or may I get you something?" the lady replied in an unfriendly tone, "No," and then she disappeared.

Accommodations: The Menger is an important part of San Antonio history. Located near the Alamo, Rivercenter Mall, and the romantic Riverwalk, the five-story, 350-room Menger Hotel offers unparalleled amenities, including the famous Colonial Room Restaurant and the Menger Bar.

The Rogers Hotel

🕊️ 🕊️ 🕊️ 🕊️ 🕊️

100 N. College Street (at Main) • Waxahachie, Texas 75165-3707
(972) 938-3688 • (800) 556-4192 • www.rogershotel.com
Room rates: $59-$99 • All major credit cards

History: Located on the Old Chisholm Trail, The Rogers Hotel is named after the founder of Waxahachie, Emory W. Rogers. In 1847, Rogers built his log cabin home and in 1850 he donated land for the Ellis County Courthouse. In 1856, Rogers built a two-story hotel where his log cabin was located, but it was destroyed by fire in 1881. A second hotel was built on that location by The Waxahachie Real Estate & Building Association, but it too was destroyed by fire in 1911.

Architect, C. D. Hill designed the present structure in 1912 and it was opened to the public in early 1913. The Rogers Hotel has twin four-story towers; the West and East towers, built of reinforced concrete. Both are faced with dark mottled brick and trimmed with Bedford stone. It is said to be "Absolutely Fire Proof".

The West tower roof was designed with a roof garden restaurant with a panoramic view of Waxahachie and the East tower roof was made for sleeping tents, so guests could doze in the open air. The basement was designed with a billiard room, a barbershop, and swimming pool, with water supplied from a nearby hot spring. The lobby looks as it did back in 1913 and it includes a comfortable sitting area.

Throughout its history, several major league baseball teams have headquartered in Waxahachie for spring training. The Detroit Tigers in 1916, the Cincinnati Reds in 1919, the Chicago White Sox in 1921, and the Buffalo Bisons in 1948. In the motion picture, *Places in the Heart*, the Rogers Hotel was used to portray the small town bank. Some of the famous guests of the hotel have included Ty Cobb, Bonnie and Clyde, and Frank Sinatra.

Activity: Staff members and guests have heard the slamming of doors and whispers coming from unoccupied rooms. The Otis elevator that was originally installed in the early 1900s has been heard moving by itself from floor to floor late at night. An employee we spoke with believes that the son of the hotel's second owner, who is said to have committed suicide in the hotel, is the ghost that haunts the elevator.

Many of the hotel's supernatural experiences have occurred in Room 409. Once a maid found a picture of a beautiful woman drawn on the canvas of a chair while cleaning. She left to retrieve something to clean it off with, but when she returned the drawing had disappeared.

Accommodations: After being closed for 50 years, the Rogers Hotel has now been refurbished to its original beauty. Its original 60 rooms have been converted to 18 spacious suites and 9 conventional rooms, all including private baths. Guests will enjoy a continental breakfast each morning, and the Hotel's restaurant, Emory's Bistro, offers fine cuisine for lunch and dinner.

While in Waxahachie, you might also want to stop in at the Catfish Plantation Restaurant, a Victorian home that was originally built in 1895. While there, you can speak with the owners about their three ghosts, Elizabeth, Caroline, and Will, who make regular appearances in and around the restaurant.

— UTAH —

Ben Lomond Historic Suite Hotel

☆ ☆ ☆ ☆

2510 Washington Blvd. • Ogden, UT 84401
(800) 333-3333 • (801) 627-1900
Room rates: $75-$225

Courtesy of The Ben Lomond
Historic Suite Hotel

History: Known as the grand dame of Ogden, the Ben Lomond Hotel was designed and built as the Reed Hotel in 1890. The structure was later sold to H. C. Bigelow, underwent major renovations, and reopened to the public in 1927 as the Bigelow-Ben Lomond Hotel. Several historic architectural elements were used to enhance the hotel, including ornate ceilings, gold glass, polished woods, marble-inlaid floors, intricate carved stone masonry, and a grand staircase.

Some of America's greatest vaudevillians and celebrities played Ogden, and many stayed at the Ben Lomond Hotel, including Abbott and Costello, Douglas Fairbanks, and President William Taft.

Today, the Ben Lomond Historic Suite Hotel belongs to an exclusive group of hotels known as Historic Hotels of America. To date, only 146 hotels in the U.S. qualify for this prestigious designation. They are listed among such great hotels as San Diego's Hotel Del Coronado and New York's Waldorf Astoria. The Ben Lomond Hotel is listed on both the State and National Registers of Historic Places.

Activity: The most famous guest at the Ben Lomond Hotel is the ghost of an unknown woman who lives in Room 1106. She is described as very motherly, with a warmth about her that does not frighten anyone. When she appears, she never speaks; she only watches anyone she encounters and then fades away. Her manifestations will often include the fragrance of lilacs. The female spirit has been seen in various parts of the hotel—even in the daytime. The spirit may be that of a woman who stayed in the hotel during World War II. Her son, a soldier, had been critically wounded and was sent to Utah for recovery. The young man died, and the mother left broken-hearted.

The switchboard often receives calls from that particular room, and when the operator picks up the phone, the connection is broken. A security guard will be asked to investigate Room 1106, but the room is always found unoccupied.

Occasionally, the mysterious lady will ride the north elevator. Almost every employee has confirmed riding the elevator with her. On other occasions, when traveling up to higher floors, guests find the elevator will stop on the fifth floor. When the doors open, there will be no one there waiting—only a cold breeze followed by the scent of lilac.

Accommodations: The Ben Lomond Historic Suite Hotel offers 122 suites and 22 courtyard rooms. All rooms include a full buffet. Its voluptuously eclectic interiors provide the charm, comfort, nostalgia, and beauty of yesteryear.

WEST

— ALASKA —

The Historic Silverbow Inn

☆☆☆☆

120 Second Street
Juneau, AK 99801
(800) 586-4146, (907) 586-4146
www.silverbowinn.com
Room rates: $88-$118
All major credit cards

By Rie Munoz. Courtesy of The Historic Silverbow Inn

History: The Silverbow is Alaska's oldest continuously operating bakery. It first began in 1898 with the arrival of Gus Messerschmidt, an Austrian who built the original bakery in 1902. In 1964, the first building was demolished and a new kitchen was added, along with two other new buildings. As one of the largest kitchens in Juneau, the property served both as a restaurant and bakery. The building was sold in 1984 to new owners, and the Silverbow Inn and Restaurant was born. The Silverbow Inn blends the comfort and convenience of a bed and breakfast with the charm of a European-style urban pension.

Activity: Gus Messerschmidt was known to be a drinker in his day, and he worked alone, sometimes in the early morning while the town slept. Occasionally, eyewitnesses have seen a strange beam of light coming through the baker's rack. Also, one of the carts has been seen rolling across the concrete floor without anyone pushing it.

A wire cooling rack has been seen flying out of its holder, and often the sounds of someone walking around on the second floor will be heard. It sounds like a drunk stumbling about.

The first baker that the new owners hired was a young man with a similar build to Gus (back when the Austrian was young). The new young man was an excellent baker. He lived in an extra bedroom that Gus and his wife once shared. One morning the baker woke up at 3 A.M. to begin the day's work. He rinsed his face in the old washbasin and looked into the mirror behind the sink. To his surprise, Gus was there, looking back at him in the mirror.

Some people have said that two other ghosts inhabit the Silverbow.

The first, a small girl of age 10 or 12, may have died in the building. She has been seen around an abandoned staircase. The other apparition is of another baker who apparently does not speak English. He may have worked in the bakery sometime during its history.

There also seems to be a ghost around the sourdough starter. The present owner will sometimes hear a voice when she is stirring the sourdough in the morning. Perhaps it's Gus whispering a few baking tips.

Accommodations: Six individually decorated guest rooms are available, each with a full bath, cable television, and a private phone line. A lobby and breakfast area is on the first floor, and a historic bakery is located on-site that provides fresh bread daily for the restaurant. On June 4, 1997, bagel-making equipment was added, making the Silverbow Alaska's first traditional bagel bakery.

Golden North Hotel

🐾 🐾 🐾

Third & Broadway • Skagway, AK 99840
(314) 997-5644 (winter)
(907) 983-2451 (summer)
www.goldennorthhotel.com
Room rates: $100 • All major credit cards

By Allen Prier. Courtesy of The Golden North Hotel

History: At 104 years old, the Golden North Hotel is Alaska's oldest operating hotel. Established in 1898, the hotel was moved in 1907 by horse and capstan to its present location in Skagway, the Gateway to the Klondike.

The hotel was the gathering and meeting place for gold miners, river boat captains, and prospectors who left the diggings in the Klondike every fall to come to Skagway's tidewater in order to catch the last steamer south.

The 1997 a $1 million renovation by new owners Dennis and Nancy Corrington gave a new breath of life to the stately structure, bringing back its historic Gold Rush glory.

Activity: Legend has it that Mary lived in Seattle and traveled to Skagway to join her fiancé, a gold miner that had come to the Klondike to strike it rich. She checked into the Golden North Hotel and waited. Weeks turned into months, and her true love never returned. Some said he died, while others said he found someone else. Mary spent countless nights sitting in her rocking chair in Room 24, knowing her true love would unite them once again. As time passed, Mary came down with tuberculosis and died in the hotel, still waiting for her fiancé to return; apparently, she is still waiting.

Nowadays, the spirit of Mary has been seen roaming the hotel. A safe and untroubled ghost, she often plays little tricks on the owners and guests, like opening and closing doors even when they are locked. Once, the owners' sister was staying with a friend in Room 15 when she got up in the middle of the night. Upon her return, she slipped under the covers and felt her friend tuck her into bed, and she smelled strong perfume. The next morning, she thanked her friend for tucking her back into bed and seeing she was all warm and cozy. However, the friend replied that she had not done the tucking, and that she didn't wear that fragrance.

When renovations were underway, the owner stepped outside to retrieve something from his car. He returned to find a sheet of plastic, originally hung from ceiling to floor upstairs to keep dust contained during the renovation, slowly swaying at the top of the stairs. The owner looked up at the swaying sheet, and he observed an image of a shrouded female form through the plastic. She seemed as curious about him as he was about her. To verify he was not hallucinating, he quickly found someone walking outside and asked that she come in and confirm the appearance. To her amazement, she saw it as well and they both watched the ghost of Mary until she disappeared down the hallway.

Accommodations: On the first floor you will find a 40-foot mahogany-finished bar, an elegant Victorian-style restaurant, and an Alaskan microbrewery with over 15 specialty beers on tap. Today, each of the hotel's 31 rooms are mini-museums, with authentic period furnishings and even personal belongings and photographs of the prominent Skagway Gold Rush families of the past.

— CALIFORNIA —

Bayview Hotel

🃏🃏🃏

8041 Soquel Drive • Aptos, CA 95003
Near San Francisco, CA
(831) 688-8654, (800) 422-9843
www.bayviewhotel.com
Room rates: $149-$269
All major credit cards

By Pacific Publishing. Courtesy of The Bayview Hotel

History: The Bayview Hotel was built in the 1870s. It's a large, white Victorian with blue trim and a huge magnolia tree shading the front yard. Innkeepers Sandy and Roland Held purchased the home in 2000 after moving from Salt Lake City. Since their purchase, they have renovated the home and added antiques to recreate a period feel.

Activity: Roland was skeptical of ghost stories until one night when a ghost waved at him. He was in the kitchen, standing at the end of the counter which faces the door. He was eating a snack when he saw a dishtowel on the towel rack rise up and down in the air, as if something was causing it to wave at him. Roland checked to make sure no one was hiding around the corner, but he was alone.

On another occasion, Roland had turned an antique clock off to reset the time. The clock has a heavy pendulum that must be manually pushed to start. He walked away from it, then returned to find the clock had started on its own.

The spirits at the Bayview will sometimes use the hotel's big-screen television in a mischievous manner. On one occasion, Sandy had been meeting with an insurance agent for over 45 minutes when the television came on by itself. The agent asked who had turned on the set, and Sandy replied that it was the hotel's ghost. The agent quickly left. It seems when any meeting goes beyond 45 minutes, no matter the circumstance, the television will turn on. A friend who works in the office once turned the television to a music station. The ghost changed the channel. The worker turned back to the music channel, but ten minutes later it turned to another channel. Every time she turned it to music, the channel was changed about ten minutes later.

Some guests of the hotel have seen the image of a woman and child in the bathroom of their room. Others have heard footsteps and singing coming from the hallway. Some smell perfume emanating from areas of the hotel.

In Room 14, guests have found that small objects have disappeared only to be found later in other parts of the hotel.

The ghosts will also tilt a picture in the music room. Sandy will straighten it during the day, only to find it crooked again the next morning.

Sandy says that the ghosts that reside in her hotel are playful and friendly, and guests are curious about the opportunity to witness a ghost. Sandy says the spirits in her hotel do strange things just to let everyone know they're still around.

Accommodations: Each of the 11 rooms is beautifully decorated with period antiques and furnishings, and all have private baths. Some guest rooms include fireplaces, cozy feather beds, and large, two-person tubs. The Bayview Hotel also offers an extensive art collection and book-lined alcoves. A continental-plus breakfast is complimentary and sherry and fresh fruit is served in the afternoon.

Union Hotel

犭犭

401 First Street • Benicia, CA 94510
(866) 445-2323 • www.unionhotelbenicia.com
Room rates: $109-$219 • All major credit cards

History: Built in the 1850s, the Union Hotel is one of the few
surviving hotels from the California Gold Rush. A popular spot,
Hollywood star Humphrey Bogart once stayed at the Union Hotel in
what is now known as the Coast Lotus Room.

Activity: Ghost stories have surrounded the Union Hotel for years;
however, the appearances are infrequent. On one occasion, a guest was
checking out and heading on a trip overseas when she heard a voice say
to her, "have a nice trip." She looked around, but no one was there.

In one of the rooms, guests have reported a closet door that opens by
itself even when it is tightly shut.

One employee of the Union Hotel has found that when she walks
alone up the flight of stairs between the two guest floors, the lights in
the hallway always flicker on and off. When she walks up the stairs with
someone else, the lights never flicker; it only occurs when she is alone.

Accommodations: Located in the heart of historic Benicia, the
Union Hotel is nestled on the edge of a calm bay and is close to scenic
attractions. Each of the Union's 12 rooms is reminiscent of California's
past, with added touches of European elegance. Some suites offer
spectacular water views and spacious bathrooms with whirlpools for
two. Guests staying on weekday nights are treated to a continental
breakfast and visitors staying on a weekend night receive a two-course
gourmet breakfast each morning.

Brookdale Lodge

犭犭

11570 Highway 9 • Brookdale, CA 95007
(831) 338-6433 • www.brookdalelodge.com
Room rates: $59-$205 • All major credit cards

History: Under the giant redwoods of the Santa Cruz Mountains sits
the Brookdale Lodge, built in 1890. Judge J. H. Logan built the
property at the site of the original Grover lumber mill, and it was used
as the mill's headquarters until it was converted into a hotel.

Dr. F. K. Camp, one of the original owners, built the beautiful dining
room with a very unique feature: a natural brook running right though it.
This has made the Brookdale world-famous.

Throughout the years, the Brookdale Lodge has hosted movie stars like Shirley Temple, music celebrities, and President Herbert Hoover. During the mid 1940s, the lodge changed hands and fell into disrepair. Hidden rooms and passageways were constructed to accommodate gangsters who had become regulars at the lodge. Today, guests still enjoy the rustic elegance of the lodge and dining beside the gentle brook in this unique setting.

Activity: Over the years, there have been reports of a female spirit that resides at the Brookdale Lodge. An apparition of a girl dressed in a formal gown has been seen running across the lobby, then disappearing. In the Mermaid Room, voices and music are occasionally heard. Legend has it that during the 1940s, the niece of the owner at that time drowned in the creek that runs through the dining room. Ever since then, her spirit visits the Brookdale Lodge.

Accommodations: Guests can choose from 46 motel or cottage rooms; most with queen-sized beds. An indoor heated swimming pool, cocktail lounge, dance floor, and conference rooms are also available. The Creekside Cottage has a secluded creekside setting with a Victorian bedroom, fireplace, sitting area, antique furnishings, and Jacuzzi tub. Complimentary champagne is available for guests at the cottage.

Hotel Del Coronado

1500 Orange Avenue
Coronado, CA 92118
(800) HOTEL DEL
(619) 435-6611
www.hoteldel.com.
Room rates: $260-$700
All major credit cards

Courtesy of Hotel Del Coronado

History: California's legendary "Lady by the Sea," the Hotel Del Coronado was built in 1887. When the hotel opened, it was one of the largest buildings in America to sport a new technology called electric lights.

The hotel has played host to over a dozen U.S. presidents, and the first state dinner ever to be held outside Washington, D.C. took place at the Hotel Del. Many believe King Edward VIII, England's Prince of Wales, met Mrs. Wallis Spencer while attending a reception at the Del in 1920.

Hollywood has had a love affair with the Del for many years as a retreat for famous actors such as Mary Pickford, Greta Garbo, Charlie Chaplin, Bruce Willis, Cuba Gooding, Jr., and Dustin Hoffman. Over

the years, the Hotel Del has also been used as a setting for some of Hollywood's finest films. Today, you can romp on the same beach where Marilyn Monroe and Jack Lemmon cavorted in *Some Like It Hot*.
Activity: A beautiful young lady by the name of Kate Morgan stayed at the Hotel Del in November of 1892. Hotel employees at the time reported that she appeared ill and unhappy. She told a few people that she was waiting for her brother, who she claimed was a doctor. Five days after checking in, Kate was found dead from a self-inflicted gunshot wound to the head. Her body lay on an exterior staircase leading to the beach. News surfaced later that Kate had been seen arguing with her husband, Tom, during their train ride to San Diego. Some believe she was pregnant and that Tom left the train. She traveled on to San Diego, and committed suicide during her stay at the hotel.

Paranormal activity has been reported in the room Kate occupied. At that time it was Room 302, but today it is numbered 3312. One guest heard pipes groaning, and the window curtains would blow as if moved by a breeze (the windows were closed at the time). Also, maintenance personnel at the hotel have to constantly replace the screens on the windows of Room 3312 because they keep blowing off. Outside of the room where Kate committed suicide, the light on the staircase continually burns out for no apparent reason.

Another room that is reportedly haunted is 3502, in which some claim resides the spirit of a maid that may have known Kate. After Kate's death, the maid was never seen again. In Room 3502, the lights have been known to flicker on and off, cold drafts of air are felt outside the door on hot summer nights, and the windows open on their own. The housekeeping staff will arrange the towels, shampoo, and soap in the bathroom, only to find it rearranged upon their return.

Accommodations: From the red peaked roofs to the lush green lawns, the Hotel Del is a charming island setting in the beautiful city of San Diego. You can explore 26 acres of beaches, taste world-class dining, or visit its galleria of shops. The Hotel Del Coronado features 680 guest rooms and a wide variety of dining alternatives including two fine dining restaurants, two casual restaurants, pubs, and several other eateries and an award-winning Sunday Brunch. It is no wonder it was voted "best hotel dining" in *San Diego Magazine's* 2000 reader's poll.

Amargosa Opera House and Hotel

By C.F. Roberts. Courtesy of Amargosa Opera House and Hotel

608 Death Valley Junction
Death Valley Junction, CA 92328
(760) 852-4441
www.amargosa-opera-house.com
Room rates: $45-$60
Visa, Master Card, American Express

History: The construction of the Death Valley Junction complex began in 1923 and was completed in 1925. Built by the Pacific Coast Borax Company, the complex was used as their business center until 1939. The U-shaped complex consists of Spanish Colonial buildings made of adobe. The complex served a dual purpose, with one half of the complex used as a hotel and the remainder as a dormitory for mine workers. The complex had its own grocery store, post office, café, and infirmary. The complex also had its own community center, called Corkhill Hall, which later became the Amargosa Opera House.

In 1967, while on a western tour with her ballet troupe, Marta Becket visited what was then a mostly abandoned complex. After peering into the old Corkhill Hall, she envisioned an opera house in the desert. Giving up her career as a ballet dancer in New York, Marta leased the hall, and in 1968 she began giving performances in the newly named Amargosa Opera House.

Today the Opera House seats 125 people and receives visitors from all over the world.

Activity: Paranormal activity at the hotel has become a regular occurrence. On a daily basis, doors open and close by themselves, and the sound of a baby crying is often heard in one of the rooms. Recently, guests were treated to some ghostly room service. Their bedspreads were mysteriously pulled down, and coat hangers in the closet rattled as the guests tried to sleep. The spirits of the hotel are said to be friendly and often call the hotel staff by their names. They also move personal property around from time to time just to let everybody know they are there.

Accommodations: The Amargosa Hotel has 14 rooms. Murals depicting a gazebo, Death Valley Junction, ballerinas, and a 16-century Spanish garden adorn the walls of the hotel. Restaurants are located near the hotel. The Opera House season runs from the first Saturday in October through the second Saturday in May. The shows, presented by Marta Becket and Tom Willett, include a combination of ballet, pantomime, and vaudeville; advanced reservations are recommended since performances often sell out.

Abigail's Elegant Victorian Mansion

🏛 🏛

1406 "C" Street • Eureka, CA 95501
(707) 444-3144 • www.eureka-california.com
Room rates: $95-$195 • Visa, Master Card

History: Eureka sits on Humboldt Bay, between Ferndale and Arcata, five hours from San Francisco. Surrounded by the spectacular beauty of the giant redwoods, Abigail's Elegant Victorian Mansion, built in 1888, is one of California's most impressive and authentic Victorian "living-history house-museums."

Activity: Legend has it that the ghost of Abigail resides in the home, and she apparently loves traditional jazz. Her ghostly appearances led innkeepers Doug and Lily Vieyra to rename the inn after their paranormal resident.

A friend was house-sitting one weekend when, during the middle of the night, she was awakened by music coming from the first floor. It played for a while, then stopped, and then started again. The house sitter got up to investigate. She found on the first floor an old, hand-cranked Edison phonograph, playing a Duke Ellington record all by itself. This phonograph is unique because it requires cranking between each play. Apparently, the phonograph must have been cranked twice because there was a distinct pause between plays.

Another evening, a guest was staying in the Van Gogh Room. During the night, she complained to Doug that a ghost had opened her door. Doug asked her to lock the door. She did, but it opened again. Doug then asked her to bolt the door. She did, and minutes later it opened once again. The guest was visibly shaken, although, by profession, she was a prominent forensic scientist.

Accommodations: The home features Belgian tapestries and lace, a library full of books, and a 48-star U.S. flag crocheted by Lily Vieyra's Flemish family as they awaited liberation from the Nazis. Each of their 3 bedrooms have been beautifully restored and decorated with period furnishings, queen-sized beds, desk and a sitting area.

The elegant Victorian is an award-winning 1888 National Historic landmark, and it features spectacular gingerbread exteriors, Victorian interiors, luxurious bedrooms, and antique furnishings. An AMA recommended heart-health-friendly Continental breakfast buffet is served each morning in the elegant Victorian Dining Room.

The Groveland Hotel

🚶🚶🚶🚶

18767 Main Street
Groveland, CA 95321
(800) 273 3314
www.groveland.com
Room rates: $135-$210
All major credit cards

Courtesy of The Groveland Hotel

History: During the height of the California Gold Rush, the Groveland Hotel was known as "The Best House on the Hill." The hotel consists of two buildings. The oldest, built in 1849, was modeled after the Larkin House, the first American mansion in Monterey. The newer building was built in 1914, after the 1906 California earthquake. When innkeepers Grover and Peggy Mosley purchased the hotel in 1990, the buildings were in disrepair and close to demolition. The hotel went through a major restoration and was finally completed in 1992.

Activity: Legend has it that a miner by the name of Lyle still visits the Groveland. In 1927, Lyle was working the gold mine when he turned up missing. He was found dead in one of the rooms of the Groveland Hotel. The Mosleys have now named it Lyle's Room.

Lyle's presence has been felt on several occasions. The first time occurred when the Mosleys were refurbishing the hotel. One night, Grover was watching television when he heard the sound of running water coming from the second floor. He asked Peggy if she was running the water. Peggy joked that Lyle was probably taking a shower. Grover didn't believe in such things, so he walked up the stairs to check. When Grover reached the second floor, the water stopped. There was water in the shower, but no one was around.

Lyle's been known to be a prankster, but Peggy tells us that he has never hurt anyone. There is one thing, however, that guests will notice about Lyle: he doesn't like cosmetics in his room. He will often move cosmetics left on the dresser and deposit them over the sink. One guest told Peggy that every time she placed her lotion on the dresser, she would come back later to find it moved. Now it has become a game, and every time that guest stays at the hotel, she requests Lyle's Room, and she'll see how long it takes Lyle to move her lotion.

During another visit, one lady woke up in the middle of the night and saw a tall, slender, bearded figure in her room. She observed the figure briefly, and then it slowly disappeared into the wall. Weeks later, another female guest woke up to find one of the chairs in the room had been pulled flush, up to her bed, with the back facing her.

Accommodations: The Groveland has 17 rooms, including 3 suites. Amenities include private baths, luxurious terry cloth bathrobes, European antiques, down comforters, and period furniture. The Groveland Hotel Restaurant features an outstanding cuisine prepared from California seasonal ingredients with many herbs coming from the hotel's garden. An outdoor patio provides the perfect venue for summer evening dining or a delightful luncheon for special events. *Country Inns Magazine* rated the Groveland Hotel as one of the Top 10 inns in the United States.

Hollywood Roosevelt Hotel

7000 Hollywood Blvd • Hollywood, CA 90028
(800) 950-7667 • www.hollywoodroosevelt.com
Room rates: $119-$200 • All major credit cards

History: Named in honor of President Theodore Roosevelt, the doors of the Hollywood Roosevelt Hotel were opened on May 27, 1927. Hollywood pioneers like Louis B. Mayer, Douglas Fairbanks, and Mary Pickford were all in attendance. Soon, the Roosevelt became known as "the Home of the Stars."

The first Academy Awards presentation was held in the hotel's Blossom Room on May 16, 1929. Stars have often been seen dining in Theodore's—the hotel's historic dining room—catching an act at the Cinegrill, or attending a special event in one of the Hollywood Roosevelt's banquet rooms. The hotel has been a favorite location for television shows, feature films, music videos, and fashion photography.

Marilyn Monroe posed for her first ad for a suntan lotion on the diving board of the Roosevelt's pool. The Roosevelt has played host to stars, writers, artists, and entertainment personalities like Montgomery Clift, Rudy Valee, David Niven, F. Scott Fitzgerald, Ernest Hemingway, Salvador Dali, and many more.

Legendary Broadway musical star Mary Martin made her debut at the Cinegrill. When she couldn't find a babysitter, she would often bring her infant son along (who grew up to be actor Larry Hagman).

Supposedly, Bill "Bojangles" Robinson first showed Shirley Temple their famous staircase dance on the tile steps leading from the lobby to the mezzanine.

Today, the Hollywood Roosevelt Hotel has been restored to its original Spanish Colonial splendor. The two-story lobby, with its beautiful hand-painted ceiling, Spanish tile floors, and staircase is a delight to behold.

Activity: Montgomery Clift stayed at the Roosevelt for three months during the filming of *From Here To Eternity*. It's been said that Clift often paced the hall outside his ninth-floor room, rehearsing his lines and sometimes practicing the bugle. On particularly windy nights, one can still hear Monty's spirit playing the bugle in the hallway.

Each day, hundreds of tourists pass a full-length mirror that sits outside the elevators on the hotel's lower level. The mirror was originally among the furnishings in a room frequented by Marilyn Monroe. Several people have reported seeing the tragic actress' image reflected in the glass of this particular mirror. Every time they would stop and turn around, the image would be gone.

Accommodations: The Hollywood Roosevelt Hotel has 335 beautifully appointed rooms, including 20 luxury suites. The hotel also features elegant cabanas that offer privacy, tropical garden views, and a swimming pool.

Historic National Hotel

� � �

18183 Main Street • Jamestown, CA 95327
(800) 894-3446 • www.national-hotel.com
Room rates: $90-$140 • All major credit cards

History: Located halfway between Yosemite and Lake Tahoe, this historic California bed and breakfast was established in 1859 and is one of the oldest continuously operating hotels in California.

The city of Jamestown was founded in 1848, the same year Benjamin Woods first discovered gold. Today, Jamestown is filled with reminders of California's Gold Rush past.

Activity: In the late 1890s, a young lady arrived in town and checked into the National Hotel. She was awaiting a companion that never arrived. Residents remembered the young lady went to the Sierra Train Station daily, asking about her true love. She was heard sobbing in her room nightly. After days had passed, she grew more depressed and would often wander the halls of the hotel. A month after her arrival in town, an employee of the National Hotel found the lifeless body of the young lady in her room. Her death was ruled not to be suicide; apparently, her heart just stopped.

Today, the spirit of a young lady has been seen walking the halls of the National Hotel, and employees have nicknamed the ghost Flo. A quite friendly ghost, she's known for her harmless pranks.

Stories of her presence have been around for over 28 years. It is reported that Flo generally resides upstairs and favors the rooms in front of the building. Although on occasion, witnesses have seen her downstairs in the morning. She floats through the dining room and right through the walls.

Witnesses have reported doors slamming and lights going off and on by themselves, and clothes are sometimes dropped on the floor straight out of their suitcases. Some guests have heard a woman crying in the middle of the night, and occasionally the air is ice-cold, ostensibly when Flo is present.

Accommodations: Each of the 9 award-winning rooms has brass beds, regal comforters, lace curtains, oak pull-chain toilets, and private baths. Every room is individually appointed and includes most of the original furnishings. The National Hotel Restaurant offers both indoor and outdoor seating in European style, and guests can order from their award-winning wine list that features wines from the Sierra Nevada foothill wineries. The original Gold Rush Saloon offers the visitor a variety of spirits, including single-malt scotches and local microbrews.

Bracken Fern Manor

🎗 🎗 🎗

815 Arrowhead Villas Road
Lake Arrowhead, CA 92352
(888) 244-5612
www.brackenfernmanor.com
Room rates: $65-$190
Visa, Master Card

History: Chicago mob "bosses" were skeptical in 1925 when Bugsy Siegel concocted the idea of a $1.3 million private gambling resort in the mountains east of Los Angeles.

Courtesy of Bracken Fern Manor

Built in 1929 as one of three main buildings of Lake Arrowhead's first private resort, Club Arrowhead of the Pines was hugely popular with the rich and famous of Hollywood, and the posh new club included many state-of-the-art conveniences (like electricity).

In the Clubhouse, gin was distilled from Artesian well water, dice rolled, and starlets tangoed the night away.

Now called Bracken Fern Manor, the property once housed a market on the first floor with a soda fountain and butcher shop. Upstairs was home to the girls who came to the hotel to be actresses, but more likely became "ladies of the evening" who provided entertainment for the club members.

The manor was restored by current owner, Cheryl Weaver, and subsequently became a certified historic landmark.

Activity: Legend has it that a young lady by the name of Violet was attracted to Lake Arrowhead in search of work as an actress. She soon became one of the "ladies." With little hope of leaving, she met a young man who worked for the bosses. They fell in love, and with the aid of the other ladies, they planned to elope. The bosses found out about it, and soon the young man vanished. Some felt he had been killed, but Violet believed he ran away. She refused to work, and night after night she roamed the halls searching for her true love. She eventually decided to take her own life.

Apparently Violet still inhabits the manor, for her footsteps can be heard at night pacing the halls and guest rooms, waiting for her true love to return. The fragrance of her old-fashioned perfume fills the air when she is near.

The manor is also home to the spirit of a child. Legend has it that a 4- or 5-year-old boy named Rodney Rankin was the son of one of the girls who worked in the club. He had a dog for companionship, but he was often left to care for himself while Mom was working. One day, he was playing ball when he threw it into the street. The dog chased after it and the little boy followed. He ran into the street and was run over by a team of horses. The spirit of the little boy will play tricks on the staff and guests, move keys from one location to another, and leave footprints throughout the manor; little toy trucks have been found lying on the floors as well.

Accommodations: Each of the 10 rooms at Bracken Fern is named after a lady of the evening who lived there. There are stained-glass transoms over each of the guest room doors, with a flower depicting the room's name.

The guest rooms are decorated with comfort in mind and each has an oversized bath/shower combination. The Jacuzzi Suite has a bathtub for two, complete with a basket of water toys for the playful. A full breakfast is served in the dining room or out on the front deck of the manor.

The Queen Mary Hotel

☆☆☆☆☆

1126 Queens Highway
Long Beach, CA 90802
(562) 432-6964 • www.queenmary.com
Room rates: $109-$500
All major credit cards

History: Once called the "Queen of the Atlantic," the Queen Mary was launched in September 1934. Four

Courtesy of The Queen Mary, Long Beach, CA

steam turbines powered the mighty ship, generating 40,000 horsepower and making it faster than any other ship of the day. Britain's magnificent ocean liner could sail from Great Britain to New York in just under four days, a world record that she held for 14 years.

During World War II, the Queen Mary, camouflaged with gray paint, was successful in out-maneuvering German torpedoes as it participated in active duty. So swift was the "Gray Ghost" that Adolph Hitler put a bounty on her offering $250,000 to the captain that could sink her. Fortunately, nothing touched the ship as she transported troops. At the war's end, the Queen Mary continued her service in bringing soldiers back to their homeland. By the time she was done, the Queen Mary had carried more than 800,000 servicemen, traveled 600,000 miles, and played a part in every major allied campaign of World War II.

After the war, the Queen Mary resumed duty as a luxury liner. She carried notable passengers from all over the world—diplomats and dignitaries, ambassadors and kings, film stars and moguls have all graced the decks of the elegant vessel.

In 1967, the ship was removed from British registry and ownership was officially turned over to the City of Long Beach. Retired from active service, the Queen Mary is today enjoying a new life as a world-class floating hotel.

Activity: Each year, guests, tour guides, and crew members experience a wide range of paranormal phenomenon. During its 60-year history, there have been 49 reported deaths on the Queen Mary.

A young crewman was crushed to death in doorway 13 in the depths of the engine room during a routine watertight door drill in 1966. Eyewitnesses have reported seeing a young bearded man in blue coveralls walking the length of Shaft Alley. One couple was walking through doorway 13 when the husband felt something brush by his face. He turned around, but saw nothing. After their walk, his wife found a streak of grease on her husband's face that was not there before.

Many years ago, during its tenure as a passenger liner, a baby died aboard ship a few hours after birth, but not without heroic attempts by the ship's surgeons to save his life. Reportedly, late at night a baby's cry can be heard from the very place that was once the third-class children's playroom.

The spirit of a beautiful woman clad in a simple white evening gown is often seen dancing alone in the shadows of the Queen's Salon, the ship's former first-class lounge. While on the historic tour, a young child once observed the "woman in white." She informed the tour guide, but when the guide turned around she saw nothing, so the guide continued the tour. The little girl kept seeing the image and was able to describe the spirit in full detail.

Around the first-class swimming pool, a fine example of the ship's art deco era, many people have seen women dressed in vintage bathing suits, heard splashing noises, and discovered wet footprints on the tile. The pool, which is part of the tour but closed to the public, does not hold any water. One woman was so startled that after witnessing a lady about to dive into the pool, she yelled, "Stop!" The woman turned to alert the tour guide, only to turn back around and find the diver had disappeared.

Accommodations: The Queen Mary features 365 hotel state rooms, an elaborate Champagne Sunday Brunch, and award-winning restaurants. Enjoy the charm and art deco ambiance of one of the most beautiful ships and hotels afloat. Historic walking tours of the Queen Mary are available daily. An art gallery is open to the public, and visitors can go shopping or experience dining guaranteed to please the palate.

Mendocino Hotel and Garden Suites

45080 Main Street • Mendocino, CA 95460
(800) 548-0513, (707) 937-0511 • www.mendocinohotel.com
Room rates: $95-$275 • Visa, Master Card, American Express

History: In the 19th century, the city of Mendocino was a lumber port and lively logging town home to 19 saloons, bawdy houses, and pool halls. The population swelled to over 20,000 people.

When it opened in 1878, this yellow clapboard hotel was known as the Temperance House, a sanctuary that offered visitors scenic ocean views and beautiful garden surroundings. The original structure—which included the lobby, bar, kitchen, dining room, and upstairs rooms—has remained intact after a detailed restoration. An original bank teller's booth serves as the front desk, and a collection of glass screen dividers are displayed that once separated first- and second-class passengers in the British railway stations of the 19th century. The newer rooms offer Victorian furnishings and historical photographs that portray Mendocino's pioneer history.

In 1975, R.O. Peterson purchased the hotel, and with the aid of designers and local artisans, it was lovingly restored. Today, around 90% of the antique pieces featured in the Mendocino Hotel and Garden Suites date back to the late 19th century.

Activity: In the late 1800s, the hotel's reputation was not so pristine— it served as a bordello catering to the loggers that came through town.

Legend has it that some of the spirits from that era still visit the Mendocino Hotel. A Victorian woman has been seen at tables 6 and 8 in the restaurant, watching guests from a mirror before she disappears. Employees have also witnessed her reflection in that mirror. The ghost has visited guest rooms also; in Room 10, the housekeeping staff once left to retrieve fresh towels and returned to find an indention in the bed as if someone had lain there. Mysterious activity has also occurred in Room 307, where a mother and child watched as the image of a man appeared in the mirror. The misty image remained for a couple of minutes before slowly fading away.

Accommodations: Located in the heart of Mendocino Village since 1878, the Mendoncino Hotel features 51 guest rooms and suites and the lobby lounge features a handsomely carved antique bar and a bistro-style menu. The Victorian Dining Room is beautifully appointed with antiques for an intimate and elegant dinner and the informal Garden Room is the perfect setting for breakfast or lunch. Built with scenic views, guests can relax as they look out over the Mendocino Headlands to the mouth of Big River and the Pacific Ocean. Outside, guests can enjoy a Victorian garden that features dozens of rare roses and other plants from the 1880s.

Horton Grand Hotel

☂ ☂ ☂

311 Island Avenue • San Diego, CA 92101
(800) 542-1886 • www.hortongrand.com
Room rates: $169-$279 • All major credit cards

History: The Horton Grand Hotel is actually a restoration of two separate hotels, the Grand Horton Hotel and the Brooklyn-Kahle Sadderly Hotel. Both were built at the same time (in two different locations in town) and both opened in 1886.

The Grand Horton was built as a replica of the Innsbruck Inn in Vienna, Austria. The Brooklyn-Kahle Sadderly Hotel was less formal, with a cowboy-Victorian flavor. A saddle and harness shop occupied the ground floor where they made hand-crafted saddles for actors Tom Mix and Roy Rogers. Wyatt Earp lived in the hotel during the seven years he resided in San Diego.

Both hotels were scheduled for demolition in the late 1970s when they were purchased from the City of San Diego for $1 each. Over 10,000 pieces removed from the two hotels were cataloged and stored until the Horton Grand Hotel was rebuilt and reopened in May of 1986.

Activity: Paranormal activity is said to surround Room 309, where legend has it the ghost of "Roger" resides. No one really knows who Roger was. Some say he was killed over his gambling debts, while others say he stood up his fiancée at the altar, and later her relatives threw him in the swamp. Regardless of the method of his death, it is apparent he refuses to leave the hotel—in fact, he likes to make himself known to visitors and staff.

On the executive housekeeper's first day of work, she was startled when Roger came up behind her and gave her a big bear hug. She turned around and no one was there.

One day, a guest in Room 309 called down to the front desk to report the pictures on the wall of his room were spinning. The front desk clerk couldn't think of a reply. The guest just said, "Cool," and then hung up.

Guests have reported leaving handfuls of change on the fireplace mantle of the room, only to return and find the coins stacked neatly like poker chips. Others have found cards dealt out on the table in poker fashion. The card box was found closed nearby.

Three other apparitions have been seen in the Horton Grand. Two are known as Harry and Gus; they've been heard running up and down the halls at night. The third spirit is called the Lady in Red. She's been known to knock on doors.

Accommodations: In the heart of San Diego's Gaslamp District, the Horton Grand Hotel is a full-service historical Victorian that offers 132 beautifully appointed guest rooms, including 24 suites. Each room is furnished with antique queen-sized beds, hand-carved armoires, and lace curtains. No two rooms are alike. Some guest rooms have balconies overlooking a New Orleans-style courtyard, or you may want a room with a view of the city. Guests will enjoy Ida Bailey's fine dining for breakfast, lunch, and dinner. Ida's combines fresh California ingredients, international flavors, and European cookery to create unique and delicious food combinations. Ida's has won numerous local awards for her classic American cuisine. For some medicinal spirits, guests can stop in at the Palace Bar or the Lobby Bar.

The San Remo Hotel

2237 Mason Street • San Francisco, CA 94133
(415) 776-8688 • www.sanremohotel.com
Room rates: $65-$85 • All major credit cards

History: On April 18, 1906, an earthquake and fire leveled much of San Francisco. Following the devastation, rooms were needed to house the men that would rebuild the town. A. P. Gianinni, founder of the Bank of America, built the New California Hotel on Mason Street. The hotel became a home to city workers, sailors, fishermen, and even chocolate makers from the famous Ghiradelli plant. In 1922, the New California Hotel changed its name to the San Remo Hotel. The hotel is located in a quiet neighborhood in San Francisco's famous North Beach, just a few blocks from Fisherman's Wharf and Pier 39, and the cable car stop for Union Square is just around the corner.

Activity: A housekeeper was walking around the hotel one evening, turning off the bedside lights and locking the unoccupied rooms, when she heard a series of loud, running footsteps coming from inside a room she had checked. She reopened the door to find a light had mysteriously turned on.

Staff and guests have observed the figure of a tall, distinguished sailor in the main hallway. Reportedly, he has a dark complexion and a neatly trimmed snow-white beard. He wears a distinctive hat and a buttoned blue coat. The sighting usually occurs very early in the morning, and he's been observed walking briskly down the hallway, disappearing near the front desk.

A guest had just purchased a digital camera, and to test it, he took a series of 10 photographs sitting on the bed in his room. In reviewing the photographs, he was surprised to find a faded image of a young boy standing behind his partner. They had been alone in the room at the time.

The most famous ghost of the San Remo is called the "Madam." She supposedly moved into the hotel in the 1960s and was a long-term guest. She was an affable woman who supported herself by working as a madam in the Tenderloin district of San Francisco. In the late 1960s, she died quietly in a downstairs room. Since that time, staff members have reported seeing the Madam floating in the hallways, and she will occasionally flick lights on and off.

Accommodations: A warm European-style hotel, the San Remo Hotel has narrow, sunlit hallways, 62 comfortable rooms, and stained-glass skylights. Handpicked antiques are found throughout, as well as other items from San Francisco's history, like art nouveau prints and navigational maps of the San Francisco Bay. Opera and jazz are heard in the lobby during the day, and a fully restored 1941 Ford "Woody" station wagon is located outside. For more than 30 years, the Field brothers have run the San Remo Hotel. Along with their cheerful and knowledgeable staff, they provide elegance with a taste of the past.

Glen Tavern Inn
☆☆☆☆
134 North Mill Street • Santa Paula, CA 93060
(805) 933-5550 • www.glentaverninn.com
Room rates: $60-$80 • Cash only

History: Completed in 1911, the Glen Tavern Inn reflects the essence and ambiance of the early 1900s. A three-story craftsman with English

Tudor styling, the Glen Tavern was a favorite hideaway for many of Hollywood's stars, from past to present. Stars like Clark Gable, Carol Lombard, Harry Houdini, Kirk Douglas, Steve McQueen, and even Rin Tin Tin have stayed at the inn. In the roaring 1920s especially, the Glen Tavern Inn was the place to be.

Activity: The story goes that in 1918, a young naval captain who served in World War I visited the Glen Tavern Inn while on leave. He was drinking and playing cards one night with a few other men in Room 309 when he was stabbed and killed. Apparently, the captain is still hanging around the room where he met his end. Although he's a non-threatening entity, he likes to lock and unlock the doors and play tricks on the staff.

To this day, the employees will gladly show Room 309 to guests, but they refuse to rent it out because of the high incidence of paranormal activity that has occurred there.

Accommodations: Just 12 miles from the California coast, the Glen Tavern Inn has been described as a "living museum." A porte-cochere dominates the main entrance to the inn, and the lobby is an old-fashioned parlor, designed for comfort and relaxation. The focal point of the room is a massive stone fireplace. Fine art, antiques, and other collections are included among the furnishings. Visitors can relax and read a book or sip hot chocolate in front of a roaring fire on cold winter nights. The Glen Tavern Inn features 41 suites and a restaurant and bar will be opened to the public by the end of 2003.

The Springville Inn

🐾 🐾 🐾 🐾

35634 Highway 190 • Springville, CA 93265
(800) 4 THE INN • www.springvilleinn.com
Room rates: $80-$225
All major credit cards

Courtesy of The Springville Inn

History: The first American explorers and pioneers to settle in Springville arrived in 1849, and the Porterville Northeastern Railroad came to Springville in 1911. The Wilkinson Building, one of the first permanent buildings in Springville, was also constructed that same year. Today, the Wilkinson Building is the Springville Inn. With the arrival of the railroad, Springville transformed into a resort town. Baseball and dancing were among the citizens' favorite pastimes.

Activity: Four very special guests reside at the Springville Inn, and they have "lived" there for over 100 years. They inhabit the original 1911 main building, formerly known as the Wilkinson Hotel. The four apparitions have never ventured into the hotel's newer addition (built in 1972). They prefer to keep to the past. In the early days of the hotel, there was no coroner or morgue. When someone passed on, their bodies were placed on ice in the upstairs rooms of the hotel to await transport by stagecoach or train to Porterville. This may be the reason the four restless souls have never checked out.

One of the ghosts, who is referred to as "Young Man," appears to be an attractive logger in his 20s, who was probably working in one of the mills in the area. It is said that he was shot outside, and his body was carried into the hotel, where he bled to death. His spirit moves around the bar and up what was the original grand staircase. He is often a flirt, making his presence known by brushing up against women.

The second spirit is called "Little Girl," and she appears to be 8 years old and dressed in a turn-of-the-19th-century dress. She occasionally walks hand-in-hand with Young Man. An employee was washing dishes in the kitchen one night when she saw Little Girl watching her in a mirror that hung in the kitchen. The employee quit immediately, and the staff removed the mirror.

The third spirit is called the "Woman." She's a beautiful and elegant lady with flowing blond hair and a long dress. She has been seen floating on the balcony surrounding the Penthouse, or she wanders the second floor hallways in the hotel's main building.

The fourth and final ghost, referred to as the "Old Man," usually occupies the main kitchen of the hotel. The Old Man has been spotted staring up and down at the dumbwaiter that joins the two kitchens. The chefs and kitchen staff see him quite often.

Accommodations: Each of Springfield Inn's 8 rooms and 2 suites are filled with western pine furnishings, country quilts, ceiling fans, air conditioning, private baths, a coffee maker and satellite television. Guests of the inn will enjoy a country Continental breakfast each morning. The Stagecoach Bar and Grill serves dinner Wednesday through Sunday and brunch on Sunday. Nestled in the foothills of the Sierra Nevada Mountains, the Springville Inn has stood guard at the entrance of the Giant Sequoia National Monument since 1912. The Kemmerling family welcomes you to their warm and inviting inn, originally built as a place of lodging, food, and drink for travelers to the Southern Sierra. Today, the inn has been lovingly restored and refurbished, returning it to its past glory.

Victorian Rose Bed & Breakfast

⚜ ⚜ ⚜ ⚜ ⚜

896 E. Main Street • Ventura, CA 93001
(805) 641-1888 • www.victorian-rose.com
Room rates: $99 • All major credit cards

Courtesy of Victorian Rose B&B

History: The one-of-a-kind Victorian Rose Bed & Breakfast was once the Victorian Gothic Church. Carved beams towering 26 feet high grace the ceilings of this magnificent structure that has an abundance of stained-glass windows.

An unusual display of Victorian Gothic, Eastlake, Norwegian, and Mission architecture is present. Topping the structure is the original 96-foot steeple.

Inside, cherubs watch over the sanctuary, which itself offers sitting areas throughout. Guests can relax as they sit by an indoor fountain, relax in the large Jacuzzi, or take a leisurely stroll down the Victorian garden path around the inn.

Activity: The Victorian Rose is a very active place. They've reported over 100 paranormal sightings within the past two years. Heading up the activity is the spirit of a minister that apparently runs the show and dictates what will occur. He has been known to tuck people in at night and occasionally strokes the guests' hair. Several people have seen him, and he is only one of five spirits that reportedly inhabit the building.

Legend has it that many years ago, a lady fell to her death from the old choir loft. Today, during a full moon, the ghost of the lady can be heard singing in the sanctuary. Guests have reported hearing her spiritual solos at night.

Glowing orbs have been seen sailing around the inn, and lights occasionally turn on and off. A spirit of a little girl is present, and she plays pranks on guests. She will move beds around the room or transport guests' clothes from the counter to underneath the bed.

Doorknobs have turned on their own, and the sound of someone walking around resounds from the second floor.

On one occasion, the large chandelier in the Victorian Rose turned at a 45-degree angle and was seen suspended by itself in mid air.

Owners Richard and Nona Bogatch told us of an unusual experience that occurred one night when a little girl was staying in one of the guest rooms. She had an intense bronchial condition and was coughing continuously. During the night, one of the spirits poured warm water onto her chest. She woke up startled and went to her mother. The bronchial condition was completely gone. It's believed the warm water treatment was for medicinal purposes.

Richard and Nona are so used to hearing things go bump in the night that they don't even get up to check them out. They got tired of getting up in the middle of the night only to find nothing had been disturbed. They now say to themselves, "Oh, it's just the ghosts again."

Accommodations: Richard and Nona have dedicated two years to restoring the 110-year-old church into a bed and breakfast. The 2 guest rooms and 1 master suite are creatively decorated, and each features a gas-burning fireplace and newly appointed baths. A 3-bedroom, 2-bath ocean front condo that sleeps 10 is also available for weekly rental only. As morning arrives, a gourmet breakfast awaits the visitor, and during the day, guests can sample tasty delights during the wine and cheese hour.

— COLORADO —

The Hotel St. Nicholas

☆☆☆☆☆

303 North Third Street
Cripple Creek, CO 80813
(888) 786-4257, (719) 689-0856
www.cripple-creek.co.us/stnick.html
Room rates: $49-$90
Visa, Master Card, American
Express

History: Built in 1898 during Colorado's gold rush, the stately Hotel St. Nicholas was originally a hospital run by the order of Sisters of Mercy. Distressed miners and ladies of the evening were treated here for everything

Courtesy of The Hotel St. Nicholas

from broken bones to concussions to morphine overdoses. Today, innkeepers Noel and Denise Perran and Susan Adelbush have painstakingly restored and refurbished the hospital into a wonderful hotel, located on Cripple Creek's highest hill. A gleaming, oak grand staircase leads to the second floor sauna, and the hotel's Boiler Room Tavern is popular with both guests and locals.

Activity: Innkeeper Noel Perran once heard a baby crying in the area below the lobby. He called down to see who was there but received no answer. He checked downstairs, but the room was empty. He later learned that the room where the crying was coming from was originally the old nursery, where caregivers laid the children in the sun for the treatment of jaundice.

A friend of Noel's was a K9 police officer, and he and his police dog, Rex, often stayed at the hotel while it was being renovated. Rex is a trained drug- and bomb-sniffing dog, as well as an attack and tracking dog. One night, Rex went into alert mode as if there was an intruder in the hotel. Knowing they were the only ones there, the officer gave Rex the command to seek, and off the dog ran to the upper floor. As they followed Rex, the officer warned Noel that there must be an intruder in the hotel and for him to stay back as they reached the top floor. There they found Rex lying on the floor, whimpering, with no one in sight.

Finally, the East Wing has two floors with its own staircase. During renovations, a workman was digging under the stairs when he heard someone walking down the steps above him. He looked through the balusters and saw what looked like a dirty pair of work boots coming down the stairs. As they came down further, to the workman's disbelief, he saw nothing from the knees up. The workman dropped his tools and never returned. Evidence was later found of a miner treated in the hospital after a mine explosion ... apparently, he lost both his legs.

Accommodations: The Hotel St. Nicholas contains 15 guest rooms with individually appointed bedchambers, each different in size and décor. Amenities include king- and queen-sized beds, antiques, and in some rooms, down comforters and heated towel racks.

The Hotel St. Nicholas also has opulent parlors and a rooftop hot tub with a view of Cripple Creek Valley. When visitors are ready to see the town, a short stroll will lead them to the casinos and many fine restaurants.

Last Dollar Inn

🕊 🕊 🕊 🕊

315 E. Carr Avenue
Cripple Creek, CO 80813
(888) 429-6700, (719) 689-9113
www.cripple-creek.co.us/lastdinn.htm
Room rates: $60-$150
Visa, Master Card

Courtesy of The Last Dollar Inn

History: Janice and Rick Wood came to Cripple Creek in search of a piece of history, and ended up purchasing a brownstone built in 1898 by a businessman who wanted to emulate the brownstones of New York. The structure was first opened as a boarding house in the early 1900s, and then it was used as a bordello. The house changed hands over time, and author Linda Goodman lived in the home for several years. Goodman added stained glass to the home and a beautiful garden. She loved the home dearly, and it was even mentioned in some of her books.

In April 1995, the Woods purchased the home, remodeled and expanded, and opened it to the public as the Last Dollar Inn.

Activity: Rick Wood enjoys telling ghost stories. In fact, he is the tour guide for "The Cripple Creek Ghost Walk Tours." Visitors who have stayed in the back bedrooms of the Last Dollar Inn have heard the sounds of a locomotive. Along with the train sounds, the image of a man has been seen standing in the corner of the room. He has been described as dressed in a uniform with a flat-topped cap, like a train conductor. If that were not enough, this is the only house in town that actually has train tracks located underneath (now in the basement). The tracks date back to the original train line that went through town in 1889.

Guests have heard someone walking the halls on the second floor and knocking on doors. The ghost of a lady has been seen walking about, dressed in a nightgown. Witnesses on the first floor have seen her crossing the hallway upstairs, and guests on the second floor have reported seeing her walk the floor downstairs.

Accommodations: The inn offers 6 unique guest rooms, each with private baths. The rooms are decorated in Victorian or period style from the time when Cripple Creek was a boomtown. The main floor of the new Victorian addition has a bay window with a view of the town and the Sangre De Cristo Mountains, and 2 newly created guest rooms.

In the original 1898 brownstone are 4 completely remodeled rooms that include much of the furniture and decorations originally in the home.

A full country gourmet-style breakfast is provided to guests each morning, and for those who enjoy playing the odds at the casino, the gaming district is located directly across the street.

The Brown Palace Hotel

🧍 🧍 🧍

321 Seventeenth Street • Denver, CO 80202
(800) 321-2599 • www.brownpalace.com
Room rates: $189-$985 • All major credit cards

History: In the late 1800s, miners were still flocking to the West in search of gold and silver. Denver was a favorite stop on their way to and from the mountains. Entrepreneur Henry Cordes Brown spared no expense in the building of his grand hotel. Work began on the Brown Palace in 1888. Architect Frank E. Edbrooke designed the exterior of the hotel in Colorado red granite and Arizona sandstone. Artist James Whitehouse was commissioned to create 26 medallions carved in stone, each depicting an animal native to the Rocky Mountains. These can still be seen from the seventh floor.

For the interior, Edbrooke designed America's first atrium lobby, with balconies rising eight floors above the ground and surrounded by cast iron railings and ornate metalwork panels. For no apparent reason, two of the panels were installed upside down.

White onyx from Mexico encompasses the lobby, the Grand Salon on the second floor, and the eighth-floor ballroom. Recognized as the second fireproof building in America, no wood was used for the floors and walls. Instead, the walls were made with porous terracotta fireproofing.

Rumor has it that there is a tunnel between the Brown Palace Hotel and the Navarre building across the street. Apparently, at one time, the Navarre building was a gambling house and brothel, and gentlemen could secretly travel back and forth without being seen.

Activity: Mrs. Crawford Hill lived in Room 904 for 15 years. Many years after her death, a hotel historian was conducting a romantic tour and mentioned her romantic interludes. Suddenly, the switchboard started to light up with calls coming from Room 904, but when the switchboard operator answered the phone, there was only static on the line.

In the Ellyngton restaurant, an employee has on several occasions seen a group of ghost musicians. The employee once heard the music and found them playing in the early hours of the morning. The employee told them they couldn't play there, and one of the spirit musicians told him not to worry, "we live here."

Accommodations: Since its opening, the Brown Palace Hotel has never closed. Today, the 109-year-old hotel has 241 guest rooms and suites, 4 restaurants, 11 banquet rooms, and a vast array of specialty shops. Because of the Brown Palace's unique triangle shape, all of the rooms on its eight floors face the street. Also, the hotel gets all of its water from its own artesian wells.

The Stanley Hotel

🐦🐦🐦🐦

333 Wonderview
Estes Park, CO 80517
(800) 976-1377, (970) 586-3371
www.stanleyhotel.com
Room rates: $179-$299
Visa, Master Card, Discover

Courtesy of The Stanley Hotel

History: In 1903, F. O. (Freelan Oscar) Stanley, creator of the Stanley Steamer automobile, was suffering from tuberculosis and had been sent by his doctor to Colorado to seek the fresh mountain air. Stanley and his wife fell in love with the mountains, wildlife, and the flowers of Estes Park, and Stanley began to regain his health. Stanley eventually built a home a mile west of where he would later build a luxury hotel.

Construction began on the Stanley Hotel in 1906. Stanely chose Neoclassical Georgian architecture that resembled the resort architecture of the eastern seaboard. Today, The Stanley Hotel is almost exactly the same as it was in 1909, complete with spacious lobby, grand staircase, two large fireplaces at either end, and a Palladian window that lights the first landing.

Activity: The Stanley Hotel experiences quite a bit of ghostly activity. In the middle of the summer, a guest came down to the front desk at 5 A.M. and requested that she be given another room immediately. The staff asked what was wrong, and she replied that she was awakened by someone jumping up and down on her bed. When she sat up, she also noticed that even though it was summer, it was very cold—she could see her breath.

The fourth floor tends to attract a lot of sightings. Some feel it's the spirits of the workers from early in the hotel's history.

Other occurrences have involved lights that will suddenly go on and off in the rooms, and doors in the corridor opening and closing on their own. The Stanley staff continually receives comments from guests that when they walk down the main staircase they feel a breeze of cold air.

The night auditor and other staff members have repeatedly witnessed the image of a gentleman who arrives at the hotel between 2 and 3 A.M. He appears to be between 70 to 80 years old, and he enters through the main doors, walks over, sits down on a chair by the fireplace, reads the newspaper, and smokes a cigar. Seconds later the apparition is gone. Rumors are that the older gentleman is F. O. Stanley himself, still visiting the hotel that he loved.

Accommodations: The Stanley Hotel features 138 guest rooms (122 standard rooms and 16 suites). The hotel attracts thousands of visitors each year. Some of the hotel's most famous guests have included the "Unsinkable" Molly Brown, John Philip Sousa, Theodore Roosevelt, the Emperor and Empress of Japan, and several Hollywood personalities. Then of course, there is the very special connection between the Stanley Hotel and author Stephen King and his book *The Shining*. King wrote approximately half of that novel in room 217, and the hotel was featured in the television version of *The Shining*.

Attempts have been made to include at least one piece of the hotel's original furniture in each room, along with additional antique furnishings. The heated outdoor swimming pool is available to guests for a refreshing swim, and tennis and volleyball courts are also located on the grounds. The Stanley Hotel can tailor Murder Mystery Parties to fit any corporation or group. Cascades Restaurant, located in the hotel, serves breakfast, lunch, and dinner.

If you're in the mood for a nice stroll or some great shopping, the town of Estes Park is a wonderful place to visit. The beautiful Rocky Mountain National Park is a short drive from the hotel.

Hand Hotel Bed & Breakfast

531 Front Street • Fairplay, CO 80440-1059
(719) 836-3595 • www.handhotel.com.
Room rates: $49-$65 • All major credit cards

History: Surrounded by the quiet beauty of the Rocky Mountains, the Hand Hotel was built in 1931 by Jake and Jessie Hand. The hotel was originally furnished with Western and American Indian memorabilia from the South Park area. Jessie's extensive arrowhead collection is prominently displayed in the nearby South Park City Museum. In the summer, guests can pan for gold or go trout fishing just out the back door; in the winter, visitors can cross-country ski, ride a snowmobile, or enjoy world-class downhill skiing only half an hour away.
Activity: Some guests apparently refuse to check out of the Hand Hotel. A previous owner once saw shadowy movements in the hotel, heard doors slam, and watched as a box that had sat on a shelf for over three years suddenly flew off the shelf to the floor. Once, a light fixture even appeared in the middle of the floor when it had not been there minutes before.

In Grandma Hand's room, a scent of perfume has been detected several times, leading some to believe it was a fragrance Grandma wore. Other strange occurrences surround Grandma Hand's favorite pink rocking chair that she loved to sit in when she lived in the hotel. When employees have moved the chair to other parts of the hotel, guests have been mysteriously and unexplainably prompted to seek out the chair and return it to her room.

Legend has it that a man by the name of Ben worked as a caretaker for the Hand Hotel. Occasionally, Ben's ghost has been seen in the lobby of the hotel smoking a cigar.

Accommodations: Each of the 11 rooms carries its own distinct personality, reminiscent of the people who settled in the South Park and Fairplay area. From the Miner Room, Trapper Room, Outlaw Room, and Rancher Room, to the Grandma Hand Room and School Marm Room, the views of the neighboring mountains and rivers are breathtaking. In the morning guests can help themselves to a continental breakfast or a cup of hot coffee in the sun room overlooking the majestic 14,000 ft. peaks. Though the hotel has been remodeled several times, the new owners have taken it back to circa 1890-1910, transforming the hotel's entire décor to Western turn-of-the century. The Hand Hotel has two gift shops, one Western and the other Victorian; each offers unique items made in Colorado.

The Historic Fairplay Hotel

500 Main Street • Fairplay, CO 80440
(719) 836-2365
Room rates: $49-$70 • Visa, Master Card

History: In 1873, Louis and Marie Valiton purchased land from the Colorado Territory for $87.50 and built the Valiton Hotel. That same year, a fire destroyed much of Fairplay, but it spared the Valiton Hotel. Unfortunately, fire did finally claim the original hotel in 1921, but it was rebuilt in 1922 upon the original foundation. Over the years, the hotel has changed owners and names several times. Today, the Historic Fairplay Hotel stands much as it did in 1922, with period antiques and modern conveniences.

Activity: A young female's spirit by the name of Julia supposedly haunts the hotel. She's very active in October of each year, and guests have reported seeing Julia and hearing music emanating from the hotel's wooden dance floors, accompanied by the rhythmic creaking of the floorboards as if residents were still dancing a jig in celebration of the harvest.

Accommodations: The hotel offers 27 rooms and suites, many of which have the original lathe and plaster. Antiques fill the hotel, adding to the ambiance. The dining room features delectable breakfasts and dinners in the only old-fashioned ski lodge in Summit County and Vail. The Fairplay Hotel is a short walk from South Park, the town that inspired the popular television series. Located 23 miles from Breckenridge, the Fairplay Hotel offers easy accessibility to first-class ski slopes.

The Bross Hotel Bed & Breakfast

☆☆☆

312 Onarga Street
Paonia, CO 81428
(970) 527-6776
www.paonia-inn.com
Room rates: $70-$90
All major credit cards

Courtesy of The Bross Hotel

History: Sheriff W. T. Bross opened this hotel off of Main Street in 1906. At the time, it was considered the only first-class hotel in the county. In 1994, the hotel was renovated by a team of skilled craftsmen and artisans and turned into a bed and breakfast inn.

Today, the Bross Hotel has the charm and elegance of a historic hotel combined with the amenities of a modern bed and breakfast. Once again, it reins supreme as Delta County's premier hotel.

Activity: Reports of paranormal activity surround Room 2. In fact, the renovators sensed a presence in the room, and for this reason, they left it intact. They kept it the original size and number and only added a bathroom in what was once a closet.

The sheriff's wife, "Mother Bross" is the friendly ghost that maintains permanent residence in the room. Being a pleasant spirit, she has been known to watch over guests as they snuggle into the double bed for the night. During other times, employees and guests will find the bedspread and sheets out of place, as if someone had been sleeping there.

On one occasion, a previous owner was sitting in the dining room chatting about the Bross family. While she was making a derogatory comment about the elder couple, the mirror bolted to the wall of the room fell, hit the counter, and landed on the floor, but did not break. The previous owner then said, "Maybe I should apologize."

Accommodations: The Bross Hotel offers 10 guest rooms, each with a private bath and a full breakfast each morning. Guests can relax on the spacious porch and western balcony or read a good book in the library. A game room and conference room are also available. Whatever your pleasure, the Bross Hotel is your ticket to relaxation and comfort.

Redstone Inn

82 Redstone Blvd.
Redstone, CO 81623
(800) 748-2524, (970) 963-2526
www.redstoneinn.com
Room rates: $46-$211
All major credit cards

By R.C. Bishop. Courtesy of The Redstone Inn

History: The city of Redstone was founded by an entrepreneur, John Cleveland Osgood, who felt there was a need for a coal-mining operation in the region. Along with a small number of investors, Osgood developed a full-scale coal mining empire. In 1892, he merged his company with an iron and steel manufacturing operation in Pueblo to form the Colorado Fuel and Iron Company. The construction of the Crystal River Railroad followed.

In an effort to improve the living conditions of his miners, Osgood constructed 84 Swiss chalet—style homes in Redstone to house miners and their families. He also built an elegant 20-room inn for his bachelor employees. Today, it's known as the Redstone Inn.

In 1925, Osgood, along with his third wife, Lucille, began a complete renovation of the inn. A year later, he died, leaving Lucille his entire estate.

Activity: The Redstone Inn was built for the mining community, and naturally there are a few spirits still lurking about. Legend has it that a ghost inhabits the third floor of the inn. The staff, accustomed to strange occurrences, has nicknamed the spirit "George" and from eyewitness reports, he's a busy specter. Often there are sounds of furniture moving across the floor, doors opening and closing on their own, windows shutting by themselves, and music coming from the vacated attic. Today, George's presence remains so active that none of the housekeeping staff will go to the inn's third floor alone.

Accommodations: Beneath the massive red cliffs sits the historic Redstone Inn, a first-class hotel and resort. Nestled in the quaint 100-year-old town of Redstone, the inn is open every day of the year. Visitors from all over the state come to the inn to enjoy their versatile cuisine and turn-of-the-19th-century style, both offered at very reasonable rates. Accessible even in the winter, Colorado Highway 133 (or the "scenic byway," as it is called) is kept clear and safe for travel year-round.

The Redstone Inn features 35 guest rooms ranging from one-of-a-kind special historic rooms, quaint rooms with hand-pegged mission oak furniture, spacious rooms with veranda entrances and magnificent views, to very large family rooms that include refrigerators and private patios.

— HAWAII —

Hale Kokomo Bed & Breakfast

2719 Kokomo Road • Haiku, HI 96708
(808) 572-5613 • www.screenteam.ch/halekokomo
Room rates: $50-$80 • All major credit cards

History: Built in 1927 by a New England architect, the Hale Kokomo is an original two-story Victorian villa.

The first owner of the home was a Chinese blacksmith who reportedly kept to himself. He and his wife lived in the home for over 30 years. The wife fell over the licki tree one day and broke both of her feet. After that, she lived in the garage because she was unable to climb the stairs.

The home changed hands until it was purchased in 1998, remodeled, and opened to the public as a bed and breakfast. The original elegance and atmosphere of the property have been preserved. The garden offers tropical flowers and trees, and each morning, the Swiss management team offers guests a rich and diverse breakfast.

Activity: The 80-year-old neighbors have told the current innkeeper that they would never wait or stand in front of the house as children, since it was common knowledge the home was haunted.

The ghost manifests somewhere between the library and the living room. A friendly apparition, it often opens and closes doors.

In April of 2002, the owner was in the home with his girlfriend when they both heard the door leading from the living room to the porch open and close. After a quick investigation, they found the door was closed. They searched for an intruder but found no one in sight.

A previous owner confirmed that her son and daughter felt some type of presence in the very spot where the current owner had heard the door open and close.

Accommodations: Located on the gentle slopes of Haleakala Crater, on the north side of Maui, this Victorian-style villa offers visitors 4 guest rooms. The inn, secluded from busy tourist centers, has a living room with an open fireplace, a dining room, a library, a cozy balcony, and a tropical garden. Nestled 1,400 feet above sea level, guests enjoy pleasant day temperatures and moderate cool nights.

Penny's Place in Paradise Bed & Breakfast

1440 Front Street
Lahaina, Maui, Hawaii 96761
(808) 661-1068 • www.pennysplace.net
Room rates: $88-$124
Visa, Master Card, American Express

Courtesy of Penny's Place in Paradise B&B

History: Lahaina was once the whaling capital of the world and the royal capital of the Hawaiian Islands. The whales visit between December and April and the Pacific Whale Foundation now studies and protects the great mammals.

Front Street is the main drag through town and runs parallel with the ocean. Shops and galleries are located all over town, and as the sun sets, residents and visitors alike gather along the sea wall to watch the beautiful sunset.

This newly constructed Hawaiian/Victorian bed and breakfast was built on the site of an old plantation home.

Activity: The area of Lahaina is steeped in Hawaiian legend. Several cemeteries in the area are the final resting places of Hawaiian royalty, and there are some people who claim the graves hold the bodies of the Ancient Hawaiian Kapuna (Hawaiian Elders) who wish to be left alone.

The spirit of a lady dressed in white has been seen walking on the beaches in the moonlight. Visitors have witnessed her strolling along the sand.

It is "kapu" (forbidden) to take coral or lava rock away from the island, yet many do. Many of these same visitors mail the items back to relieve themselves of the Hawaiian curse that plagues them with bad luck until they return the pieces to the island.

A friendly ghost of an elderly Hawaiian lady has been seen often on the property. She will usually make her presence known on the balcony or in the kitchen. She wears a calico dress with a lace collar.

Accommodations: Located on the Island of Maui, Hawaii, on world famous Front Street in historic Old Lahaina, the inn has 4 beautiful guest rooms on the balcony level, 50 feet from the water's edge. Guests can pick a room with a beautiful ocean view or a view of the islands of Lanai and Molokai. As the sun rises over the pineapple fields, guests can enjoy a complimentary buffet breakfast served in the first level turret.

— Idaho —

Blackwood Manor

501 Elk Creek Road • Elk City, ID 83525
(208) 842-2591 • www.blackwoodmanor.com
Room rates: $75 • All major credit cards

History: Located in the mountains near Elk City, the Blackwood
Manor is like a step back in time. The original house was a stagecoach
stop when Genevieve and her first husband bought it. At the time, they
were raising a foster child named Harold. After Genevieve's husband
died, she and Harold married. They tore down the stagecoach stop and
built the Blackwood Manor in 1968.

Genevieve had a reputation of being an eccentric lady. Her father
was a sea captain, and he brought her Victorian furniture that he had
found in a bordello in France to outfit her new home. While working on
the home, Genevieve decided to have the whole manor decorated in red.

When Genevieve passed away, her husband Harold remarried and
moved away, leaving the manor unoccupied for years until Carol
Doherty and her husband purchased it and transformed it into an inn.

Decorated in Tudor and Jacobean style, this 5,000-square-foot
country home is located on 56 acres, with views of woodlands,
meadows, and mountains. Guests will enjoy the old-world-style
sanctuary, where Medieval history is the inspiration for an atmosphere
reminiscent of a European castle. Heavily carved dark-wood antique
furniture, tapestry-hung walls, canopied beds with full bed curtains, and
three wood-burning fireplaces adorn the home.

Blackwood Manor is perfect for small weddings, receptions, and
family gatherings. Guests have even held Renaissance-style weddings
there, complete with period costumes.

Activity: When the Dohertys purchased the manor it had sat vacant for
some time and had the reputation of being haunted. Mature, college-
ages employees would not even stay alone in the manor at night.

The first night Carol was in the manor alone, she was sitting on her
bed with her dogs, and she heard footsteps coming down the hallway.
She knew she was alone in the manor, but she decided not to go and see
what was causing the disturbance. From that moment forward, she
believed it must be the spirit of Genevieve coming around to make sure
everything was in order.

Carol told us that Genevieve's visits are rare nowadays, so she must be pleased with the operation of the manor and its new owners.

Accommodations: Blackwood Manor offers 2 guest rooms, each beautifully decorated. A full English breakfast is served family style each morning in the formal dining room. On the grounds, guests can relax and watch horses frolic. Longhaired Scottish Highland Cattle, the oldest registered breed of cattle, also roam and graze in the pasture. Lincolnshire sheep, peacocks, rabbits, duck, and geese can be found grazing or foraging on the lawns.

Outdoor recreation in the area includes fishing, hunting, hiking, and swimming at the hot springs. Guests can ride mountain bikes, jeeps, four-wheelers, or horses up to Hump Lake, and winter activities include cross-country skiing and snowmobiling.

Historic Jameson Restaurant, Saloon, and Inn

☆ ☆ ☆ ☆

304 Sixth Street
Wallace, ID 83873
(800) 556-2544
www.wallace-id.com/jameson
Room rates: $69-$89
All major credit cards

History: The historic town of Wallace, Idaho, known as the "Silver Capital of the World," is rich in heritage. This 115-year-old

Courtesy of The Historic Jameson Restaurant, Saloon, and Inn

mining town is located midway between two recreational ski areas. Every building in this small hamlet (population 1,010) is on the Historic Register. Visitors can enjoy a plethora of jewelry and antique shops, or take a tour of the Sierra Silver Mine, the only tour of its kind in the Northwest.

Activity: Innkeepers David and Gelly Wilcoxen call one of their ghosts Willie, since all that have met him have gotten the willies. Willie's image once appeared suddenly in an old photograph, startling a guest.

Their other ghost is Maggie, who was reputedly a legendary lady of the evening from the 1890s.

Maggie's reflection has been seen in mirrors, the doors of vacant rooms slam shut on their own, windows open by themselves, and old items keep appearing in the guest rooms. Also, there have been reports of unexplained voices in the night.

One of the inn's waitresses also encountered Maggie. The waitress took a break one night to go to the restroom. She noticed that a lady was in the stall next to her. She assumed it was her girlfriend who must have come in before her. As the waitress left the restroom, she said, "I'll meet you back out front, Linda." The voice in the stall, said, "I'm not her, I'm Maggie." The waitress walked out the door and met her friend Linda coming in. She immediately turned around and looked in the restroom, but no one was there.

One day, a lady guest was sitting and eating by the door of the saloon. She felt something around her head. Thinking it was a fly, she swatted her hands around to push away the pesky thing. She then went to the ladies room to run a comb through her hair. When she did, it became stuck. Leaning toward the mirror, she turned to find a plug of her hair had been braided in the back!

Accommodations: The historic structure is topped off by 6 rooms on the third floor, and all are lavishly decorated in Victorian style. The larger rooms look out over the Depot Railroad Museum, and on occasion, they have a visitor or two of the paranormal kind. Guests receive a full country breakfast, cooked to order.

— MONTANA —

Chico Hot Springs Resort

#1 Chico Road • Pray, MT 59065
(800) HOT-WADA • www.chicohotsprings.com
Room rates: $39-$209 • All major credit cards

History: Built in June of 1900 by Percie and Bill Knowles, the Chico Hot Springs Resort offered visitors a touch of elegance in the heart of mining country. Guests like President Teddy Roosevelt and artist Charles Russell have stayed at the hotel.

After Bill Knowles' death in 1910, Percie and her son, Radbourne, transformed the luxurious hotel into a respected medical facility. Patients came from all over the Northwest to bathe in the healing waters. In the 1940s, the hotel took a different turn when gambling and dude ranching were added.

In 1974, Mike and Eve Art purchased the hotel and began to recapture the hotel's turn-of-the-century ambiance. Today, with Georgian-inspired architecture, the Chico Hot Springs Hotel is one of Montana's best-preserved early-20th-century hot springs hotels and health resorts.

Activity: There have been many ghostly sightings around the Chico Hot Springs Resort. Two security guards refused to believe the employees' ghostly tales until one night when both witnessed an apparition. They saw a white transparent figure hovering just above the floor next to an old piano. Only the head and upper body were pronounced, as the remaining torso was a formless mass dissolving to nothing. One guard decided to try and take a picture of the spirit, so he went to the office and retrieved a camera. The picture was taken, and a hazy spot appeared on the photograph. The figure hovered around the piano for almost two minutes, but after the picture was taken, the figure vanished like smoke.

Many believe the ghost is that of Percie Knowles. Percie lived her final hours in Room 349. She had become quite senile, and spent her days in a rocking chair, staring out the window at Emigrant Peak behind the hotel. Today, Percie's spirit is often seen returning to Room 349. The door will often be found left open. Security has locked the door, only to find it open minutes later. The rocking chair has been seen rocking on its own, and wherever you place the chair elsewhere in the room, it will always return to a spot in front of the window.

A bible located in the attic has mysteriously remained dust-free, and it is always opened to the same page of Psalms, even after employees have intentionally left it open to other pages. Sometimes, a feather or handkerchief has been found marking the page, only to go missing later. One such handkerchief was later found inexplicably transferred to the saloon.

Accommodations: Chico Hot Springs offers a diverse selection of lodging, from 44 cozy guest rooms in the turn-of-the-century main lodge, to 13 deluxe rooms overlooking the front lawn, to the lower lodge, a western inn with 17 spacious rooms and sweeping verandas. They also offer a small modern fisherman's lodge, rustic log cabins, fully equipped chalets, a honeymoon cottage, and a 5-bedroom log home.

The Dining Room at Chico offers elegant fine dining in a relaxed atmosphere and a special Sunday Brunch. E.R.'s House of Ribs in the Chico Saloon serves E.R.'s famous and fabulous barbeque ribs, and casual fare can be found at the Poolside Grille. Located on 150 pristine acres only 30 miles from Yellowstone, the Chico Hot Springs Resort is the essence of western hospitality. Large verandas, period furnishings, and healing waters invite visitors to experience what the native peoples have long appreciated.

— OREGON —

Colonel Silsby's Bed & Breakfast

111 Third Street
Ashland, Oregon 97520
(800) 927-3070
(541) 488-3070
www.silsbysinn.com
Room rates: $75–$175
All major credit cards

Courtesy of Colonel Silsby's Bed & Breakfast

History: Step back in time to the charm of a bygone era as you visit Colonel Silsby's Bed & Breakfast. The inn was originally built in 1896 for Colonel William H. Silsby, a Civil War hero of the battles of Vicksburg and Atlanta. Now restored, the bed and breakfast is a fine example of Queen Anne architecture and is one of the best-preserved Victorians in Ashland.

Activity: Colonel Silsby's Bed & Breakfast has a resident ghost named Elizabeth Silsby, the granddaughter of the original owner of the home. Elizabeth is a very friendly spirit, and she reportedly likes to play practical jokes. She often opens and closes doors, turns on the showers in the guest rooms, and has even been known to sit on the bed next to guests. This has happened on numerous occasions.

Known to be a little out-of-step with her family, Elizabeth's headstone is turned completely around from the other headstones in the family plot. The innkeeper has seen her frequently, and Elizabeth even has a favorite room in the inn, called The Elizabeth Suite.

Accommodations: Located one block from town and five minutes from the Oregon Shakespeare Festival, this 1896 Queen Anne Victorian is listed on the National Register of Historic Homes.

The inn offers 6 guest rooms—3 two-room suites, 2 standard guest rooms, and a studio cottage with a kitchenette, Jacuzzi tub, fireplace, and private courtyard. All guest rooms have queen-sized beds, antiques, and period furniture. Guests will enjoy a wonderful breakfast, featuring a variety of teas, homemade jellies, freshly baked scones, fruit, and a delicious entree.

McMenamins Grand Lodge

☆ ☆ ☆ ☆

3505 Pacific Avenue
Forest Grove, OR 97116
(877) 992-9533
(503) 992-9533
www.mcmenamins.com/grandlodge/index.html
Room rates: $45-$200
All major credit cards

Courtesy of McMenamins Grand Lodge

History: In 1922, the Masonic Lodges of Oregon created Greek Revival-style structures to house their aged, infirm, widowed, and orphaned brothers and sisters. The buildings of red brick, Ionic columns, marble accents, and French doors are settled on 13 beautiful acres. Area children believed the property to be a home of royalty. The fraternal organization created several interior welcoming spaces for gatherings within the building. There is a cozy reception room, a magnificent auditorium, open porches, and sun parlors. Fireplaces, natural light, and hardwood floors add to the feeling of warmth.

When the Masonic and Eastern Star Home relocated in 1999, McMenamins, named for Mike and Brian McMenamin, pioneers in the Northwest microbrewing industry, purchased the buildings and began a creative and respectful renovation that enhanced the original features while adding several modern improvements.

Activity: Legend has it that a few of the early residents of the home still enjoy the comforts of McMenamins Grand Lodge. The most famous ghost has been seen in the octagonal sunroom on the second floor. The female apparition always wears lavender perfume, the scent of which is noticeable when she appears. Witnesses have seen her more often during the early hours of the morning.

The Masons used the Children's Cottage as an orphanage. Today, guests have reported hearing the sounds of small children laughing and playing in the upstairs rooms of the cottage.

After the Lodge was opened to the public, an artist doing mosaic work decided to stay one wintry night. Before turning in, she packed up all of her tilework and placed it on a cart. She placed everything in a locked closet, not taking the time to organize it. The next morning, she found all of her bed covers tucked tightly into the mattress around her—odd since she normally slept with loose covers. When she unlocked the closet, she found everything on the cart neatly organized. She looked on top of the stack of materials, and spelled out in tiny ceramic tiles was the word "leave."

Accommodations: McMenamins Grand Lodge offers 77 comfortably furnished guest rooms. Guests are welcome to enjoy a warm dip in the soaking pool or a cup of coffee in the Rounder Room. The Ironwork Grill, located in the original formal dining room, features delicious entrees, ranging from blackened prime rib to pasta. The Doctor's Office Bar is anchored by a massive 6' x 12' snooker table from England and an extraordinary German back bar built in the 1860s. The room serves up games, pastimes, and beverages amidst a sporting atmosphere of playful artwork. The Yardhouse Pub offers an intimate, indoor setting, and casual seating for lunch and dinner.

Hotel Oregon

310 NE Evans Street • McMinnville, OR 97128
(888) 472-8427 • (503) 472-8427
www.hoteloregon.com/McHO/index.html
Room rates: $75-$155
All major credit cards

History: Local restaurateur and farmer Thomas A. White opened the Hotel Elberton in 1905. In 1932, following White's death, new proprietor Arnold "Nick" Nicolai changed the name of the establishment to the Hotel

Courtesy of Hotel Oregon

Oregon. The hotel prospered during World War II, and a new restaurant was added, along with several street-level storefront shops to house individual businesses.

In 1967, freezing temperatures caused pipes to burst and the guest rooms were vacated as water flooded the building. The extensive damage forced the hotel to close. In 1998, a major renovation took place to revive the historical structure, reopening the hotel business after a 30-year absence—and completing the fourth floor to match the original 1910 plans.

Activity: The ghost of the Hotel Oregon has been nicknamed John, and he makes his presence known in several unusual ways.

The hotel has several bars within the building, one of which is the

Cellar Bar; the hotel offices are located nearby. On one occasion, the Cellar Bar had not been open all day. The innkeeper stocked the bar, then went back to her office. At the time, only three employees were in the building. A few minutes later, she left her office, and as she walked by the bar, she saw something odd inside: four candles burning. They had just been lit, since there was no melted wax present. The innkeeper called the other employees and found that no one else had gone near the bar that day.

The manager was in the kitchen one evening talking to another employee. Near the kitchen are two hallways, one with an ice machine at the end. As the manager was chatting, she noticed a man in brown shorts, shirt, and hat was walking down the hallway where the ice machine was located. The manager followed, but she found no one there.

In Mattie's Room, which is also the Hotel's catering room, the innkeeper once discovered the six of spades playing card stuck to the ceiling by the light fixture. The card was left there awhile for amusement value. Though it was eventually taken down, six months later the same card was found stuck to the same spot.

Accommodations: Located in the heart of Oregon's wine country, the Hotel Oregon offers 42 cozy guest rooms, each with natural lighting, king- or queen-sized beds, and unique furnishings. Guests can request rooms with private or shared baths. For over a century, guests have enjoyed the hotel's restaurant, lounge, dance spot, and soda fountain. It's also an ideal location for weddings and receptions.

McMenamins Edgefield

2126 SW Halsey Street • Troutdale, OR 97060
(800) 669-8610, (503) 669-8610
www.mcmenamins.com/edge/index.html
Room rates: $20-$200 • All major credit cards

History: McMenamins Edgefield was built in 1911 and served for several decades as the Multnomah County poor farm. Residents operated a self-sufficient environment where they raised hogs and poultry; grew fruits and vegetables; operated a dairy, cannery, and

Courtesy of McMenamins
Edgefield

meatpacking plant; and worked in the laundry, kitchen, and hospital. In 1947, it was renamed Multnomah County Home and Farm until the farm operations ended in the late 1950s.

In 1962, the facility was renamed Edgefield Manor and it functioned as a nursing home until it closed in 1982. The property was purchased in 1990 from Multnomah County, and over the next four years the condemned buildings and land were converted into a unique European-style village. The new facility includes lodging, a pub with a movie theatre, fine dining, a winery with vineyards, a brewery, a distillery, a golf course, gardens, and meeting, wedding, and banquet space.

The historic Georgian revival-style manor dominates the village atmosphere and is surrounded by numerous smaller buildings that now share a role in entertaining visitors. Guests can enjoy local artists showcasing their artwork, and the sculpted grounds and gardens tie the 25 acres together.

Activity: In the 1930s, an infirmary was added to what is today the winery wing, with lodging rooms on the main floor of that wing. It is assumed that as an infirmary, quite a few people passed on in that wing of the building. The winery wing receives the greatest number of reports from guests who have experienced heavy or sad feelings or sensations while in the particular rooms.

The Ad House was once the old administrator's building. Guests of the lodging rooms in that building have been awakened in their bed at night by someone or something shaking their ankles. Others have reported waking up and seeing the image of a little girl standing by the foot of their beds.

One guest woke up to find a large African-American man in tattered clothing standing in the corner of the room. The guest turned to wake up her husband, but when she turned back around, the apparition was gone.

Employees at McMenamins Edgefield often hear their names being called. When they turn around, they will find no one there.

Accommodations: McMenamins Edgefield offers over 100 bed and breakfast rooms as well as hostel accommodations, creating a unique lodging experience. The guest rooms are spacious with inviting décor from the turn of the 19th century. To encourage a tranquil retreat atmosphere, televisions and telephones are absent from the rooms. Shared baths for men or women are centrally located in each wing, and most rooms offer individual bathrooms with total privacy.

The Black Rabbit Restaurant is located in the main lodge and is open daily for breakfast, lunch, and dinner. Guests can choose from a menu of Northwestern cuisine and traditional favorites as well as handcrafted ales, wines, and spirits. During the summer, alfresco dining is available in the New Orleans-style Black Rabbit Courtyard for lunch and dinner. The Power Station Pub & Theater is a classic English-style pub serving burgers, fries, and sandwiches as well as ales and wines. Guests can take their favorite pint next door to the Power Station Theater for a full-length feature film, showing nightly. The Little Red Shed is a cozy hideaway where guests can relax and enjoy favorite McMenamins ales and free live music played under the neighboring alder and maple trees. The Ice House is another gathering spot fitted with Edgefield's only television for special sporting events.

Heceta Head Lighthouse

92072 Highway 101 South
Yachats, OR 97498
(541) 547-3696
www.hecetalighthouse.com
Room rates: $137-$220
Visa, Master Card

Courtesy of Heceta Head Lighthouse

History: The Heceta Head Lighthouse and lightkeeper's house were built in 1894. Both are listed on the National Register of Historic Places. The area was named for Captain Don Bruno de Heceta of the Spanish Royal Navy, an explorer whose expedition passed along the Oregon Coast around 1775.

The lighthouse is a working lighthouse towering 205 feet above the Pacific Ocean. One thousand barrels of blasting powder were used to create a flat table on the rocky cliffs to hold the structure. Ships as far as 21 miles away can see its "first order" Fresnel lens. It is said to be the most photographed lighthouse in the U.S. and the brightest light on the Oregon Coast.

The Keeper's House Bed & Breakfast is located on a cliff overlooking a magnificent view of the Pacific Ocean and the beach below.

Activity: The only images of light you will find in the lighthouse are man-made. However, the Light Keeper's House has a ghostly resident. Unexplained noises have been heard in the inn, and on one occasion, the former owners were playing cards with two guests when a high-pitched scream was heard.

Two students were relaxing on the front porch when they witnessed a gray mist ascend the porch steps. They described the misty image as long and flowing, like a puff of smoke.

A workman was cleaning a window in the attic one day when he noticed strange reflections in the glass. He turned around to find a gray-haired, elderly woman dressed in an 1890s-style gown. The apparition peered at the workman until he decided to vacate the area. He refused to ever enter the attic again. One day, he was working on the exterior of the house when he accidentally broke an attic window. He repaired it from the outside, but the broken glass remained on the floor of the attic. That night the owners were awakened by the sounds of scraping coming from the attic. It sounded as if someone was sweeping up glass with a broom. The next morning, the owners went into the attic and found the glass had been swept into a neat pile.

Accommodations: The Keeper's House is a Queen Anne-style inn that offers 5 guest rooms, each restored to its original splendor. By day, it serves as an interpretive center, and by night it becomes a bed and breakfast. Guests are encouraged to view the lighthouse and its awesome light in the sky after dark. Described as a "magical" experience, the brilliant light can be seen from the base of the tower, and it's become a very romantic place for marriage proposals.

— WASHINGTON —

Cooney Mansion
Bed & Breakfast Inn

1705 Fifth Street • Cosmopolis, WA 98537
(800) 9-SPRUCE, (360) 533-0602 • www.cooneymansion.com
Room rates: $80-$185 • All major credit cards

History: Built in 1908 as a home for lumber baron Neil Cooney and a showcase for his mills' timber, the Cooney Mansion is a State and National Register Landmark. Throughout the mansion, visitors will find an abundance of woodwork and turn-of-the-19th-century Arts & Crafts period furniture.

Activity: Research shows that at one time, the Sisters of St. Rose— which later founded St. Joseph's Hospital—may have once lived dormitory-style in the ballroom of the mansion. Regardless of whether this is true, several people have sensed wonderful, positive, female energies in the home.

The Cedar Room has always been rumored to be haunted, and to this day the staff notices a pleasant scent there. Even after all curtains, bedding, mattresses, and carpeting have been changed out, the scent has remained.

One night, a guest who was staying in Room 6 awoke to find the picture hanging above her bed was tapping against the wall on its own.

A couple of female friends were staying in the Hemlock Room when one of the guests awoke to find an older lady in a housecoat sitting in the rocking chair. The guest thought it was her friend, until she spoke to her from the bathroom. When the guest looked back at the chair, the lady in the rocker had disappeared.

Accommodations: Originally known as the Spruce Cottage, this 10,000-square-foot mansion offers guests a relaxed atmosphere with an old-fashioned warmth and hospitality. Cooney Mansion offers 5 guest suites (each with a full private bath) and an additional 4 guest rooms with a shared bath on the former "servant's floor."

The Cooney Suite is over 600 square feet of total privacy and comfort, featuring fireplace, sitting area, enclosed porch, and a bathroom larger than most bedrooms, complete with an old fashioned "Rainfall" showerhead. Each morning, guests are treated to a "Lumber Baron's Breakfast," served at the massive, original dining table. In the afternoon and evening, visitors can enjoy complimentary tea and coffee.

To relax, guests may use the Jacuzzi, sauna, and exercise room, or curl up with a good book from the Cooney Mansion's extensive library.

The Captain Whidbey Inn

2072 West Captain Whidbey Inn Road
Coupeville, WA 98239
(800) 366-4097, (360) 678-4097
www.captainwhidbey.com
Room rates: $85-$285
All major credit cards

Courtesy of The Captain Whidbey Inn

History: The Captain Whidbey Inn was built in 1907 by Judge Lester Still as a place for the elite of Seattle to come and visit. Early guests arrived at the inn's pier by way of a paddlewheel steamer. It soon became the destination of discerning travelers from all over the world. The Judge died in 1960 at the age of 89.

Activity: Judge Still once rented the building to a diet doctor by the name of Dr. Hazard. Her methodology was to prescribe water and vitamins for patients to lose weight. A lot of people lost weight, but of course you can't live on just that combination. Reportedly, one young girl from England lost weight, but also tragically starved to death. Dr. Hazard was charged for manslaughter and was actually tried in Judge Still's court. The Doctor was convicted and sent to prison.

To this day, guests of the inn reportedly see an apparition of a young girl in a turn-of-the-19th-century nightdress. Many believe she is the young girl who died of starvation so many years ago.

Accommodations: The Captain Whidbey Inn offers 32 rooms, plus 3 two-bedroom cottages and 4 rustic one-bedroom cabins, each complete with feather beds, down comforters, and fireplaces. This natural paradise has exquisite views of Penn Cove. If you're in the mood for fine dining, the inn offers fresh baked breads and the chef's culinary specialties.

Manresa Castle

7th and Sheridan
Port Townsend, WA 98368
(800) 732-1281, (360) 385-5750
www.manresacastle.com
Room rates: $70-$175
All major credit cards

Courtesy of Manresa Castle

History: Port Townsend became the first incorporated city in Jefferson County in 1878, and its citizens elected Charles Eisenbeis as the first mayor. The castle was built in 1892 as the home of Charles and Kate Eisenbeis. Prior to becoming mayor, Eisenbeis was a prominent member of the early Port Townsend business community. His business holdings included a bakery, brickworks, lumber mill, brewery, bank, and hotel.

His castle was the largest private residence ever built in Port Townsend, consisting of 30 rooms and designed after the castles in Eisenbeis' native Prussia. Locals referred to it as "Eisenbeis Castle." The walls were 12 inches thick, and the roof was made of slate. German artisans installed tiled fireplaces and finely crafted woodwork. After Charles Eisenbeis died in 1902, his wife Kate later remarried, and the castle was left empty for almost 20 years.

In 1925, a Seattle attorney bought the castle as a vacation place for nuns teaching in the Seattle schools. In 1927, Jesuit priests purchased the building to be used as a training college. In 1928, a large wing housing a chapel and sleeping rooms was added. They named the new complex Manresa Hall after the town in Spain where Ignatius Loyola founded the order.

In 1968, the Jesuits left, and the building became a hotel, now dubbed Manresa Castle. Since 1968, three different owners have all done their part to lovingly renovate and the restore the building to modern standards while maintaining its Victorian elegance.

Activity: The current innkeeper does not believe any ghosts reside in the castle. However, he does receive reports from guests that feel otherwise. In one guest room, the toilet reportedly flushes constantly during the night. Guests have reported hearing music occasionally throughout the night—sometimes it's a piano, sometimes a violin, and sometimes a full orchestra. A glass has shattered in a bartender's hand, and guests have reported seeing a strange light under their doors coming from the hallway. When they opened the door, there was no one there.

Guests on the third floor have reported hearing footsteps as if someone was above them. The only problem is that there are no floors above the third.

Occasionally during the night, guests will feel something like a small cat jumping on the foot of their bed. When they turn on the light, nothing is there.

Accommodations: The 40-room, century-old Manresa Castle offers comfortable surroundings that include a restaurant and lounge, spacious gardens, and breathtaking views of the Olympic and Cascade Mountains. It provides the perfect setting for a special retreat or conference.

Thornewood Castle Inn and Gardens

8601 N. Thorne Lane S.W. • Tacoma, WA 98498-2129
(253) 584-4393 • www.thornewoodcastle.com
Room rates: $175-$400 • All major credit cards

History: Thornewood Castle is a magnificent three-story manor home dating back to the turn of the 19th century. With over 27,000 square feet of living space, the Thornewood is one of the few genuine private castles in the United States.

The home was built to the specifications of Chester Thorne, one of the founders of the Port of Tacoma, whose fascination with the grandeur of old English castles and estates led him to design his dream home.

Architect Kirtland Cutter converted Thorne's dream into an amazing reality. Construction took three years to complete, from 1908 to 1911, with many of the materials—including the brick, oak paneling, oak staircase, and the medieval stained glass—coming from a castle in Europe. Three ships were commissioned to transport these building materials to the Pacific Northwest. The massive grand staircase greets visitors, along with a priceless collection of artwork. Much of this collection is hand-painted on glass surrounded by panes of crystal mounted in windows throughout the estate. The artwork was created in the 15th to 17th centuries, and it was previously owned by an English duke who spent 40 years acquiring the collection.

Activity: Along with Thornewood's majestic architecture, a few spirits linger. One ghost is believed to be that of Chester Thorne.

Light bulbs in the gentlemen's parlor and in the blue room unscrew from the socket by themselves. Lamps switch off and on in the ballroom, and on separate occasions, a punchbowl broke to pieces and the bottoms blew out of some liquor bottles.

Thornewood has held numerous weddings and receptions, and occasionally brides have stood in front of an old mirror that has been passed down through generations. While admiring their gowns, the brides will see a lady sitting on the window seat behind them. When they turn around, she is gone. From the garden, visitors have looked up at the bedroom window and have seen that same image of the woman standing at the window.

Accommodations: Thornewood Castle is nestled on four acres at American Lake. A gracious country inn, Thornewood has been lovingly restored. The Castle offers 54 guest rooms, including 28 bedrooms and 22 baths and complimentary chocolates in the rooms. Guests can stroll through the same halls where presidents and dignitaries have walked. Presidents William Taft and Theodore Roosevelt stayed in the presidential suite during each of their visits.

Visitors can roam the grounds and the beautiful half-acre sunken English perennial garden, or they may swim, fish, or boat on the picturesque American Lake. Guests can relax at the end of the day and watch the beautiful sunset from Thornewood Castle's hand-tiled lakeside patio. Guests can have breakfast delivered to their rooms or served downstairs in the castle dining room.

— WYOMING —

The Plains Hotel

1600 Central Avenue • Cheyenne, WY 82001
(307) 638-3311 • www.theplainshotel.com
Room rates: $109-$199 • All major credit cards

History: On March 9, 1911, one of the most elaborately furnished hostelries in the West opened to hotel patrons. Cattle barons, oil tycoons, and travelers on their way to Yellowstone and the Grand Tetons all enjoyed the Plains Hotel. One of the most notable patrons of the hotel was Chief Little Shield, an Arapaho high chief who played an integral part in negotiating peace treaties.

Activity: Legend has it that shortly after the hotel opened, a couple arrived at the Plains to spend their honeymoon. When the new groom failed to return to the bridal suite in a timely fashion, his new bride, Rosie, set out to find him. From the second-floor mezzanine, Rosie spotted her husband with a lady of the evening. She followed them to the lady's room, and in an act of passion, killed them both and then herself.

Since that time, images of all three spirits have been seen throughout the hotel. Employees and guests have caught glimpses of Rosie walking on the mezzanine and peering down into the lobby. Occasionally, the sounds of laughter and crying can be heard in unoccupied guest rooms. The ghost of Rosie's husband has been seen walking through the hotel. He appears in the clothing of that time period: a formal black waist coat, a black cowboy hat, a white shirt with no collar, and a shiny silver top button.

The hotel is filled with original Western artwork, drawings, and photographs. Among them is a black-and-white photograph taken in the bar of the hotel. We encourage guests to take a good look at it, for it depicts two patrons sitting at the bar, while the mirror behind the bar reflects three people. The mysterious third figure in the picture has never been identified.

Accommodations: Over $5 million has been invested in the restoration of this historic hotel, which includes a restaurant, gift shop, banquet facilities, and 131 guest rooms and suites.

The Historic Sheridan Inn

856 Broadway Street
Sheridan, WY 82801
(307) 674-5440
www.sheridaninn.com
Call for rates

By Mike Johnson. Courtesy of The Historic Sheridan Inn

History: The Burlington and Missouri Railroad built the Sheridan Inn in partnership with the Sheridan Land Company during the winter of 1892. The inn was opened to the public in May of 1893. Architect Thomas Kimball modeled the structure after a hunting lodge he had visited in Scotland. The inn was immediately touted as the finest structure between Chicago and San Francisco.

William F. "Buffalo Bill" Cody admired the inn and invested in the inn's original furnishings. Buffalo Bill lived in the inn each time he came through town, and he conducted talent auditions for his *Wild West Show* on the massive front porch. A collection of pictures of Buffalo Bill is available for viewing.

In 1964, the National Park Service honored the inn as one of 17 National Historic Landmarks in Wyoming. The inn stands as a symbol of the spirit of the people who ventured West through the wilderness to create a better life. Through the years, notables such as Ernest Hemingway, Will Rogers, Robert Taylor, Bob Hope, and countless others have enjoyed the comfort of the Sheridan Inn.

Activity: In 1901, at the age of 22, Miss Kate Arnold traveled to the Sheridan Inn from Virginia to work as a seamstress. During her tenure of 64 years, she worked as desk clerk, housekeeper, hostess, and sitter for the many children who stayed at the inn with their families. She loved the place dearly, and her final request was for the inn to be her final resting place. Following her death in 1968, her remains were cremated and buried in the wall of a room she occupied on the third floor.

Today, Miss Kate's loving and caring spirit is still a part of the Sheridan Inn. Her guardian presence is felt on an almost daily basis. Lights have turned off and on by themselves, and doors have opened and closed on their own. Those who spend a great deal of time at the inn have grown to love Miss Kate as did so many people years ago.

Accommodations: The lobby, main dining room, and bar all have exposed hand-hewn beams made from Georgia pine. The building is designed so each room has a gable or dormer, which provides access to the roof. This unique feature has earned the inn the nickname of "House of 69 Gables."

Three fireplaces are located on the main floor, and the original Buffalo Bill Bar, which is made of oak and mahogany, was built in England and shipped to the United States. It was a gift from Queen Victoria of England to Buffalo Bill, following the private performance of his *Wild West Show* that he gave following her husband's death.

Tours are available, both guided and self-guided, including bus tours. Lunch and dinner is served at the inn and banquet and party catering is available. At the current time there are no sleeping rooms available for rent at the Historic Sheridan Inn. Their board of directors are in the process of seeking a permanent operator that will become partners in the renovation of the building and become long-term operators of the inn.

SOURCES

All information received for *Haunted Inns of America* was gathered by first-hand interviews with the owners and/or employees of the hotels/inns. In some cases, additional information was used. We would like to thank all who participated.

— WEBSITES —

Lone Star Spirits
www.lonestarspirits.org

Obiwan's UFO-Free paranormal page
www.ghosts.org

Haunted Travels
www.hauntedtravels.com

Real Haunted Houses
www.realhaunts.com

The Shadowlands
www.theshadowlands.net

Washington State Ghost Society
www.washintonstateghostsociety.org

Cathe's Ghost Encounters of the Civil War Kind
www.hauntedfieldsofglory.com

The National Trust for Historic Hotels of America
www.historichotels.org

— BOOKS —

Dinner and Spirits by Robert and Anne Wlodarski pub. iUniverse; Lincoln, NE

Best Tales of Texas Ghosts by Docia Schultz Williams pub. Republic of Texas Press; Plano, TX

Haunted Inns of the Southeast by Sheila Turnage pub John F. Blair; Winston-Salem, NC

Haunted Highway: The Spirits of Route 66 by Ellen Robson and Dianne Halicki pub. Golden West Publishers; Phoenix, AZ

The Ghosts of Virginia by L.B. Taylor Jr. pub. L.B. Taylor

Lighthouse Ghosts: 13 bona fide apparitions standing watch over America's shores by Norma Elizabeth and Bruce Roberts pub. Crane Hill Publishers; Birmingham, AL

Haunted Hotels by Robin Mead pub. Rutledge Hill Press

Nantucket Hauntings by Blue Balliett pub. Down East Books

Haunted Ohio by Chris Woodyard pub. Kestrel Pubn.

Cape May Ghost Stories Book 2 by Charles J. Adams III pub. Charles J. Adams III

Ghosts of the Klondike: They Haunt the Frozen North by Shirley Jonas, Chris Caldwell pub. Lynn Canal Pub.

Big Sky Ghosts: Eerie True Tales of Montana by Debra D. Munn pub. Pruett Publishing Co.

Haunted Texas Vacations: The Complete Ghostly Guide by Lisa Farwell pub. Westcliffe Publishers

U.S. GHOST TOURS

Selma's Ghost Tour
Selma, AL
800-45-SELMA

Eureka Springs Ghost Tours
Eureka Springs, AR
501-253-6800
www.eureka-springs-ghost.com

Haunted Houses of Pasadena
Walking Tour
Pasadena, CA
626-791-1129
www.icghosts.com

Cripple Creek's Ghost Walk Tour
Cripple Creek, CO
877-858-4653

The Daytona Ghost Walk
Daytona Beach, FL
386-253-6034
www.hauntsofdaytona.com

Gunslingers, Ghosts, and Gold
Ghost Tour
Denver, CO
800-275-8802
www.denverhauntedhistory.com

Ghost Tours of Amelia
Amelia Island, FL
866-446-7870
904-548-0996
www.ghosttoursofameliaisland.com

Ghost Tours of Key West
Key West, FL
305-293-8009

Ghost Tours of St. Augustine
St. Augustine, FL
888-461-1009
www.ghosttoursofstaugustine.com

Hauntings Tour
Savannah, GA
912-234-3571

Ghosts and Graveyards Tour
Des Moines, IA
515-270-6654
www.magicalhistorytours.com

History and Hauntings Tours of
Alton Illinois
Alton, IL
888-446-7859
618-465-1086
www.prairieghosts.com

Haunted Pub Crawl
Chicago, IL
708-499-0300
www.ghosttours.com

Supernatural Chinatown
Chicago, IL
708-499-0300
www.ghosttours.com

Excursions into the Unknown
Haunted Chicagoland Tours
Oak Lawn, IL
708-425-5163
www.ghostresearch.org

Haunted History Tour
New Orleans, LA
504-861-2727
www.hauntedhistorytours.com

New England Ghost Tours
Boston, MA
781-235-7149
www.members.aol.com/nehaunts

Colonial Lantern Tours
Plymouth. MA
800-698-5636
www.lanterntours.com

Spellbound Tours
Salem, MA
978-745-0138
www.spellboundtours.com

Fell's Point Ghost Walk
Baltimore, MD
410-522-7400
www.fellspointghost.com

The Hauntings of Ellicott Mills
Ellicott Mills, MD
800-288-8747

Candle Light Ghost Tours
Frederick, MD
301-845-7001

St. Louis Spirit Search and
Haunted History Tour
St Louis, MO
314-776-4667

Haunted Cape May Tour
Cape May, NJ
609-463-8984
www.capemay.com

A Spook About Ghosts Tour
Santa Fe, NM
505-988-2774
www.whitington.com/santafe/ghost

East Village Ghosts Tour
New York, NY
212-969-8262

North Coast Ghost Tours
Cleveland, OH
330-225-1519

Ghost Tours of Gettysburg
Gettysburg, PA
717-337-0445

The Historic Farnsworth House
Candlelight Ghost Walks
Gettysburg, PA
717-334-8838
www.gettysburgaddress.com

Ghosts of Philadelphia
Philadelphia, PA
215-413-1997
www.ghosttour.com/Philadelphia.htm

The Ghosts of Charleston
Charleston, SC
800-854-1670
www.tourcharleston.com

Ghosts of Galveston
Galveston, TX
409-766-7957
www.ghostsofgalveston.com

The Walking Ghost Tours of Old
Town Spring
Old Town Spring, TX
281-528-0200

Hauntings History of San Antonio
San Antonio, TX
210-227-ECTO (3286)
www.webspawner.com/users/ghost
tour

Leesburg Ghost Tours
Leesburg, VA
703-913-2060

Capital Hauntings Walking Tour
Washington, DC
202-484-1565

ALPHABETICAL LISTING OF INNS

THE GHOST STALKERS

Photo: Verner Stenstrom

Terry L. Smith performed as a magician, illusionist, and escape artist before his passion and interests were drawn to film and video production. A graduate of Texas Christian University, Terry has worked as a film, video and music producer/publisher, director, editor, screenwriter, cameraman, and journalist for more than fifteen years. While creating historical documentaries for the city of Fort Worth, Terry uncovered material on haunted locations there. This unexplained activity sent him on a journey into the mysteries of the paranormal and supernatural experiences worldwide.

Mark Jean has been working for more than twenty years in photography and photographic imaging. After owning his own black-and-white photographic lab for more than ten years, Mark decided to devote more time to researching paranormal phenomena. Today, Mark continues to work in photography and paranormal research.

In 1989, a local newspaper dubbed the duo The Ghost Stalkers, and from that time forward they have conducted interviews and paranormal investigations around the country. Terry and Mark have been featured in five books on ghosts, in periodicals in America and the United Kingdom, and on BBC Radio.

The Ghost Stalkers would love to hear from you if you know of a hotel or B&B that is believed to be "haunted." You may contact them at:

The Ghost Stalkers
P.O. Box 126033 • Fort Worth, Texas 76126
Web: www.ghoststalkers.com
E-mail: ghosttx@ghoststalkers.com